THE
MANUFACTURING
MAN
AND HIS JOB

Contributors

K. J. Allen
Roger W. Bolz
Edward M. Brabant
Frank Buese
James F. Collins, Jr.
Peter deK. Dusinberre,
  Jr.
Romeyn Everdell
James G. Everhart
John W. Faus
Chester Gadzinski
Earl R. Gomersall
Donald G. Hall
Erich Hardt
Joseph E. Kochmar
Harry S. Mann
William H. Markle
Lawrence M. Matthews
George J. Michel, Jr.

H. J. Moore
Leon B. Musser
James A. O'Hara
Walter R. Olson
Richard F. Perdunn
Howard A. Pilkey
George W. Plossl
Richard F. Powell, Jr.
Bayard F. Rowan
Richard A. Seagrave
Philip C. Shaak
Glen R. Simmons
John V. Smonig
R. D. Sonderup
Arthur B. Toan, Jr.
John W. Wade
John D. Wait
Oliver W. Wight
Edward Wisnewsky

THE MANUFACTURING MAN AND HIS JOB

Edited by

ROBERT E. FINLEY
  Production Manager—Publications, American Management Association, Inc.

HENRY R. ZIOBRO
  Management Development Specialist, Xerox Corporation

AMERICAN MANAGEMENT ASSOCIATION, INC.

CONTENTS

5

PART THREE
Related Functions and Services

INTRODUCTION: THE ROLE OF THE MANUFACTURING FUNCTION IN THE COMPANY AND IN THE AMERICAN ECONOMY

By JOHN W. WADE

American industry is on the threshold of an economic era that could change the destiny of this and every other country for centuries to come. Manufacturing will play a role in shaping this destiny, not only by its operations within the individual company but also by its impact on the overall American economy.

Let us evaluate the responsibilities that manufacturing has now and will continue to have in this new era to its owners and stockholders, its employees, its customers, and finally, the general public. Each of the functions singled out in this introduction is treated more fully by an expert elsewhere in this book. Therefore, all that is needed here is to give some indication of the immense scope of manufacturing management in all its activities and of its impact on all members of our free society.

Today's organization must be managed in such a way as to be able to deal with decisions which affect not only its present course of action but possibly its very future. What are the steps that must be taken to guarantee at least in some small measure that the decisions and actions taken today within the organization will be logically sound and prove to be ultimately successful?

One of the first things we as managers should assure ourselves of is that the employees at all levels within our organization are properly indoctrinated in the objectives of the total manufacturing concepts and that all are informed about their specific roles and responsibilities in the company's overall plans

JOHN W. WADE is Executive Vice President, Tecumseh Products Company, Tecumseh, Michigan.

and ultimate goals. If this task seems Herculean, then perhaps the only solution is re-organization before proper results can be obtained.

One of the most important needs of the manufacturing organization is proper manning by qualified employees in its each and every segment, then an adequate system of controls to assure successful performance in terms of day-to-day activities and future planning. After the necessary organization for effective action has been structured, the individuals who are charged with making it work must be assured that they will have the full support of management in the accomplishment of their duties. They also must know that the responsibilities assigned to them are essential to the efficient operation of the entire organization and that unless they fulfill them to the greatest extent of their capabilities, the entire organizational structure may be in jeopardy.

The modern business organization, by comparison with that of a few years back, is large and complex, and the incidence of a clear-cut understanding of relatively simple problems between management and labor has fallen to a very low level in too many companies. Today, many managers of business enterprises have become what we may call "professionals" and in many instances have become distinctly separated, not only from supervision within the management organization, but also from the workers in the plants and offices. As a result, these "professional managers" are sharing less and less the problems of either management or labor, to the extent that some out-of-line conditions reach catastrophic proportions. Where there is no communication there is no understanding on either side. And while managers must specialize, as managers their primary responsibility is to get things done through people. Too many companies today take the attitude that the less "the people"—employees down the line—know, the better off they all will be and the less trouble they will make and the less they will interfere in the successful operation of the company. The fact of growing size and complexity is too many times merely an excuse, and consequently lines of communication are harder to work through. But today more than ever, with competition at fever pitch, management—particularly in manufacturing—must achieve a more harmonious balance between local labor and the associated "service organizations" of labor, or the future security and well-being of the organization will be in constant jeopardy.

Management must devise some system of reporting facts as clearly as possible to the employees down the line and, in doing so, must include enough information that every employee fully understands what he is expected to do, what the aims and objectives of the company are, and where his efforts contribute to the overall plan. Reporting of essential facts cannot start somewhere in the middle of the organization but has to come from the very top and be in language plain enough for all to understand. Similarly, communications from below cannot be ignored or treated lightly. Above all, this chain of communication must not be allowed to stop in the middle of the organization, and it is the inherent obligation of manufacturing management to see that it doesn't. Information must be presented in such a way that it reflects the interests of all concerned with the whole business, who most certainly include not only the immediate company employees but also the stockholders, the public, and, last but not least, the customer. For the customer, in the end, is unmistakably the major source of wages, income, and profits.

It is also apparent on reflection that the world's economic well-being depends to a great extent upon introducing new products. Any successful business organization at least must be able to develop new or improved products, and it must have talent to manufacture them in the best way known. In this day of highly competitive industries, when a "captive" product is practically an oddity, it is imperative that all of manufacturing, from product engineering to the distribution function, concentrate its efforts on making certain that all products, whether in the developmental stage or in actual production, are serviced to assure that they are at their maximum in quality and profitability. One axiom that reflects this statement quite well is the often-heard sentiment to the effect that "the fact that we have been doing the same thing for an appreciable amount of time is pretty good evidence that it needs changing." When any one of us looks back on the achievements of the past, how many examples can he think of that this statement could apply to? In this dynamic world the static organization will be passed by!

The prime responsibility of the product engineering or research and development division is not necessarily new product research and development but also existing product improvement. For by "development" is meant the various ways and methods of improving existing products in the areas of labor, materials, and processes or, in some cases, developing an entirely new replacement product. Development is successful only if the merits of improved or new products, in the overall evaluation, outweigh the total merits of the products they replace; certainly they must offer equal or improved market potentials.

Following closely behind—in fact, many times paralleling—the efforts of manufacturing product research and development are product engineering, manufacturing engineering, and plant engineering. These segments of the overall manufacturing endeavor, along with product development in many instances, have interrelated responsibilities and should be so organized, wherever possible, as to operate in a manner that reflects this fact. Their common objective should be to engineer products that, to the extent feasible, are satisfactorily turned out with the most efficient manufacturing equipment and processes conceivable. After this common objective is accomplished, the products and equipment used in their production should be maintained, or again improved upon, to realize their full potential over the life expectancy contemplated for them.

There is no really satisfactory way that these important segments of the manufacturing function can be wholly or partially divided and still realize their full potential. To allow them to be divided is to invite serious problems or inefficiencies in one or more of the segments or in the function as a whole.

The successful accomplishments of any manufacturing business are not just day-to-day improvements of the materials, processes, and equipment which it utilizes for its existing products, for most certainly these accomplishments are affected by advance planning of new products, processes, and plant improvements. Planning is necessary in order to be as certain as possible of future survival at a reasonable level of profit. So it is not surprising that there are frequent references to planning in the pages that follow. Many a potential product development, and occasionally a business itself, has failed because the three segments of engineering have not worked in unison toward a common goal, whereas cautious planning and careful execution and control of the plan would have done much to assure success.

Other "services" within manufacturing which share equally important roles in the overall American economy are inventory and production planning, quality control, industrial engineering, and the other functions which have a direct influence on whether the business is profitable. It must always be kept in mind, however, that no company should create functions or systems just for the sake of having them. The organization structure should be created and altered only as indications dictate, in response to internal conditions which require adequate controls. Any change, of course, must be made in a way which insures efficiency and satisfactory profits.

The plant is the arena in which the final efforts of all the various members of the organization are directed to the end that manpower, materials, machines, time, and facilities can be utilized to the maximum of their potential and, as well as is humanly possible, kept in balance to produce the maximum quality and value of product. Let us not forget that if the plant doesn't run smoothly and efficiently, all our procedures, plans, and efforts are for naught. So let us be constantly aware of the potential hazards that can unwittingly be placed in the way of good, sound manufacturing economics and that create obstacles to logical and effective decision making on the part of each and every employee within the organization. For in the end—and it bears repeating—the ultimate objective of any manufacturing organization is to achieve the finest operation—one that will produce sound and realistic profits for all who have an interest in it.

It is rumored, and probably rightly so, that our competitors in both hemispheres are making more rapid technological and industrial strides in all areas than we in American industry and that, consequently, our competitive advantages of the past are becoming less and less visible. In view of this trend, it is up to American industry to accelerate its efforts toward progress in all areas. Full cooperation and the utmost effort from all employees in our industrial complex are definitely required; otherwise deterioration is bound to set in and, probably, result in eventual failure. Let us be positive in all our actions within the manufacturing function and so retain our prestige as world industrial leaders. With renewed efforts, constant vigilance, and a positive attitude in the face of possible adversity, success in world leadership can still be a certainty.

PART ONE

Organizing and Manning the Function

THE MANUFACTURING MANAGER'S SKILLS

By WILLIAM H. MARKLE

The skills and abilities required to be a successful manufacturing manager are numerous and various. The special combination of skills that any one position demands obviously depends upon the type of work that position is expected to accomplish. Even so, some skills are absolutely essential, and it is to a discussion of these that this paper is directed. Most of the points are covered at length elsewhere in this book by experts in their respective fields. All that is attempted here is to give the reader some indication of the essential talents of the manufacturing manager and the way in which these talents are exercised by the successful manager.

THE ABILITY TO DELEGATE

Today's complex industrial organizations with their many interpersonal problems had their beginnings in Biblical antiquity. Jethro's advice to his son-in-law Moses in Chapter 18 of the *Book of Exodus* is appropriate to our age:

> And thou shalt teach them ordinances and laws, and shalt shew them the way wherein they must walk, and the work they must do.

> Moreover thou shalt provide out of all the people able men, such as fear God, men of truth, hating covetousness; and place such over them, to be rulers of thousands, and rulers of hundreds, rulers of fifties, and rulers of tens:

> And let them judge the people at all seasons: and it shall be, that every great matter they shall bring unto thee, but every small matter they shall judge: so shall it be easier for thyself, and they shall bear the burden with thee.

WILLIAM H. MARKLE is Vice President, Stainless Processing Company, Chicago, Illinois.

There we have it in capsule form—the start of the whole business of management through the orderly delegation of authority and responsibility. Although the leader retains the ultimate authority for himself, and although all power and authority emanate from him, he must break down this authority and responsibility into segments of manageable size so that the people who help him get the job done can function effectively on their own and in keeping with the goals and aspirations of the organization.

This sounds logical and rational. And yet how many of us have done this job well ourselves? How many of us know men occupying high places in industrial organizations who cannot bring themselves to an orderly divesting of the more routine aspects of their jobs? We can almost see them drowning in a sea of myriad and miscellaneous minutiae, unable to sort out the important from the trivial.

High on the list of skills needed to manage a manufacturing operation is the ability to delegate the more routine aspects of a job, to divide the routine from the unusual, and to assure that the usual aspects of operations function well in the hands of subordinates and only the unusual or exceptional situations are forwarded up the line to the boss for a decision.

Of course, hand in hand with delegation goes the recognition that each man will be held accountable for activities for which he has authority. The top man in an organization can never unload his ultimate accountability; however, he can structure his organization in such a way that accountability for actions and judgments can be maintained from the very bottom to the very top of his organization. A failure to recognize this essential tenet of organization structure is often at the core of a manager's reluctance to divest himself of the more routine aspects of his job.

Another facet of delegating authority and responsibility is what some people call the opportunity cost of time. Perhaps it is more aptly called the tyranny of time. Jobs fall into four basic categories: routine, emergency, special, and creative work. Now, just as a law of physics states that no two objects may occupy the same space at the same time, so it is axiomatic that the human brain cannot effectively cope with more than one situation at a time. Thus, if we are doing routine work, the other three types must wait, and the same is true of emergency, special, or creative work.

The skillful manager invests his time and energy in such a manner that the best interests of his organization are served. Of course, there are some areas of our jobs over which we have control and others in which situations are imposed on us. Time to be invested in routine and creative work can be planned for. On the other hand, the only thing predictable about emergencies is that they will happen, the when being uncertain. And, as for special work, who knows when the boss will call? All these considerations are parts of the manager's job, and planning for balance and flexibility in time investment is an important skill. Many managers run into rough sledding because, unlike Moses, they retain too much routine and are buried when emergencies and special assignments come upon them.

THE ABILITY TO COMMUNICATE

Once authority and responsibility have been delegated, we have a vertically integrated organization available for action. Nothing will happen, though, until it starts receiving orders from the top, and so another important skill in the effective functioning of a manufacturing organism is communication. Most operating problems come about through poor communicating, just as most time wasting is traceable to poor delegation. Many managers take problems of communication quite lightly, and yet language is one of the most complex tools for getting work done through other people.

How many times have we heard the cliché, "Say what you mean, and mean what you say"? It sounds simple, doesn't it? But it is not what we say that counts, it is what people *think* we say. All too often the implication of the word "communication" is only that somebody is telling something. Too little attention is paid to the other half of communication: what is going on at the receiving end, the listening end, which is not only the subordinate listening to the superior, but also the superior listening to the subordinate. How much we miss that could otherwise contribute to our success as managers because we are too busy to listen to what people tell us.

If we are to become better managers, every one of us would do well to sharpen the skills which comprise the art of listening attentively to people: maintaining eye contact, asking open questions, drawing people out, showing interest, making people feel comfortable when they talk with us, and, perhaps one of the hardest skills of all, playing dumb once in a while. Few things in life are so embarrassing and frustrating to a speaker as to be telling a story or presenting an idea and to have the listener stop him in the middle and say, "Oh, I've heard that before."

THE ABILITY TO SOLVE PROBLEMS

Making decisions, solving problems, and thinking creatively are the bread and butter of management. If we have delegated well and communicated well, a substantial portion of our time will be available for making major decisions and solving unusual problems. Frequently, of course, we make decisions in order to resolve a problem. The managers who succeed, who rise to the top, must have a good batting average in successfully solving problems.

Some years ago the head of the Industrial Engineering Department of Yale University said, "If I had only one hour to solve a problem, I would spend up to two-thirds of that hour in attempting to define what the problem is." This statement warrants thinking about. What is a problem? A problem is usually a mess, and often hand in hand with messes go tension, excitement, and a desire to swing into action, even if the appropriate direction of action is unclear. Voices rise, tempers shorten, and clear thinking is all too often in short supply. Such situations place a high premium on the manager's skill in bringing order out of chaos, sense out of nonsense.

Problems fall into two categories: new situations and old situations. In handling either, the procedure is the same, with minor modifications. When he is faced with a new problem, a skillful manager frequently calls a meeting of his immediate subordinates. He attempts to define his problem, get the facts, establish alternatives, evaluate the alternatives, plan a course of action, assign authority and responsibility for implementing the course of action, and, finally, establish a means of following up. This procedure appears to be the essence of simplicity; yet to carry it off well requires all the manager's skills. Often the manager who conducts such a meeting is on the spot. He may have all sorts of reasons for bringing tension and hostility into such a meeting, attacking subordinates, and working people over. Yet the manager who would improve the odds that he will come up with the best solution must conduct his meeting in a permissive, relaxed environment.

The manager who is skilled in creative problem solving is aware that in gathering the facts surrounding a problem, people tend to come up with opinions and not with facts. This confusion substantially reduces the odds that the best alternative will be found.

When something goes wrong in a hitherto smooth-functioning operation, the skillful manager usually insists on finding out exactly what part of his operation has changed before contemplating any remedial action.

In making decisions one of the major responsibilities of the manager is to make a choice between alternatives. He must plan his work, as well as the work of his subordinates, in such a manner that when a decision has to be made, he is aware of his best alternatives. If the choice of action is made from an orderly array of alternatives, it will probably be successful; but even if it is not, much of the heat normally generated by failure will probably be eliminated.

THE ABILITY TO TRUST OTHERS

Some of the best managers have developed a mutuality of faith with other people in the organization which acts as a kind of lubricant to its smooth functioning. Day in and day out we must put our faith and trust in our associates, whether they be above or below us in the organizational chart and whether they have line or staff functions. The good manager, the real leader, is the one who goes far beyond lip service in placing his faith in other people.

A man would be a fool to place responsibility in anyone in whom he did not have trust and confidence. Nevertheless, all too often managers tend to use purely intuitive judgment in hiring and promoting people. Choosing people to fill jobs is not an exact science; there certainly is quite a bit of art in it. Nonetheless, the skillful manager, before hiring a man, uses whatever psychological tools, sound interviewing procedures, and other sources of information that are available to him.

THE ABILITY TO TEACH AND COUNSEL

Having filled out the organization through hiring or promotion, the manager must constantly be aware of his responsibility as a mentor for his subordinates. His role of teacher is one of the most important that he commits himself to by being a manager. The strength of his organization and its ability to grow, to handle unusual situations, to create, are in large measure the result of his ability to bring out in his subordinates those managerial skills which can achieve the organization's goals.

In a sense the manager is always teaching, since his subordinates are always watching him; and, in his role as teacher, his personal example is always subject to inspection. The leader may say, "Do as I say, not as I do," but the subordinate's reaction may be, "Your actions speak so loud that I can't hear a word you say."

Having picked his people and taught them, the successful manager must counsel them regularly and objectively. People have a right to know where they stand with the boss. Preparation for a constructive performance appraisal cannot be handled in a hit-or-miss manner. In U.S. Reduction Company, for example, the plant manager prepares a detailed written report with supporting evidence which he reviews with his own boss in order to account for his stewardship of the men who report to him. It also helps him prepare for his counseling session with his subordinates.

In these counseling sessions, which are held away from the formality of an office, the plant manager attempts to help a man recognize where his strengths lie as well as his weaknesses and to obtain a commitment to a course of action for improving the areas of weakness. If a man is in danger of losing his position, he should know that the situation exists, why it exists, and how long he has to straighten it out. A sound manager should recognize that if a man is failing, the manager himself must bear some measure of responsibility for the failure; he must map out some constructive course of action so that the subordinate knows he has an opportunity to prove his worth and keep his job.

COMMUNITY RESPONSIBILITY

One final point is particularly relevant to the manufacturing manager—responsibility to the community. A good manager realizes that his organization does not exist in a vacuum. Industrial leadership is looked to for substantial help in maintaining the day-in-day-out workings of the community. The manager who walks away from this responsibility is failing to discharge his function for helping maintain the company image. By his own involvement in community affairs such as the United Fund drives, American Red Cross, Junior Achievement, church, and other voluntary social and charitable activities, the manager reflects his organization's social interest.

Even more important, if he can encourage his subordinates to participate in community activities, he is accomplishing two things: First, he is helping the corporate image by indicating an interest in activities which the community feels are important and in its best interest. Second, involvement in voluntary activities improves managerial skills. The lessons about motivation and administration learned in a volunteer organization stand managers in good stead in running their bread-and-butter operations. There is a lot to be said for learning how to motivate people without having the clout of salary administration firmly in hand.

A SUMMATION

To review, it is the job of the manager to—
- Delegate authority and responsibility, but maintain accountability.
- Invest time intelligently, with an awareness that the penalty of doing anything is that something also must be left undone.

- Give substantial care to the manner in which he communicates.
- Work hard at being a good listener.
- Make decisions and solve problems, for this is what he is paid to do; adjust the odds his way with a factual, thoughtfully oriented, creative approach.
- Pick his people carefully, teach them constantly, and counsel them constructively.
- Be aware of community responsibilities.

THE SELECTION AND DEVELOPMENT OF SUBORDINATES

By HOWARD A. PILKEY

The manufacturing job, like any other, is more complex today than it was several years ago. The technology of automation and electromechanical devices has raised the standards for selection of candidates who are expected to serve as operators and supervisors. Then too there is an ever increasing demand to produce more, better, and faster at lower cost per unit. This invariably means that we in the manufacturing establishment are going to turn out more goods with fewer people both on the production worker level and in management. Managers consequently must look for better-qualified personnel to fill positions at all levels than was absolutely necessary in the quite recent past.

SOURCES OF EMPLOYEES

There are two major sources of employees—one is within the company, and the other is outside the company. Most companies prefer to follow a policy of promotion from within wherever possible to fill the higher-level positions and of recruitment from outside for the opening or starting positions. This procedure has the distinct advantage of creating high morale among employees; however, its success depends upon the initial selection of employees to fill the lower-level or opening positions. Definite consideration at the time of selection, therefore, must be given to potential for advancement. One problem of advancement from within is supervisors who are reluctant to give up some of their good men to fill higher-level positions. Such managers fortunately are

HOWARD A. PILKEY is Manager, Salaried Personnel, Administration & Training, The Carborundum Company, Niagara Falls, New York.

becoming fewer since many people in supervisory jobs have reached their positions through just such a process.

When no one is available at a lower level with the potential to fill a higher-level position, companies are required to look outside. This means that they must bring someone from outside to direct the work of others who are already in the company, and although such a situation may be necessary, it does have an adverse effect on the attitudes of the current employees. Companies that follow such a policy find they have a morale problem and a higher than average turnover in personnel.

A company can become too inbred, and caution is required to strike a happy medium. There are very large and successful companies in the United States that have had long-established policies of filling their higher-level positions only from within. In recent years some of them have altered their thinking and have started to hire personnel for various positions from outside. Perhaps the best practice is a combination of inside and outside recruiting, with greater emphasis on selection from within.

In addition to the favorable effect on other employees the practice of choosing people from within has definite advantages. The individual chosen is more familiar with the company, he is happy and well motivated because he has received a promotion, and more useful information is available about his work performance. He need not be someone from the same department but can come from another department. This has a decided benefit in that employees know that they have opportunities for advancement not only in their own group but also in other areas in the company. This practice also has its advantages when hiring someone from outside, since most applicants want to know if they can be considered for positions outside the department which originally hires them.

There are a number of sources which can be used for securing candidates from outside. Given the level of unemployment in the United States during the past several years, industry has had little difficulty in finding people for unskilled and semi-skilled positions. There has been, however, a marked change on the part of industry in educational requirements. Most companies are now requiring a minimum of a high school education, and, further to refine their selection, some have started to use tests, although this practice is not so prevalent for the unskilled and semi-skilled as for the skilled, administrative, supervisory, technical, and managerial levels.

The State Employment Services offer a ready pool of unskilled and semi-skilled employees. Some companies, however, find their current employees a major source of applicants. They notify their employees of openings and in this way are able to secure an adequate supply of good new employees. They may use a referral card that the employee gives to the individual he is recommending. This procedure helps to make the current employee feel he is more a part of the company, thus enhancing his motivation to produce.

It is, on the other hand, becoming increasingly more difficult to find applicants to fill positions in skilled occupations, particularly in the trade areas. Since World War II there has been a decrease in the number of people entering the skilled trades. This fact, combined with an increase in demand, has created a shortage. The once-flourishing company-sponsored apprentice programs have been curtailed for one reason or another, and industry is beginning to feel the effects. The only solution to the problem of finding candidates to fill skilled-trade positions is to train the unskilled through well-administered apprenticeship plans. It currently appears that there will be, for some time to come, a greater scarcity of skilled craftsmen than of engineers. The vocational schools and technical institutes are a good source of applicants for apprenticeship programs, although graduates from regular high schools with mathematics, science, and drafting majors are likewise acceptable.

There are a number of ways in which to secure candidates for administrative, technical, supervisory, and managerial positions. Colleges and universities are among the best sources of well-qualified candidates with potential for advancement. Most companies have some type of program for recruiting at such institutions, and many have special college relations managers whose primary function is to coordinate the recruitment of graduates. In some of the very large companies these recuiting activities are set up on a regional or areal basis. Most institutions of higher education have a placement office with a staff under the direction of a full-time placement officer. Representatives of hundreds of companies flood the campuses each year, starting in October and continuing on through June. Since a number of the universities are operating on a trimester or quarterly basis, the college recruitment activity is becoming a year-round function.

One of the prime sources of candidates is still direct advertising through newspapers, technical journals, magazines, and other printed media that have been developed exclusively for recruitment purposes. Depending upon the nature of the position to be filled and the level and availability of possible candidates, advertising for help is done either locally or nationally. Ads may run anywhere from a few lines under "Help Wanted Classified" to full-page "display" ads. The financial section of several newspapers, such as the Sunday edition of *The New York Times* and the *Chicago Tribune,* are used continuously by companies particularly to advertise for high-level positions. *The Wall*

Street Journal provides a similar service from Monday to Friday; the employer has the opportunity to select the edition or editions he wants to use, such as Eastern, Midwestern, or Far Western. Such ads get wide coverage and generally reach the people to whom they are directed.

Technical magazines also are available, but in using them it is well to remember that they have long lead times. Most are monthly publications, but some, like *Chemical & Engineering News,* are weekly.

There has been a continued increase in the use of private employment agencies, according to recent studies made by national organizations. The private agencies charge a fee, usually a percentage of the first year's salary. Although formerly the fee was nearly always paid by the applicant seeking a position, today most companies pay it. One of the advantages is the screening done by the agencies, although its quality varies from one agency to another and according to whether a list of candidates is readily available. The agency, when used correctly, can give a company's personnel staff considerable assistance. Since the demand for well-qualified personnel is increasing, companies must utilize all the resources available to meet their employment requirements. The supply of good applicants is short today, and it does not appear that the situation is going to get any better in the near future.

JOB SPECIFICATIONS

Selection is not something that can be done haphazardly. It requires skill, effort, and judgment. When we are selecting from among candidates for *any* position, we must remember that in some respects all people are the same, as in having two legs, two arms, two eyes, and a brain. In other respects they are different—for example, in aptitude, personality, skills, and intelligence. In selecting a person for a position we are concerned with the differences in relation to the qualifications required. Thus this investigation of differences becomes an important function of managers who are responsible for selecting and hiring personnel for their organizations.

The first thing a manager should have when he is selecting a person is a good, accurate description of the position to be filled. From this he is able to determine certain basic qualifications that are required in the person who will fill the position. The result of his determination has been referred to as "man specifications." Without such a description a manager may select a person who does not have the qualifications or one who has more qualifications than required, either of which conditions causes problems in the future, except when the overqualified person is being trained and prepared for advancement.

From the job description the manager is able to determine some basic qualifications—primarily experience and education. They are not the only factors to be considered in selection, of course, as we shall see later. In addition to serving as a basis for determining certain man qualifications, the position description serves as a guide for training and development and for establishing goals and objectives.

EXPERIENCE

While from the position description the manager is able to ascertain what experience is needed, he should further define this information according to type and amount. The manager should also determine how closely the experience of the applicant must be related to the duties of the position. For example, if he is trying to select a maintenance supervisor or manager, obviously it is best to find someone with experience in maintenance. It may not be necessary, however, for the candidate to have experience in supervision, depending on his other qualifications and on how large a maintenance staff he has to supervise. Or the position to be filled may be one purely of production supervision. Unless the nature of the production is highly technical, the manager may be able to fill the position with a person who has experience in supervision without regard to the type of production he has formerly been working with. In the first instance the technical aspect of the experience is more important than in the second instance, where supervisory experience is paramount.

It is difficult, however, to establish rigid guidelines, for each position requires something different. Experience, nonetheless, is a basic factor except for a starting position, for which "zero" experience is acceptable.

EDUCATION

From the position description we can also determine the level and type of education required, whether it has to be specific—as in the case of the mechanical engineer, electrical engineer, or industrial engineer—or whether it can be any type of discipline. Perhaps no scholastic degree is required at all. In some instances, if a degree is required, it may be either undergraduate or graduate. For example, a foreman's position may not require a degree man, but, if it does, any discipline may be satisfactory. On the other hand, for a position as an industrial engineer a manager probably will want to hire a person with a degree in industrial or mechanical engineering.

In evaluating education the manager should consider the school, the subjects taken, and the level of achievement. The longer a person is out of school and the more experience he has, the less emphasis is placed on grades. When there is no experience, as with a new graduate, more emphasis is placed on grades. Some people feel that high grades do not always mean a similarly good result in terms of job performance. We can assume, however, that, everything else being equal, the person with the higher grades will perform better.

EVALUATION OF FACTORS

In selecting a person for a position we should collect as much information as possible about him. The more information we have, the better decision we can make. We have already mentioned two areas where we can collect information—experience and education. In addition there are aptitudes, behavior, interests, performance on previous positions, and evaluation of potentials for advancement.

From the applicant's previous work experience can be obtained considerable information on how he will fit into the position for which he is under consideration. Experience may have been acquired within the company, outside the company, or—it may be—a combination of both. In the preliminary stages we are interested in what the candidate has done and how it matches with what we want him to do in the new position. However, as we proceed further, we find that additional information—such as *how* he actually accomplished his work—may be more important. A careful evaluation of the individual's work history will show us how he has progressed on the job. Has his progress been slow, has it been fast, or has he maintained a status quo? Has his achievement been outstanding or mediocre? Is it beyond what is expected as normal, or is it below? These are some of the judgments a manager must make. Some of this information is gathered at the time of the interview, and some of it is gathered through reference checks with other people for whom the applicant has worked.

Another important piece of information is concerned with motivation. Past work history enables us to determine how well an individual is motivated and perhaps what it is that motivates him. This knowledge is important not only for job performance but also for training and development. It is generally assumed that the person who is well motivated has the best chance for success.

From the applicant's work history we are also able to determine something about his behavior. Is he an outgoing, gregarious type of person, or is he retiring? Does he demonstrate initiative? Is he a loner, or does he work well with others? Previous experience shows us, too, what leadership and managerial ability he possesses and whether he is able to accept responsibility or give directions to others. The information we obtain from work experience has a high level of validity since it is based on what a person has actually done. We should try to collect this information, however, from as many different people as possible, so that we can check what one says against what another says. The comments normally are consistent, and the information usually falls into a discernible pattern.

In the same way that we obtain information about a person from his work experience, we can obtain certain information from his education. Everyone is aware that grades are somewhat of an indicator of an individual's abilities and achievements; however, other information is often overlooked that can easily be obtained. For example: How was his education financed? How much of his expenses did he pay himself? Did he work while going to school? Perhaps he was married and even raising a family while getting a degree. Extracurricular activities are likewise a good indication of abilities. Did the job candidate demonstrate leadership or managerial abilities in various activities? For example, was he chairman of various functions, an officer of his class, or a member of some other school organization?

Another factor to be considered is aptitude. We are able to obtain some information about this from a person's program in school and his grades. It can be further established through his work history as indicated by achievement and progress on the job. Many companies also use psychological testing. Much has been written about the use of psychological tests in the selection process. Some of the popular writers have been quite critical—they ridicule the validity of tests for this purpose. However, professionals in the field of testing recognize its value and recommend its use. And, regardless of the fact that some doubt has been cast on tests' usefulness, their application by business and industry is on the increase. Their effectiveness lies in the way they are used and the weight given to them in the selection process. Any test is misused when it takes prominence over all other factors and becomes the major basis on which the selection is made. Psychological test results, used correctly, give us some additional information on which to make a decision. They should never be used as a crutch or to take the place of judgment.

Since people are more likely to do things better when they are interested in what they are doing, it is well to investigate the interests and the career objectives of the candidate and determine whether they are compatible with the position being filled.

Of considerable importance to overall success is behavior. Even though a person may have a good education, with high academic achievement and a marked interest in a particular field, he may fail in a position because he does not display the behavior required. For example, if the position requires a considerable amount of detail with a high degree of accuracy, a person who does not naturally have this ability will be most uncomfortable; he will not be able to do his best and, in all probability, in time will either quit or be fired. In the same sense, if the position is one with a considerable amount of responsibility, with challenge and incentive, a person who does not lean toward such responsibility will not be so successful as one who does.

It is often difficult for a manager to evaluate behavior. He should try to observe behavioral characteristics during the interview and ask questions that will provoke behavioral responses. Certain aspects of behavior are readily discernible. It is not hard to determine that the person who does little talking during the interview is probably low in sociability, whereas the one who is able to express himself well and carry on a conversation without too much difficulty has skill in this area. He is most likely to be gregarious and outgoing. It is, of course, easier to judge the type of behavior which is characteristic of a person when it is magnified than when it is subtle.

MAKING THE DECISION

Determining which person or persons to offer a position is one of the most important decisions a manager is called upon to make. In arriving at his decision he should consider all the information he has on the qualifications of all the candidates and check it against the requirements of the position. Deciding what emphasis to place on one factor in relationship to other factors is always difficult. For a person with little or no experience it is obvious that education, test scores, behavior, and impressions are going to carry more weight than they do for an applicant who has several years of work experience. The amount of weight that experience carries depends upon how closely it relates to the amount of experience required for the new position.

A great mistake is commonly made in this connection. In selecting someone for a supervisory position it is not unusual for a manager to choose a high-production worker from the ranks and then to find out that he is not suited for supervisory work. The very characteristics that made him an outstanding production worker are not those required to make him a good supervisor. The net result is the loss of a good production worker with the questionable gain of a mediocre supervisor.

The important point to remember is that all these factors that we have looked at should be considered in arriving at the hiring decision. The manager should review all the information he has. The following list presents a systematic approach to making a selection. Although it is not foolproof, this systematic way of arriving at a decision will help managers to improve their batting average in selecting subordinates.

I. *Experience*
- What kind of experience does the person have?
- What is the length of this experience?
- How closely does it match the qualifications for the position?
- How does it relate to other positions in the company?
- How long was he in his previous positions before being promoted?
- How many promotions has he had?

II. *Education*
- What kind of education does he have?
- What was his scholastic achievement?
- Did he work while going to school?
- Was his education interrupted? If so, why?
- Did he receive all his education at one school? If not, why did he change?
- How does his education relate to the requirements of the position? To advancement to other positions?

III. *Behavior*
- What are the major aspects of his behavior?
- How do they fit in with the requirements of the position?
- Is he well motivated?

IV. *Interest*
- Is the position in line with the interests and overall career objectives of the individual?

V. *Aptitude*
- What are his aptitudes?
- How do they relate to the requirements of the position?
- How do they relate to advancement to higher-level positions?

VI. *Reference*
- What do people for whom he has worked have to say about him?

VII. *Potential*

- Does he have potential for advancement beyond his present position? If so, to what level?

TRAINING AND DEVELOPMENT WITHIN THE COMPANY

Fundamentally, the modern manager must subscribe to certain philosophies if he is to be effective in training and developing his subordinates. According to these philosophies, each manager of a function, regardless of how small or large it may be, is responsible for the training and development of all the people under his jurisdiction, whether they report directly to him or through others. Furthermore, training and development—a continuous process—is a conscious, planned activity not to be left to chance. If the manager observes these precepts, the employee's chances of success are greatly enhanced.

Training and development may be carried on within the company or outside. Inside training is divided into two parts—on the job and off the job. It is generally considered that the most effective training is done on the job. It is effective for a number of reasons involving such factors as transfer of skills, readiness, timing, association, and motivation.

When training is given off the job, there must be a successful transfer of the skills acquired to the job itself. In the process of transfer there generally is a loss of skills between the time when the training was received and the time when it is actually used. Or the loss may result from the fact that the off-the-job situation is not exactly the same as the on-the-job application. When training is given on the job, the transfer of the skills acquired is immediate, without any time lag. There is no need to relate the training to the actual work situation since the training itself is applied directly to the work.

A person learns most quickly when he is *ready* to receive the training. In an on-the-job situation this preparedness or readiness is enhanced because the trainee receives the training at the exact time when he needs it.

Through proper timing, direct association with the work, readiness to receive the training, and the opportunity to apply the training immediately to the work situation, a person's motivation to learn and his receptivity to training can be greatly improved. On-the-job training is carried out on a continuous, day-to-day basis as the need arises. The trainee under such conditions is less likely to become discouraged since he is not required to muddle through situations himself on a trial-and-error basis, as often happens when proper instruction is not given.

In addition to training on the job, other, closely related training techniques are effective. In certain instances an individual may need training which he can't get from his job situation, because the areas of work to which this training applies are not directly related to his present position. Examples are quality control, production control, labor relations, and safety. In such instances the employee can be taken off his job and given a special assignment in areas where the necessary training is actually given.

In other training situations, off the job but within the company, classes, conferences, or meetings dealing with a variety of subjects may be set up on a group basis. They may be scheduled to run for one or two days a week or for varied periods anywhere from two to four weeks or even longer. They may be concerned with methods improvement, safety, grievance handling, contract interpretation, conference leadership, or a number of other subjects. These courses are most effective when the people who are selected to participate in them have a definite need for the training being offered.

An effective development technique that has come into use within the past several years is assignment to a task force. The task force, usually made up of people with varying backgrounds, makes a study of a particular problem and comes up with a solution or recommendation. This provides exposure to areas of work outside those of the regular job activity. The task force members have the opportunity to learn to work with others, most of whom are in different lines of work, such as accounting, data processing, and sales.

PERFORMANCE APPRAISAL AS A MEANS OF DEVELOPMENT

Many companies, particularly large ones, have for a number of years appraised their employees' performance on a systematic basis. The *modus operandi* of these programs is similar throughout industry. The immediate superior, using a specially devised form, evaluates the performance of those employees who report to him. At predetermined intervals he sits down with each person and discusses his performance. The manner in which this is done varies from company to company—and even within a company from one manager to another. The original approach involved the use of a list of traits that the boss would check off; he would then call in the subordinate and proceed to tell him about his shortcomings. The premise was that the subordinate would heed the advice of the boss and improve his performance accordingly. It was difficult for the boss to understand why this improvement rarely occurred; why, in fact, the opposite type of behavior usually resulted—a letdown by the subordinate.

EXHIBIT 1

ONE-WAY EXCHANGE OF INFORMATION DURING PERFORMANCE APPRAISAL

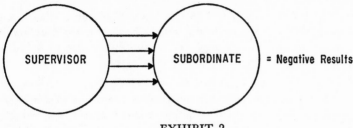

EXHIBIT 2

TWO-WAY EXCHANGE OF INFORMATION DURING PERFORMANCE APPRAISAL

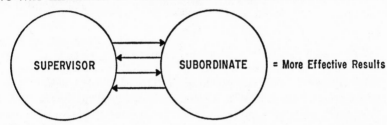

As a result of the failure of such misguided programs, newer approaches were developed to improve performance more effectively. One of the first steps was to eliminate the use of traits and to speak in terms of job improvement or job activities. This approach was more effective since it was job-oriented and did not touch directly on the personal characteristics of the people being appraised. However, in many instances the boss was still telling his subordinates where he felt they needed improvement. All too often a subordinate would not agree with the superior; as a result, he did nothing to bring about the suggested changes. This one-way exchange is depicted graphically by the diagram in Exhibit 1. When this situation was studied, it was decided that one way to overcome the problem was to give the subordinate an opportunity to participate more actively in determining those areas where he needed improvement. The diagram in Exhibit 2 portrays this situation.

This latter procedure began to show signs of achieving better results; however, it was soon recognized that even more refinements were needed. These involved setting up objectives or goals for the subordinate to shoot at, the appraisal being based on how well he was able to achieve them. Such a program has been discussed by Edgar F. Huse and Emanuel Kay, both of the General Electric Company. One of its important aspects, as they see it, is the role of the manager in his relationship to his subordinates.

An employee must be able to obtain assistance when and as needed.
For the employee to improve job performance, he must be able to obtain assistance, coaching, and guidance as needed.

First, the employees must feel free to request assistance when necessary. Employees will ask for assistance only when they are not "punished" for such an action—for example, when this is not seen as an admission of weakness or as ultimately resulting in criticism.

Second, the supervisor must feel free to offer assistance as necessary. At times, every supervisor sees a need to give assistance to a subordinate. This may come in the form of pointing out mistakes, suggesting a different approach, or in any one of a number of ways. To be most effective, this *must* be done in a constructive rather than threatening fashion. He must avoid causing a defensive reaction from the employee which would only reduce his effectiveness.

Third, to establish this climate, the supervisor must act as a *helper* rather than a judge. In work planning and review sessions, the emphasis shifts from the judging implicit in appraisals to concentration on accomplishing mutually acceptable goals. The emphasis is shifted from the weaknesses of the man to a job-centered operations approach. A climate is established for the employee to receive assistance when and as needed. In other words, work planning and review is a process which establishes a climate of *mutual* cooperation. Instead of stressing or accumulating past mistakes or successes to justify a salary action, the man and supervisor should use the review sessions as opportunities to learn how to improve future work performance. Instead of dealing in subjective opinions, praise, or criticism, they should mutually search for better measurements of mutually acceptable goals. The subordinate is a partner not a defendant.*

THE DEVELOPMENT PROCESS

Two major areas are involved in the development of subordinates. One is knowledge; the other is skill. Much of our training and development activity will be concerned with these, although attitude is also important. Starting with the knowledge and skills the individual already possesses, we assign to him work that will require a little more of each. When he has mastered this assignment, we repeat the process—which can best be understood by imagining a diagram consisting of two concentric circles. The inner circle represents what knowledge and skills the individual already possesses, the outer circle represents

---

* "Improving Employee Productivity Through Work Planning," in *The Personnel Job in a Changing World,* American Management Association, Inc., New York, 1964.

the additional knowledge and skills the new assignment will require. When he reaches the periphery of the outer circle, we assign him work that will reach out still further to a third circle. And so we continue, adding more and more circles. What is important is to give the trainee an assignment that will push him beyond the level of what he is doing currently. We must remember two things:

1. We must never give him an assignment that is too far from what he knows and the skills he possesses. Should such a situation occur, he will be unable to bridge the gap from the inner to the outer circle; becoming discouraged and frustrated, he will withdraw within himself and will no longer strive to improve but, instead, he will actually decline.

2. We must be sure to give him sufficient time to finish each assignment. Too short a time will have the same effect as giving him an assignment that is beyond him.

SELF-DEVELOPMENT

Much of what we have been considering up to this point places the burden for training and development on the manager. This does not mean, however, that the subordinate himself is not also responsible for his own development and growth. In fact, a good manager will, in some way or another, promote self-development on the part of his subordinates. When any one of them shows initiative in this direction, it indicates interest on his part and a desire to grow to something beyond what he is. It is indicative of his willingness to accept responsibility and not depend on someone else to provide the impetus and means for progressing. It may be surprising to a manager to discover that although he has put forth great personal effort to help a subordinate grow and develop, his efforts are not so productive as those of the subordinate himself.

We too often tend to associate self-development with voluntary enrollment in courses at local schools and colleges, outside reading, membership in technical or similar organizations, and so on. However, much of the really lasting self-development takes place right on the job. The employee who is interested in self-development does a little more than is requested or expected of him in his position; seeks out new things to do and may ask to be assigned to certain additional tasks in order to increase his breadth of knowledge and skills.

MORE ABOUT TRAINING OUTSIDE THE COMPANY

A large number of training and development programs are available outside the company. They should be used as supplements to the training and development that subordinates receive within the company, both on and off the job. Two factors govern the selection of a program: (1) the individual's immediate needs and (2) what is required to prepare him for advancement to a higher-level position.

With reference to the first factor, the more closely the program is related to the job situation and the quicker the training is applied on the job, the greater the benefit. It is important that the immediate superior play a major part in the selection of the program in which the subordinate is to participate. In this way the superior will be receptive to the new ideas and concepts the trainee has received during his training and encourage and permit him to use them on his job. Too frequently, employees return from expensive training programs only to have the boss (who wasn't in on the act) say, "That's nice, but it won't work here."

When selecting programs for employee development, the manager must assure that the nature of the training is not too far removed from what the trainee will be doing within a reasonable period of time. It is obvious that when training is being provided for the future needs of the individual, it is more difficult to apply it quickly. However, every effort should be made to give the trainee special assignments in the area of the training he has received so that he can, as it were, get in some practice shots.

Some of the major advantages in using outside training facilities are these:

1. The trainee gets to know people from other companies.
2. He is exposed to new ideas and concepts with which he otherwise might not come into contact.
3. He has the opportunity to receive instruction from leading authorities in the field.
4. He is motivated to do better when he returns to his job.
5. The change in environment enhances the relearning process.

*   *   *

There are, essentially, four points to any good program of selecting and developing subordinates. Observing these points faithfully will add greatly to a manufacturing manager's chances of success in his operations.

1. The effectiveness of any organization is dependent upon the people who make up the organization, from the worker at the lowest level in production to the executive at the highest level in management.
2. This effectiveness is increased when all employees are well trained in the performance of their work.
3. The growth of the organization is insured when its people are developed to assume positions of greater responsibility.
4. In order to achieve this effectiveness and growth, we must have good material to start with, and this is dependent on good selection.

TRAINING AND MANPOWER DEVELOPMENT

By ERICH HARDT

The average manufacturing manager recognizes the importance of his training and manpower development responsibilities; but, for various reasons, he frequently feels uncomfortable in a discussion about them. The major reasons for this feeling fortunately can be turned to his advantage rather easily. Let's examine them one at a time; their cures we'll get to later.

1. He is questioned about this phase of his work in the inquiring presence of professionals (training specialists) and feels a little bit like a layman being quizzed by a prominent physician at a medical convention about how he is meeting his family's health needs. He knows he ought to be doing something about it—in fact, wants to—but is too unsure of himself even to comment. In the same way, the manufacturing manager realizes he should be doing something about training and developing his subordinates, but he feels inadequately informed in comparison with the well-informed company of professional evaluators.

2. The training and manpower development responsibilities of the line manager have rarely been defined in his position guide (or job description) with the same clarity that his production, quality, or financial responsibilities have been stated. Again, he recognizes that he should be doing something but has not been told what is required.

3. His superior may not have made clear exactly what he (the superior) thinks is meant by line management's responsibility for training and manpower development. The manager's situation is thus worsened. He now is in front of experts, has no guide sheet, and does not really know what he can say that will please his superior.

4. The situation becomes more complicated for the line manager when no specific goals or measures of results expected are spelled out as they are for production and other manufacturing areas. A manufacturing manager has learned to study measurable goals and resourcefully direct

---

ERICH HARDT is the Manager of Management Planning and Development for The F. & M. Schaefer Brewing Co., Brooklyn, New York.

his energies toward them. He likes measuring results. He likes seeing
how well he can perform against goals. In training and manpower development he can't measure as clearly what he has accomplished. Results thus become matters of discussion and opinion, not specifics which
he and others can measure in an agreed-upon fashion.

5. Finally, the manager's dilemma is complete when the approaches
   offered him bear little resemblance to his usual problem-solving
   methods. Normally he searches for what went wrong and sets up clear
   safeguards against its repetition. When he plans, his steps are clear.
   When he controls, he can measure precisely, and when he forecasts,
   it is on the basis of known facts and understood experience. This is
   all too rarely so in the training and manpower development actions
   he takes. No two problems are the same; therefore, no method of solution is ever exactly re-applicable. He thus finds himself in the company
   of experts, without road map or instructions, without the end of the
   road noted, but with a vehicle that operates like no other he has ever
   used before. Little wonder the manufacturing manager feels uncomfortable!

If we try to help him by putting him on a common technical footing with
the training specialist, we will lose a great deal of his valuable production
time in teaching him subject matter relatively little of which is directly useful
in meeting his profit obligations to the company. If we give him more specific
guidelines in his job description, we can impress him with the fact that training and development of subordinates is one of his major responsibilities. If
we get his superior to commit himself on what, exactly, he expects, the manager will feel no more uncomfortable discussing this subject with his superior
than he is discussing cost with his superior in front of the accountants. If
we additionally establish goals and spell out expected results, the manufacturing manager will be able to converse in his own language. And, finally, if
we offer him approaches (problem solution methods) more nearly akin to his
normal operating methods, he will be quite comfortable discussing his responsibilities for training and manpower development with the specialists.

UNDERSTANDING THE TRAINING SPECIALIST

Like anyone trained in a limited field, the training and manpower development specialists have evolved a language somewhat different from that of the
rest of the people in industry. Despite the fact that they claim a great deal
of interest in the ability to communicate, they frequently find themselves *not*

understood rather than misunderstood. The words they use are not in themselves uncommon, but the concepts they express are based on research and principles unknown to the manufacturing manager. It is this "apparent familiarity" of the words which makes the line manager feel he should understand what is being said. Since, however, he does not understand (he is operations-oriented and finds staff work considerably less specific than his own), he concludes that it is better to remain silent than to reveal what must be his ignorance of seemingly obvious facts.

Things which seem simple to the professional are not at all simple to the layman. The latter often feels it is a revelation of his own inadequacy to confess ignorance. He is wrong. Only a neophyte in any profession would condemn the man who asks for clarification. It is in the nature of a competent training specialist to want to be understood.

Thus, to cure this first symptom of his discomfort, the manufacturing manager will do well to ask questions, to test his own understanding, and to discuss his own specific training and development needs in the terms he himself understands. If the manager asks questions (thus making certain that he understands the training man's suggestions correctly) and then focuses the discussion on specific issues of interest to him as a line manager, the training man is forced to make himself understood. The manufacturing manager can always control the conversation by insisting on discussing the development of his people in terms of realistic plans which he can administer. Since the line manager is responsible for achieving results through his subordinates, the staff man must be resourceful enough to meet the specific development needs of each member of line management.

STRENGTHENING THE POSITION GUIDE

Most manufacturing position guides or job descriptions contain 15 to 25 items, all of which refer to production and cost situations with the exception of perhaps two. One of these cites "all other duties assigned," and the other contains a generality in regard to the manager's responsibility for the training and development of subordinates.

This generality is obviously inadequate, and some corrective action should be taken as soon as possible. The single statement in regard to this major responsibility should be at least as precise and demanding as others. The same applies to management performance standards, which are frequently written with the position guide as a base.

Standards should include the following four elements:

1. Quality expected.
2. Quantity expected.
3. Completion time expected.
4. Manner of performance expected.

This principle is just as applicable to standard elements related to training and manpower development as to those related to cost. A stated standard is not just a "hope." For instance, a definition of a goal can indicate how many future general foremen must be developed out of the present number of foremen, and the date by which this is to be done can also be indicated. Also, a properly detailed specification sheet for the general foreman's job can project the objectives and serve as a progress checklist.

If performance is evaluated on generalities such as "ability to get along with people," "personality," "willingness to work overtime," "emotional stability," and the like, the manufacturing manager will find it difficult to evaluate a subordinate without exposing himself to disputes and questions from both his superior and his subordinate. No two people will agree on the meanings of such phrases or on evidence of what *constitutes* behavioral pattern. Again, if the "number of grievances" or "number of accidents" is used as a measure, too many deceptions are possible. Grievances are caused by many factors other than performance alone; accidents must be charged, and the center charged is not in all cases actually at fault. But if evaluations are based on attendance record, safety record, production record, reject ratio, cost per unit, units per hour, percent of downtime, and the like, the manufacturing manager has little difficulty discussing an evaluation with a subordinate. They are discussing job performance and meeting of goals in a language both understand the same way.

FILLING IN THE BOSS'S UNDERSTANDING

Frequently, the superior has no definite knowledge of what he is looking for, but since the head of the company makes an annual speech at a trade function about the "importance of our people" or "our greatest asset," he recognizes that there must be something here that requires his attention. He is not at all certain what it is. Because of his own lack of understanding of what the professionals have to say and the fact that his own requirements are not well spelled out in his position guide, he may actually be hoping his subordinates can perform in such a way as to give him a useful clue. They are perhaps college men and have studied "this sort of thing." Thus, if each subordinate does something along the lines of training and development, the superior can compare methods and results, and from these numerous observations he may learn what is expected of him.

We are back at the basic point: Every manager must ask questions, test his understanding of what is being said, and discuss problems in the language and orientation of his subordinate line managers. He must concentrate on situations that exist in his own function as he sees them. This holds true for all levels of line management.

A physician studies a good many years before he practices medicine, but if a patient has to give himself a hypodermic needle every few hours, the doctor tells him specifically what to do, cautioning him about related symptoms and dangers. He does not give the patient a full medical course. The training and development man is a trained specialist with wide knowledge. The manufacturing manager should not concern himself with all the research data and background reading available in the field. It is enough for him to be able to diagnose the development needs of subordinates and apply the appropriate methods to get the needed results. The training specialist can suggest many approaches, but the line manager should accept and use only those he can understand and apply in a practical way.

The manufacturing manager does a good job of controlling costs without a degree in accounting, and he does a good job of controlling quality without an engineering degree. By the same token he can do a very good job of developing people without the broad staff training and experience the specialist should have. Thus, once he gains a practical understanding related to the on-the-job situation, he can begin to set down guidelines for his subordinate managers, give necessary task assignments, set up controls, and make reasonable demands in training and development.

SPELLING OUT GOALS AND RESULTS

It is customary for a good manufacturing manager to have established his goals and detailed the precise results that are expected of him. Once more the exception to this rule appears all too frequently to be training and manpower development. But fortunately, again, specifics can be spelled out in terms of quality and quantity, terminal date, and manner of performance. For example, it can be the responsibility of a manager to develop at least one assistant in the next year (or two) who is qualified for promotion on the basis of his proven qualifications as judged by the company specifications for the next-higher position.

At a given level such as foreman the objectives for the year can be defined in terms of volume, reject rate, absentee rate, labor cost, and so on to be attained by a certain date. After an evaluation has established whether the goals are underachieved or overachieved, specific training can be designed to develop the skills and impart the knowledge needed to achieve the results wanted. It need have nothing to do with promotion. Every manager must improve performance and raise his own and his subordinates' standards. This is best done as objectively as possible on the basis of specific goals and measured results.

CHOOSING AMONG VARIOUS APPROACHES

The manufacturing manager approaches his training needs from the simple, practical point of view that he has set up specific goals, then measured results, and found that someone did not perform adequately. The subordinate in question is being paid to perform as a foreman, let's say, and he must certainly maintain at least a standard level in all respects. To the extent that the expected criteria have been spelled out, the specific performance results can be measured.

The line manager's approach to a problem of substandard results is to find the cause of the deficiency, apply a remedy, and try again. There is no reason for him not to use this approach in training subordinates. Let him tell the subordinate what is wanted in all respects and in all areas, then encourage (motivate) successful performance. He can measure results against what was expected, make corrections, and set up new goals. It is a constant process, like cost and quality control. The acceptable product quality of 1950 is no longer good enough in 1966, and the managerial performance level of 1950 is just as outdated.

When it comes to potential, again let him set clear objectives, offer an opportunity to perform, and measure results. Evaluation, counseling, and coaching present no terrors for the manufacturing manager if he and his subordinates are talking in terms of performance results.

In some companies the group approach is used, but the formula remains the same: Establish well-understood goals, give the opportunity to perform, and measure results. The difficulty with group evaluation is not than an incompetent man is "hidden" by well-meaning associates but that the superior is not sufficiently specific and challenging in his demands for results. It has been proved that group results can be greater than the sum of individual results. This is because, not only is each man just as effective in the group as he is on an individual assignment, but he takes on an additional effectiveness because of group interactions. Too many managers in setting goals for subordinate groups do not adequately challenge the group-interaction bonus of talent available to them. Thus they look at groups as "time wasters" or "conversational committees." If the results wanted are spelled out in terms of quality, quantity, time, and means, and if they are set at a challenging level, the manager has no difficulty. Potential leaders tend to emerge rather consistently from the various groups to which they are assigned, so that the identification of future leaders is not lost in group interaction.

*   *   *

In short, the manufacturing manager need no longer feel uncomfortable in discussing his training and manpower development responsibilities. He is now discussing a situation which he understands fully within the context of his own responsibilities as well as of his superior's understood requirements and in terms of specific goals and results which must be achieved. The approach to training and development he uses is a practical one, consistent with his handling of a cost, a maintenance, or a pure production problem.

The manufacturing manager is basically results-oriented. He can effectively use this inclination with his training and manpower development specialists by discussing his problems in three simple areas:

1. What are the results wanted in terms of performance or potential specifics?
2. What opportunities to achieve these results can be offered on the job or in job-related individual or group task delegations?
3. How can results be measued?

The manufacturing manager will be as expert as he need be in training and developing his own people, and he will find the staff man of greatest professional help, if he keeps these questions always in mind. There is a big difference between the doctor who knows all the medical terminology and research studies, and the man whose son needs specifically prescribed medical help regularly. The manufacturing manager is the stronger for seeking the advice of the expert and is at his best when he knows the specific problem for which he seeks help and can define the ultimate result he wants.

REPORTING RELATIONSHIPS AND SUPERVISORY DUTIES OF THE MANUFACTURING MANAGER

By JOHN D. WAIT

The scope of the manufacturing manager's duties, as well as of his reporting relationships, obviously varies—and greatly—company by company, depending on the size of the firm, the extent to which it is formally organized, its volume of business, the complexity of its manufacturing operations, the extent, if any, of its staff functions, and so on. Furthermore, an industrial organization, like political, social, educational, institutional, and other organizations, is made up of people, and for this reason and others too numerous to list, no two organizations are alike. No simple, single, fixed organization structure suits all situations. It is with these two points of view in mind that this chapter must be read.

Any treatise on the subject of the supervisory duties of the manufacturing manager, or of any manager, should begin with the simple premise that the first and foremost duty of a manager is to get things done through people. We may perhaps say that this premise is too simple, but it is not so simple when we consider the difficulties we encounter when we attempt to find good managers. Not so simple, that is, when we recall the tendency of many managers to rely on a system, rather than on their own ability to manage—to lead—or to play it safe by leaving to committees the making of decisions that rightfully belong to these men themselves.

To manage requires not only education, training, and experience but also—and possibly of even greater importance—

- A desire to manage.
- A willingness to accept responsibilities.

JOHN D. WAIT is Plant Manager, Morrison Steel Company, New Brunswick, New Jersey.

- A willingness to work hard.
- Enthusiasm, remembering that enthusiasm is contagious and can create wonders.
- The courage to make and stand by decisions.
- The recognition of a manager's job for what it is—a demanding occupation.

ORGANIZATION OF THE WORKFORCE

A primary responsibility in any endeavor involving people is that of properly organizing them into effective work groups, which is, really, solving the problem of who is to do what. The complete determination and understanding of this fact is the crux of success in management. The good manager will make certain his organization is sound. This means that he will assure—

1. That it is carefully and adequately planned. This prerequisite demands that a manager not only fully understand and appreciate his own scope of responsibility but that he likewise understand and appreciate the overall organization as a whole.
2. That the table of organization is as simple as it's possible to make it and that it's fully understood by all concerned, keeping in mind that if it won't work on paper, it won't work.
3. That it is staffed with the right persons in the right places.
4. That such persons have the full authority to carry out the responsibilities assigned to them.
5. That it is maintained and constantly updated.

With respect to maintaining and updating the organization structure, it is most important never to lose sight of the fact that an organization is dynamic; that, as such, it is subject to the constant need for change, and that, also, changes—which can be insidious—tend of their own dynamics to creep in. The manager who ignores the need for constant updating and revision of his organization structure runs the risk of finding himself not only with a confused and demoralized staff but also with high production costs, missed delivery schedules, and impaired quality.

THE DUTIES OF THE MANAGER IN MAKING THE ORGANIZATION STRUCTURE WORK

Developing the organization structure isn't enough in itself. Plans don't work of their own accord; they must be made to work. It is the manufacturing manager's duty, therefore, to follow through to make certain the organization functions as intended and, where it does not, to correct the malfunction before it gets out of control.

He must keep close watch on the members of his staff so as to support them when they need support, not only in their direct work responsibilities but also in their relationships in and out of the manufacturing organization. He must continually indoctrinate them in the precepts of the organization structure as well as in the objectives of the company as a whole. It is also his duty to encourage and assist them in furthering their own development. He should keep them apprised, as fully as possible, not only of the company's long-range plans but also of the important day-to-day happenings which affect it. This type of knowledge can do much to promote an atmosphere of high morale and close effective relationships between superiors and subordinates.

It is by doing these things that a manager assures himself that an organization becomes a smooth-working and productive team.

THE "HOW" OF SUPERVISION

Having established "who is to do what," the manufacturing manager must concern himself with the "how." It is here that his duties can encompass many functions of overall management responsibility. Just how many and to what extent depend on the composition of each particular company. In addition to the manufacturing operation itself, the many functions which fall under the guidance of the manufacturing manager can run the gamut of quality control, engineering, industrial relations, production control, purchasing, physical distribution, and so on, as the papers in this book suggest. Thus the duties of any specific manager may vary considerably from what is considered normal in another company.

However, there is no escaping the "how" of the manufacturing operation; it is basic in the manufacturing manager's duties. It is his duty to make certain that the necessary systems, procedures, and methods, both administrative and operative, are developed to achieve the highest possible efficiency in all the functions reporting to him. Furthermore, he must thoroughly understand his product line, manufacturing techniques, manufacturing capabilities, production requirements, personnel requirements, cost standards, and so on and implement this knowledge in his daily supervisory activities. It is in the implementation of these basic functions of the manufacturing manager that other duties come into focus.

Of primary importance is the manufacturing manager's duty of coordinating production, inventory, and sales requirement with manufacturing capabilities. It in turn leads to another duty, a most important one—establishing and maintaining good reporting relationships. By this is meant interdepartmental cooperation, not superior-subordinate relations—for example, keeping the sales department advised of the status of manufacturing in terms of servicing customers' orders. The sales department cannot function effectively without information. It is the duty of the manufacturing manager to provide it, accurately and in time to be useful. Failure to keep the sales department fully informed, particularly when problems of maintaining schedules exist, usually results in such discord throughout the entire organization that distracting side issues can exhaust any manager's usefulness.

Reporting relationships do not, of course, start or stop with the sales department. They are many and varied, and their status is important to the success of the manufacturing operations. Particular attention must be paid to the finance department's reporting needs (accounting, budgets, and so on). In this respect the intelligent manufacturing manager will cooperate to the fullest, recognizing not only the importance of the finance function but the value of the end results of its effort to himself in administering the manufacturing operation.

While sales and finance are singled out as departments demanding the best in relationships, the need to engender good relationships is general and must not be confined to a few major areas. Nor can good relationships be maintained on a hit-or-miss basis; they must be fostered continuously—first as a personal obligation of a manager's day-to-day responsibilities and secondly as a principle of administrative management to be inculcated throughout the organization. Cooperation is a two-way street. The following aphorism, though old, still makes good sense: "As ye sow, so shall ye reap."

It makes particularly good sense when applied to labor relations, which is the Achilles heel of many otherwise good managers. Unfortunately, too few are aware that good labor relations does not begin at the bargaining table, that it cannot be bought at the bargaining table, that it is not a fringe benefit of a generous contract. On the contrary, developing and maintaining good labor relations are most important aspects of the manufacturing manager's day-to-day supervisory duties, requiring as they do—

• An understanding of, and genuine interest in, people.

- An understanding of the contractual obligations and a desire and willingness to apply them fairly and honestly.
- A supervisory force thoroughly trained to understand, appreciate, and effectuate the policies laid down to bring about the desired good working conditions.
- A daily unrelenting effort by the manager to know fully the status of his labor relations in order to take quick corrective action should any deterioration set in.

That one consistently practices good labor relations does not mean that the economic demands presented at the bargaining table will in any way be reduced. Such practice, however, does minimize the noneconomic demands and, what is more important, brings about a relatively high level of morale which is reflected in overall operating efficiency.

"As ye sow so shall ye reap" paraphrases another important phase of the manufacturing manager's daily supervisory duties: preventive maintenance. The more extensive the mechanization the greater the emphasis on the preventive. "Preventive" is the key word in high operating efficiency, and the manufacturing manager, if he is to avoid unscheduled and costly shutdowns, must keep abreast of the effectiveness of the particular system in operation, of the status of the preventive maintenance schedule or work orders, and of the latest in preventive maintenance techniques.

The manager with an up-to-date, smooth-working organization, one whose channels of communication are kept open and operating, will find his own relationships with top management much simplified and for the most part satisfactory.

INSURING EFFECTIVE AUTHORITY AND DELEGATION IN THE ORGANIZATION

By EARL R. GOMERSALL

The subject of delegating authority is fraught with platitudes and confusion in all types of organization structures. Most truisms regarding delegated authority state categorically that authoritative power parallels organizational responsibility. In fact, however, authority diffuses from strict line and staff structures. It is this diffusion that has created a need for a better understanding of delegated authority in varying organizational schemes.

The industrial trend toward centralized policy with decentralized execution has further confused many aspects of delegation because it parallels diffusion of authority—by intent and by default. To put the subject in perspective, we need to define what delegation is, what authority is, how the two interact, and how they come into being.

Delegation is empowering one person to act for another. *Authority* is the right to act. The two words are practically synonymous when defined in this manner. A further empirical definition would state that to have authority, one must be a delegatee. However, it is common to find both authority without portfolio and people who are authorized to act but do not. The anomalies of authority without justification and empowerment without execution can keep the finest organizational structure from operating efficiently.

DELEGATION AS A MATTER OF PROCEDURE

In order not to mistake real delegation for other types of authority we must think of delegation as a matter of procedure, rather like a chain of command.

EARL R. GOMERSALL is Manager of Manufacturing, Integrated Circuits Department, Texas Instruments Incorporated in Dallas, Texas.

EARL R. GOMERSALL is Manager of Manufacturing, Integrated Circuits Department, Texas Instruments Incorporated in Dallas, Texas.

50

This chain begins when the stockholders empower the president to act on their behalf. Subsequently, in writing, the president may procedurally empower certain of his subordinates to act for him.

It is the formalization of authority through written procedure that should distinguish delegated authority from other types of industrial influence. Illustrations of formalized authority through corporate procedure or charter abound. For example:

1. The treasurer or controller is authorized to sign checks on the company account by written approval of the president or board of directors.
2. The buyer or purchasing agent is authorized to commit the corporation to contracts for goods or services.
3. The receiving dock foreman is authorized to accept goods previously purchased.
4. The production and inventory control manager is authorized to requisition materials and supplies in accordance with approved production schedules.

These examples of authority through delegation are common to all businesses; they are generally recognized as matters of procedure; and they are absolutely essential. Furthermore, specific authority to act on the behalf of the corporation in the manner described does not usually cause any concern or controversy among operating personnel.

What factors of delegation do cause concern or controversy? Since we have defined delegation as a procedural matter, then we must examine the possibility of corporate personnel obtaining delegated authority in some manner other than by writing. In addition, we must look at the reasons why some people are given authority procedurally yet refuse to exercise their responsibility.

First, let us examine what is sometimes called the "field promotion" phenomenon. During a production crisis a manager who has been procedurally delegated the authority to sign, purchase, hire, fire, and contractually commit declares, "I want everybody to understand that your supervisor is to get whatever he needs to get this job done." (The supervisor in question is the manager's unauthorized subordinate.) "When your supervisor asks for anything, you may assume it's me asking."

Thus, during a period of tension, one supervisor has been orally delegated to act for his immediate superior. Individual members of the organization have been told to disregard the fact that their supervisor's authority is not valid. The delegating manager actually intended to empower his subordinate only temporarily. During the crisis, however, he did not fully transmit his intentions.

"Field promotion" delegation throws the organization into chaos once the "justifying" crisis has passed. No one can really be sure who is boss. Therefore, although it takes slightly longer to delegate authority in writing, even if the delegated authority is only temporary, it is necessary to do so in order to assure long-range organizational continuity.

Our next look will be at the delegatee who refuses to exercise his authority. We shall call this phenomenon "the philosophy of programed mediocrity"; that is, avoiding tough management decisions and getting ahead on seniority. Managers who have authority but refuse to exercise it are usually insecure in their responsibility. They may be spotted by their use of such phrases as the following:

- "Let's give this a lot more thought."
- "I doubt if the vice president would go for this right now."
- "Why don't we check around and see if other operations are going this way?"
- "It's a good approach, but not for our company."
- "I really hate to break with tradition right now."

No doubt there are occasions when such statements are appropriate. However, the programed inhibitor will use such statements, or variations thereof, routinely when he feels his "responsibility" (security) may be in jeopardy.

Unfortunately, there is no effective way to combat the delegatee who refuses to meet his authority head-on. Generally, such a manager must be approached obliquely with overwhelming data to move him from dead center. It may even be necessary to get tacit approval from the next organizational level to neutralize the insecure feelings of the authoritative inhibitor.

Caution must be used in dealing with programed mediocrity. When forced to make too many security-attacking decisions, the insecure manager may recommend removal of the prime motivator. He may also welcome de facto authority to relieve him of decision-making responsibilities.

In summary, while delegation must stem from procedure to be effective, delegation in itself does not assure execution. When organizing a line operation, therefore, the manager must be sure that those men and women he places in responsible positions are ready and willing to execute their responsibility to the fullest extent in accordance with the end objectives of the corporation.

AUTHORITY AS A DISCRETIONARY MATTER

Although authority in industry takes many forms, they may be reduced to four major categories. We shall examine each in turn.

Delegated authority. The simplest type is delegated authority, which comes from the procedural authorization of the corporate officers to empower someone to act as their representatives, as we have seen. Delegated authority is misconstrued where internal communication is so poor as to disseminate improperly information about who really has authority to act to all levels of personnel. Improper dissemination can occur both vertically and horizontally.

Some humorous situations can arise through poor vertical communication of officially delegated authority. The vice president, for instance, officially empowers the manufacturing manager to requisition goods and services costing not more than $25,000. In turn, the manufacturing manager officially authorizes his production planning manager to act in matters of material and supplies up to and including $5,000. Subsequently, to assure himself that the work for which he is responsible is properly executed, the production planning manager issues instructions to the central stockroom supervisor that nothing may be withdrawn without his authorization.

The vice president, on one of his tours of the plant, finds himself without paper and pencil. One of his aides suggests that he stop by the stockroom and requisition the material he needs. The stockroom supervisor, not being acquainted with the vice president, refuses to issue the note pad and pencil because his signature is not the authority he needs to permit withdrawal of the material. So he requests the vice president to ask the production control manager to countersign the requisition.

The network of delegation too often does not outline the entire authorized chain of command, nor does it take into account the local inhibitors that individual managers place on delegation to protect themselves and insure satisfactory performance. It is usually lack of cross-referenced authority on a parallel, rather than vertical, basis that delays effective action within the plant.

De facto authority. This type of authority also is gained by errors in communication within the corporation. For instance, an unauthorized group leader in the machine shop urgently requisitions two $50 carbide tools from the central tool crib. The tool crib foreman, impressed by the urgency of the request, issues the tools, not demanding a requisition but asking for a signature on a standard receipt form. The foreman, when reviewing the receipts for tools at the end of the month, notes that the unauthorized tool withdrawal by the group leader was not questioned by control or by his supervisor. Henceforth, the tool crib foreman no longer questions requests from the group leader because of the favorable audit of his tool withdrawal receipts. Thus, for all intents and purposes, the unauthorized group leader is now authorized to withdraw up to $50 worth of tools from the crib.

In another example of de facto authority, a manufacturing engineer visits one of the corporation's vendors. He, by definition in this case, cannot commit the corporation for either quantity or price, since such an authorization is the sole responsibility of the purchasing agent. The manufacturing engineer has been sent to the vendor to resolve specification problems only. During the negotiation of specifications the vendor mentions to the manufacturing engineer that if the quantity purchased were increased by 25 percent, a 2 percent reduction in price could be given. The manufacturing engineer agrees to the increased quantity and tells the vendor to go ahead and purchase raw material. Upon returning to his plant, the engineer mentions his negotiations to the inventory control manager who, in turn, goes along with him and increases his requisitions to the purchasing department by 25 percent. Purchasing issues a change order, and the corporation receives the 2 percent discount.

In review, a manufacturing engineer has committed the corporation to a purchase he was not authorized to commit, and the corporation has backed him up. Therefore, on any future negotiations the vendor may, in good faith, react to instructions from the manufacturing engineer. The pattern thus set up can be legally binding for any further business between the two parties. The corporation will find it difficult—if not impossible—to default on "deals" made by the manufacturing engineer which it does not like when it backs up those it does like. If procedural authority is assumed and the corporate organization backs it up, either expressly or by implication, the unwarranted authority has, in essence, been given full approval. Authority has become de facto.

These examples of de facto authority may sound far-fetched, but in fact such situations occur repeatedly. They may be prevented only through constant and diligent auditing of procedures and communications, both internally and externally. If incidents of de facto authority are uncovered, they may be effectively cut off by an internal memorandum or by a business letter to the appropriate outside concerns.

Authority through influence. This type of authority is insidious because it deals more with emotions than with facts and procedures. Authority can come about through esteem, character, special knowledge, procrastination, physical size, and many other aspects of influence, whether witting or unwitting.

Let us consider the auditor whose sole function is to assure that materials requisitioned have been authorized by individuals procedurally appointed to procure them. Note that the auditor is not authorized or empowered to approve what is purchased or how much is purchased as long as it is within the limits approved by management. Because all requisitions must be inspected by the auditor before being processed, he may appropriately hold them for questions of procedure. If he has spent a great deal of time with the company and has become knowledgeable about company practices and procedures, he may gain authority through influence. That is, he may—

- Make it so difficult to get requisitions approved, through tedious and detailed questioning, that he actually blocks the authority vested in the requisitioner.
- Advise the requisitioner that what is being purchased is, in his opinion, of dubious value to the corporation and suggest that either it not be purchased or a substitute be procured. The requisitioner, feeling that the auditor's opinions are to be respected, may decide to follow his advice. Thus the requisitioner has abrogated his *authority* to the auditor. He has not, however, passed on his *responsibility*.

Authority can be abrogated only when the delegatee permits it. Recognition of what has happened may be difficult. Many strong personalities can be most convincing in asserting that they have authority when in fact they don't. For example, it takes considerable fortitude for a second-level manager to purchase a set of Brand X tools when he has been told by one of his peers, "At lunch the other day J. S. [the vice president] was talking about his bad experience with Brand X. He said if he ever saw another Brand X tool in the plant, he'd personally take action!" The manager may know that J. S.'s experience happened some ten years ago. Brand X now makes a reliable and economical tool, and tests have demonstrated its quality and usefulness. Under these circumstances the manager with authority must make two decisions—one emotional and one businesslike.

Staff authority. Generally, we can correctly assume that staff personnel do not have any direct line authority. However, because of their role of service and consultation, they almost automatically achieve some degree of authority over line operations. In dealing with staff members, line managers must be acutely aware of exactly where their authority and responsibility lie. This authority and its concomitant responsibility must be constantly checked against the advice and counsel of staff personnel.

The association between line and staff personnel can give rise to considerable confusion regarding authority and responsibility. As long as staff advice results in good business decisions, little is said regarding whether the line manager depended upon it or made his own decision independently. In practice, however, negative results from staff advice usually lead to the line manager's being reprimanded for his poor judgment. The justification for such reprimanding is that the line manager cannot relinquish his responsibility to staff personnel.

The dilemma is that the line manager is expected to accept all "good" advice and reject all "poor" advice, the criteria being whatever the line manager's superior sets as good or acceptable performance.

There is no easy solution to the problems of the eternal triangle of the staff man, the operating man, and the operating man's superior. As a rule of thumb, the man in authority must ask the following questions when receiving staff advice:

- Does the advice seem reasonable and sound?
- Does the advice coincide with past practices and future claims?
- What has the staff department's record of performance been when asked for similar advice on processes and procedures?
- Is the line manager being advised to do something that is physically and economically impossible; is he being overscheduled, undermanned, or specified out of business?

If the staff's advice coincides with what the line manager feels he can accomplish, he may put the advice into action. But if the staff viewpoint seems questionable, he will most likely and very wisely discuss the pros and cons of marginal business decisions with his immediate superior before he authorizes its execution.

CENTRALIZATION—THE ULTIMATE AUTHORITY

The old adage, "If you want something done right, do it yourself," is the psychological basis for centralized authority and responsibility. It is not usually stated in so many words but is described instead in glowing terms of economies and efficiency. In fact, some of the advantages of centralized authority can spell economies. These are as follows:

1. Special knowledge. Special processes and technical or customer knowledge may make it desirable to centralize authority with the personnel best qualified to make business decisions.
2. Administrative and auditing economies. If only one to two people are authorized to make decisions and commit the corporation to expenditures of various types, auditing becomes simple and straightforward. Furthermore, the expense of communicating to all employees exactly who is authorized to do what does not present a problem.

There are also disadvantages to centralized authority. In a small company these are of lesser importance, but if business grows and expands, they can become obstacles to growth and profit.

1. The entire organizational structure must be so constituted as to direct all decisions to a central authority. As the organization enlarges, the process of obtaining approvals becomes unwieldy and slow.
2. The centralized supervisor must manage by intuition rather than facts. Although most seasoned line managers manage intuitively, they modify their intuition with considerable business details. As a company grows, it becomes virtually impossible for a manager with centralized authority to acquaint himself with all the significant details of a business.

A central manager often receives reports so voluminous that he cannot read them in any given 24-hour period. He finds himself spending his whole day authorizing detailed business papers rather than making management decisions. He may hire an assistant, but by doing so he opens the door to questions of authority through influence. He finds no way out except to delegate and assign responsibility lower in the organization—in other words, to decentralize his authority.

DECENTRALIZATION—AN EVOLUTION OF DELEGATION

Decentralization is the diffusion of central power or the delegation of central authority. Decentralization requires a restructuring of the organization to allow the effective execution of business at the best possible decision level. The advantages and disadvantages are essentially the converse of those listed for centralization. Where specialized knowledge and business association are lost, speed and response are enhanced.

The most important ingredient of decentralization is "freedom to err." As decisions are made at progressively lower levels in the organization structure, overall direction and perspective become increasingly difficult for satellite managers to perceive. The more broadly based manager may look backward on executed business decisions and criticize their objectivity. The key is redirection rather than a negative outlook. Too much hindsight on questionable decisions will inhibit the freedom to err or, more positively, the freedom to make timely decisions at the best possible level.

CENTRALIZATION VERSUS DECENTRALIZATION OF AUTHORITY

Because today's business is dynamic, most corporations have formalized decentralization of authority, coupling it with broad central policy direction. Because decentralization is the trend in industry, we need to examine what happens when we decentralize and how it can be made effective.

First, we must realize that decentralization is actually a diffusion of authority. As we know, authority is diffuse regardless of the type of organization structure. Therefore, under decentralization, all the problems of authority discussed so far are compounded.

The most effective way to put authority into perspective in a decentralized organization structure lies in achieving strong procedural support. Each employee with a "need to know" must understand who is in authority and to what degree. Note that this need to know has to be disseminated throughout the organization to be effective.

In many instances there is strong opposition to revealing authority and reponsibility in general because frankness in this connection tends to eliminate authority through influence. Those who have informal authority do not want to see their positions endangered by outlining the facts to line and staff managers.

Decentralization also requires proficient staff support groups that are attuned to the corporate end objectives rather than to their own staff objectives, for, psychologically, service groups tend to behave quite the opposite. They will, if left unguided, ride their hobbyhorses roughshod over company profits.

- The control department may improve its reports for the sake of accounting efficiency, but by doing so it removes effective line management controls.
- Central inventory control may emphasize raw-material inventory at the expense of the manufacturing schedule or customer shipping requirements.
- A central work measurement group may concentrate on carrying out the highest number of labor measurements possible rather than attempt to uncover the highest percentage of costly labor points.

In a decentralized environment, staff groups must look beyond the perfection of their own functions to the betterment of their business. If not, they obtain de facto authority by inhibiting line managers from achieving corporate goals through the suboptimization of their own functions.

THE KEY TO EFFECTIVE AUTHORITY

Because a great deal of emotionalism surrounds delegated authority and responsibility, the most effective way to clarify the corporation's standpoint is through written communication, preferably in the form of procedures. Organization charts, along with authoritative responsibility, must be made available to all personnel in the company with the need to know. If such procedures are followed, each line and staff manager will know exactly where the limits of his authority lie and how they interact with others on a parallel level.

These solutions to a very complex problem may sound easy. Though they are easy to contemplate, unfortunately they are difficult to execute. Organizational changes coupled with corporate growth can make outlining changing authority and responsibility a very difficult task. It may even become expensive and burdensome. The undesirable alternatives are (1) power and authority by influence and character, (2) authority through seniority, and (3) de facto authority.

These are easy traps to fall into because it is tedious to maintain procedural control over the organization structure. Unless the manager is willing to take the time and effort necessary to outline the interaction of all authority at all levels, he must revert to complete central control or let his responsibility be taken over by those who desire to maintain authority without responsibility.

COMMUNICATION WITH OTHERS IN THE ORGANIZATION

By PHILIP C. SHAAK

One of the most difficult questions facing managers today is how to communicate effectively. Communication on occasion simply does not take place, despite seeming carefulness in assuring that it does. We must first look at some of the reasons for this breakdown before we can begin to look at some ways the manufacturing man can improve communication in the plant.

WHY COMMUNICATION FAILS

A prime reason for lack of communication is simply the increased specialization of so many plants. Factory managers find—much to their discomfort and confusion—that engineers talk one language and production people talk another. Systems analysts work with one set of words and quality control people work with another. Terms such as "negative variance," "critical path," "standard deviation," "value analysis," and "performance standard" have particular meanings for some people in the organization but little or no meaning at all for others. It is often difficult to get the research chemist who works in the laboratory to understand what problems are encountered when his process is introduced into the plant in a large production run. The process that ran almost perfectly back in the laboratory simply may not work economically in the factory. The chemist is convinced that costs are high because the production people are stupid, and the production people are convinced the chemist still has his head in the clouds and knows absolutely nothing about how a plant operates. As technology advances, both managers and professionals find

PHILIP C. SHAAK is Associate Professor of Business Administration at the School of Business, Rutgers—The State University—in Newark, New Jersey.

it increasingly difficult to keep abreast of developments in their areas of interest. It is even more difficult for them to understand changes affecting other parts of the company's operation.

A second reason for the communication problem is the number of layers of management from the top executive to the foreman. Each layer acts as a sending station, and each acts as a receiving station. How the communications are sent out from one level of management to another, how these messages are received, and their timing are crucial factors in the communication process.

Let any manager consider his own situation and look at the subordinates below him. Are they more likely to tell him things they think he wants to hear, or things they think he does not want to hear? Are they more likely to tell him things which will please him and make him think how effective they are, or tell him things which will disturb him and lead him to put additional pressure on them? More specifically, is he more likely to hear about the 31 orders which were shipped on time, or about the three other orders which are still two weeks behind schedule?

Managers are more likely to be told things their subordinates want them to know and less likely to be told things they want to hide. Every layer of management acts as a filter as communications go down *and up* the line. For example, a foreman is told only certain things about promotion policy that his superiors want him to know. Similarly, the senior executive is told only certain things about the implementation of the policy which his subordinates want him to know. By the time information gets all the way to the top, it has been very carefully filtered, just as other information is carefully filtered on the way down to the foreman.

A third major reason for lack of communication is the confusion between the "ceremony" of communicating with others and the act of communicating. Frequently managers go through all the motions of communicating with others but still fail to get their messages across.

One case which illustrates this confusion between ceremony and act involves a senior manager who had a large number of subordinates in locations throughout the United States. His usual practice was to receive reports from the field during the week, and on Saturday morning he dictated a message from the home office to all field men. This message was 10 to 12 pages long. On Monday the home office message was duplicated and mailed, so the field men received it either late Tuesday or early Wednesday morning. The senior manager was convinced this was an effective way to communicate with his field men; however, his assistant manager in the home office was not so convinced. One Monday this assistant manager inserted in the middle of the letter a short paragraph stating that the first field man to call the home office on Wednesday to acknowledge receipt of the letter would receive $50. Not one person called on Wednesday. This assistant manager was sure the field men were at best reading the first and last pages of the home office letter each week and entirely missing what came between. The evidence suggests he was right. Perhaps the worst part of this case is that the senior manager still insists on his weekly ten-page letter to the field men, even though he is aware of what happened. He is still confusing the ceremony with the act of communicating.

COMMUNICATIONS CHANNELS

Scores of definitions of "communication" can be found, but as used here it simply means "getting a message through to another person." Of course, more than two people may be involved, but the following remarks about the roles of the sender and the receiver apply nonetheless. All that concerns us now is getting a message through to another person.

Well, how *do* we get a message across? What means or channels are open to us for sending ideas, thoughts, and attitudes to someone else? They are basically three:

1. Speaking.
2. Writing.
3. Acting.

We may do these things in various ways. For instance, we can talk to someone face to face, or speak over the telephone or radio, or go on closed-circuit television, but still we are speaking to get a message across. Or we can write a memo, draw a diagram, or rough out a sketch. Fundamentally, we are writing in one way or another. The third way we communicate is through our actions. Things we do, places we go, people we meet—all communicate something to others around us. In fact, we have no choice in whether we will or will not communicate through our actions. We will, and do, whether we like it or not.

For example, suppose a manager has a particularly busy day coming up at the plant and has to leave early for an afternoon meeting at a nearby plant. He drives into the parking lot in the morning, passes up his usual parking spot, and takes another which will let him out a little faster in the afternoon. As he walks into the plant he is preoccupied, and he fails to give his usual morning greeting to several people on the way to his office. He sits down at his desk and starts to work, not having said a word to anyone and not having written a thing. Has he communicated? Yes, indeed he has. Parking his car in an unusual spot may have sent a message to some people, failing to greet others no doubt sent out messages. He may not be certain what was communicated, but he can be certain that people received some message from his actions.

Furthermore, these actions do not have to be unusual. As he goes about the plant during the day, he communicates through all his actions. The sequence in which he tours the plant, or the way in which he checks production records from the previous shift, will very likely be significant to some people.

Just as our actions communicate to others, our inaction—or failure to act—also sends messages. It may be that a bottleneck has developed on a production line, and the plant manager knows how to clear the trouble quickly. However, perhaps he decides to let the foreman on the line handle the problem, and so he stays away until the bottleneck is cleared. In this case his failure to act may well communicate to others. The foreman may feel that the manager has confidence in his ability to solve problems, or he may get an opposite impression and feel that the manager is really not interested in what is going on in the foreman's area. Often we cannot be sure just what the message will be in the mind of the receiver, but we can be quite certain that on many occasions our failure to act will transmit some message to others just as surely as if we had acted.

Thus far, we have been talking about communication in terms of sending messages, but what about the other side of the process: receiving messages? In order to have effective, meaningful communication we must have someone getting messages. The other half of the communication process, then, is:

1. Listening.
2. Reading.
3. Observing.

A manager probably does not have much difficulty getting others to observe his actions. He is in the spotlight, and people make it their business to know where he is, whom he sees, and what he does. A case in point is the signal system set up by employees in a generating station of an electric utility company. When the plant manager arrives at the plant, he frequently hears the "alarm" being sounded over the public address system. "Bird dog, bird dog, bird dog" goes all through the generating station, and all employees are alerted to the fact that the plant manager is on his way. (He never has heard the "all clear" signal.) The point is that employees do keep a reasonably close

watch on their boss, and his actions and inactions communicate a great deal
to them.

A manager may share the difficulty of so many other managers in getting
people to understand the full meaning of messages he is trying to get across
to them. More than one production manager, for instance, has painstakingly
explained an up-coming production schedule to a group of foremen and requested them to ask questions if they failed to understand. When no questions
are asked, the production manager may conclude that all the foremen understand the schedule. It is only after the schedule has gone into effect that he
finds that two foremen apparently had no idea of what it meant in terms
of their part of the plant's operations. Some communication breakdowns are
caused by not using the channels which are best for the receiver.

What things does a manager do by way of communication during the course
of a typical day? This question has been posed to many groups of managers
from foreman up to plant manager, and the following answers are usually
heard:

1. Interpret company policy.
2. Announce production schedules.
3. Check production reports.
4. Report inventory levels.
5. Report employee discipline.
6. Give operating instructions.
7. Make safety reports.
8. Submit budget reports.

When performing these communication jobs, the manager can use any one
or a combination of the following two-way channels for communicating:

- Speaking—Listening.
- Writing—Reading.
- Acting—Observing.

If a manager is going to get his message through to someone else, he has
to be sure he is using the best channel or channels. His skill as an effective
communicator lies at least partially in his ability to select the most appropriate
channel(s) for any given situation.

The most important factor to consider when selecting the best channel is
the receiver. Who is supposed to receive and understand this message? What

are his abilities? What is the best way to get a message across to this particular person? Does he need a demonstration, or will a brief verbal explanation be enough?

Time is a second important consideration in selecting the best channel. If we had all the time in the world to introduce a design change, perhaps we could afford the paper blizzard approach. Not many managers have the luxury of unlimited time to effect change, and it may be necessary to talk directly to the people involved to accomplish the change even though under other circumstances it would be better to have detailed written instructions for everyone.

The necessity for a record is a third factor to weigh when deciding the best way to communicate. An old foreman, so the story goes, carried a pad and pencil with him at all times. When he made an assignment to a worker, he wrote it on top of a sheet of paper and also on the bottom of the same sheet. Then he tore the paper in half, handed the bottom half of the sheet to the worker, and kept the top half himself. When following up to see if certain jobs were accomplished, few workers made the mistake of saying to him, "You never told me to do that." In such cases the foreman would pull out his top half of the sheet and ask the worker to find the matching half. This may be a simple approach to record keeping, but it was reportedly effective. There are many situations in which a record of what was said or was requested is necessary or desirable. When communicating more important items, it is wise to anticipate the necessity for a record and to select the proper channel with this requirement in mind.

A fourth factor to consider is whether the receiver's reaction to our message is important to us. If it is, we may decide against writing and talk to him face to face instead. That is, if we are interested in knowing whether Fred Smith feels confident about handling a particular assignment in the plant, it may be far better to discuss the assignment with him so we can see his reaction. His actions upon hearing of this assignment can communicate things he may not be willing to write or say directly.

Certainly the cost factor also weighs heavily in deciding on the best channel of communication. It may be far less expensive to pick up the telephone and call a purchasing agent to solve a problem than to exchange a series of letters. Still other factors to consider are the number of people affected by the message we are trying to get across, the location of the receiver, the facilities available, company policy, and the complexity of the message.

It would be nice if we had a unit which would take all these factors—the abilities of the receiver, time available, necessity for a record, importance of the receiver's reaction, cost, number of people affected, location, facilities—and evaluate them so as to indicate the best channel for communicating in any one situation. The surprising thing is that we do have one—the human mind. That is, managers go through at least some of this evaluation quite regularly and quite unconsciously. The selection of the most appropriate channel(s) for the more important communications should be made deliberately and thoughtfully. The most important message in the plant may not get through to the receiver if there has been a failure in selecting the best way of getting it across. Furthermore, what is best solely from the sender's point of view may not be best from the point of view of the receiver.

THE MANAGER AS COMMUNICATOR

The role of the manager in the company's communication network is often not fully appreciated. Too often he is seen as a link in a chain of command, and if a message starts at the top of the chain, it is supposed to pass down from one link to another until it gets to its intended destination. This view of the manager's communication role is not sufficiently descriptive to show fully what is going on.

Organizationally, each manager can be pictured as being in the narrowest part of an hourglass, particularly if he is a first-line supervisor. Top managers exert direct pressure from above, and typically staff personnel exert indirect pressure by submitting advisory reports or making suggestions and recommendations. On the other hand, the people this manager is supervising also exert pressure from below. They may resist certain job assignments or refuse to do certain kinds of work. "Oh, that's not my job." "I've never done that before." "No one has shown me how to do that." "I can't work with her." This manager is truly the man in the middle, and in this spot he must communicate effectively with both those above and those below him.

Insofar as the communication process is concerned, he is much more than a mere link in a chain of command. He serves often as a filter. That is, the manager may decide to pass through only certain parts of a message that he gets from above; or he reports only segments of a situation in his department of which he is aware. Certainly a manager cannot communicate everything he sees and hears to those above and below him. He necessarily selects some information to communicate and rejects or withholds other information.

In addition to serving as a communication filter, as we see in the drawings in Exhibit 1, a manager also can be likened to a prism through which light is passed, as we see in the drawings in Exhibit 2. That is, the manager may redirect or deflect a message. For instance, something intended for the plant manager may be sent instead to the assistant plant manager or to the personnel director.

Furthermore, the manager may intentionally, or unintentionally, color the

EXHIBIT 1

THE MANAGER AS A COMMUNICATION FILTER

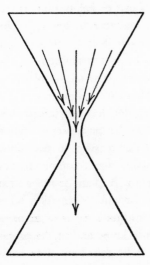 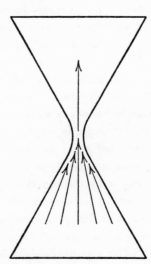

EXHIBIT 2

THE MANAGER AS A COMMUNICATION PRISM

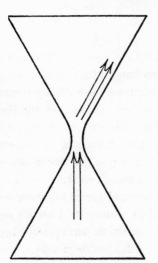 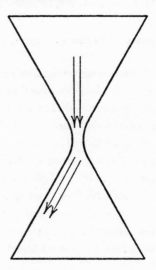

information so that the receiver gets something which appears to be quite different from what was originally intended. Another possibility is that this manager who acts as a prism magnifies or diminishes the importance of the communication as it passes from him to someone else. He focuses on certain aspects of the problem and diminishes others.

Another part of the manager's communication role has to do with timing. Quite frequently he has a substantial amount of discretion in deciding when certain information will be passed along to those above or below him. It can make a great deal of difference to a production manager to know if Line 1 is in trouble at 9:30 A.M. rather than find out about it at 10:30 A.M. The one-hour delay, during which the foreman thinks he can straighten out the mess, can cause serious rescheduling problems in other parts of the plant.

A manager, then, is more than a link in the chain of command when it comes to his job as a communicator. He must often decide what information to pass through, how it should be presented, what are the most essential points to communicate, and when is the best time to get this message across. These decisions are equally important whether we are talking about communication moving from the top down or from the bottom up. A plant manager can make some decisions which assure him of getting certain information when he wants it, but it is unrealistic to assume that subordinate levels of management will automatically report everything he needs to know and at the proper time. The intermediate levels of management must be relied upon to make many decisions of what, how, and when to communciate, whether these communications are going from the bottom to the top of the organization or flowing in the reverse direction.

FORMAL VERSUS INFORMAL COMMUNICATION

Formal communication can be thought of as messages which pass through the established organization structure. Much of what we have discussed thus far has presumed that the chain of command has been the basis for the flow of information throughout the plant. It is usually fairly easy to identify the path that formal communication should take; it goes down, up, or laterally across the organization at identifiable places. This is a nice, formal, textbook approach to internal plant communication, but it just doesn't work.

A more realistic approach has to include the informal communication system. Informal communication can be considered as messages which do not pass through, in sequence, the established organization structure. More simply, we are talking about the grapevine, rumor mill, scuttlebutt alley.

In contrast to formal communication, the origination and flow of informal communication are very difficult to trace. Any manager who can trace the grapevine accurately through five or six people is doing quite well. Often, of course, information on the grapevine is distorted and inaccurate. It is not at all unusual for a great deal of a manager's time to be spent spiking rumors which are running rampant on the grapevine and causing a major upheaval in the plant. Sometimes firms go to great lengths to trample out or strangle the grapevine. One company put in a special telephone number in its home office in its efforts to snip rumors on the vine. If anyone in the home office wanted to get the company version about a rumor, he could simply pick up the telephone, dial a certain number, and hear a recorded message. This recorded message was changed frequently to keep abreast of the grapevine.

A fundamental question to be asked is, "Should a manager use the grapevine?" This question has been posed to hundreds of managers in training sessions, and the general consensus, but by no means the uniform one, is that a manager should—indeed—use the grapevine. He can do so in at least three possible ways:

1. To get information from those below him.
2. To get information from those above.
3. To prepare people below him for possible future changes.

No one, of course, should rely exclusively or wholly on rumors to learn about what is going on in his department. Certainly it can be costly to act on just grapevine information that filters up from below. However, there is a great deal to be said for keeping attuned to grapevine information. Information about employee discontent or helpful suggestions from workers may not always come up through the formal communication network.

Many managers listen just as closely to the grapevine to get information from above as they do in getting information from below. Sometimes a manager will use a rumor as leverage to get information from his boss. For example, Joe Smith approaches the plant superintendent and says, "Fred, I heard that two men might be moved out of my shop next month. Can you tell me anything about it?"

Using the grapevine to prepare people for impending change has been successful in numerous instances. The introduction of new machinery or the change in a departmental layout is sometimes deliberately rumored by management to cushion the effect on the employees. Sometimes a rumor is passed about tightening up on long coffeebreaks in order to get a group to discipline itself before formal action has to be taken.

An important point to bear in mind about the grapevine is that it must be used with a great deal of care and discretion. Relying exclusively on rumors, taking action based only on grapevine information, making changes because someone heard someone else say something in the washroom can lead to all sorts of trouble. In a sense, the grapevine is like fire; properly controlled it can do a great deal of good, but out of control it can destroy.

BARRIERS TO COMMUNICATION

Although we spend a good portion of our waking hours communicating with others, and so get a lot of practice doing it, we encounter some barriers which are difficult to break down. As any factory-experienced manager knows, it is all too easy for the simplest message to get so garbled in the mind of the receiver that it defies the imagination. A seemingly innocuous question such as, "Why did you do it that way?" can result in a paper blizzard hitting his desk some morning, justifying a fairly simple routine procedure. Let's focus on a few of the significant barriers.

Words themselves are sometimes barriers to communication. Although we may think of words as being the core of communication, they often impair a message rather than help it get through. After all, words are only symbols of thoughts, ideas, attitudes, or emotions. We have to encode these things into words and then transmit the words to the other person. He, in turn, hears the word or words and has to go through a decoding process so that he can get the message—with luck, the one which was originally intended. Furthermore, this process is often a two-way affair, and an enormous number of opportunities present themselves for breakdowns in the system.

For example, a plant manager speaks with a general foreman about the urgency of a particular order in the shop. At the end of the conversation with the general foreman the plant manager says, "Let's get it through the shop soon." Now, what is "soon"? Does it mean this afternoon? By the end of the shift? By the end of the week? The receiver has to take the word "soon" and decode it in such a way that it matches the sender's encoding, or the message gets garbled. Unless we encode our thoughts into words which will carry precisely the message we want conveyed, the receiver quite unintentionally misses the point. Had the plant manager said, "Let's get it through the shop by the end of today's second shift," the general foreman would have had less chance of missing the message. The encoding and decoding process is shown in the diagram in Exhibit 3.

An interesting illustration of this encoding and decoding process took place

EXHIBIT 3

THE COMMUNICATION PROCESS

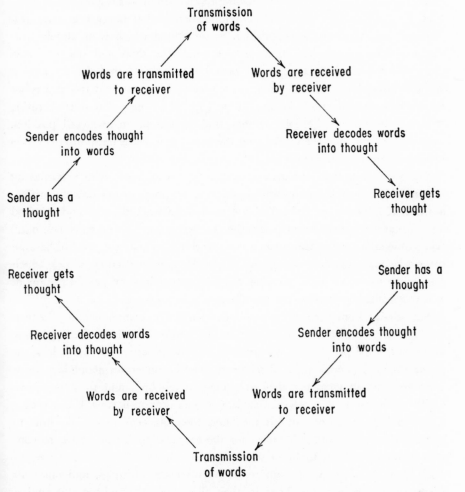

in a Connecticut plant which manufactured precision instruments. One of the plant executives was very much concerned about good housekeeping and hit on what he considered a novel approach. He had small cards printed which carried just three letters: "DDH." They were intended to mean "Day to Day Housekeeping." After the shift had left for the day, this manager went through the plant and put a card in every place where he saw evidence of poor housekeeping. It did not take long for him to get a response to his card campaign. However, the surprising thing to this manager was the interpretation placed on DDH by some people in the plant; they thought the three letters stood for "Damn Dirty Hole." In this instance the decoding process resulted in an even more pointed message for the receiver than was originally intended.

A second common barrier to communication is that many times we treat inference as fact, that is, supposition as something which is absolutely true. For example, a supervisor may walk through the shop and see four men gathered at a machine that is not operating. The fact that the machine is not operating and that four men are gathered there can lead this supervisor to conclude that they are loafing. If he goes to the men and starts berating them for loafing on the job, he may find himself in an awkward position. Perhaps the four men are working on the machine to get it back into operation and are discussing how best to fix it.

The story is told of the new manager of a warehouse who was making a tour of the building and came upon a young man sitting down whittling a stick. This new manager asked the man if he worked there and received an affirmative reply. At that point, the manager said, "No more, punch out." Some time later, an arbitrator ruled that the discharge was not justified because the young man was not loafing on the job. He was sharpening a stick which was going to be used for packing purposes. Here is a prime illustration of a manager making an observation and treating inferences as facts.

Attitudes and emotions sometimes act as barriers to communication. In fact, when subordinates talk, they frequently experience a barrier because of their attitudes toward people in positions of authority. Because the boss is in a superior position, people in his department may be uncertain about how he is likely to react to whatever they are going to tell him, and thus they have difficulty expressing themselves. Fear is a communication barrier. If a manager assigns a big job to one of his men and then proceeds to explain how to approach it, the subordinate may miss the explanation because he is so concerned about his ability to do the job.

All these barriers—words, inferences versus facts, attitudes, and emotions —are internal in a sense. That is, they all occur either within the sender, within the receiver, or both. Other difficulties in communication can be characterized as external because they occur outside either the sender or receiver. They include environment, facilities, and other features which might impair getting a message through to others. Their importance should not be overlooked. An office may be a poor place to conduct an appraisal interview, particularly if the telephone keeps ringing or if people are likely to interrupt. The efficiency of the in-company mail system and the quality of a telephone connection are other potential external barriers to communication.

It is much easier to overcome external barriers than it is to overcome internal ones. A prime reason is that a person is more likely to be aware of them than of the internal barriers. Furthermore, it is much easier to change the location of an appraisal interview than it is to change an attitude or an emotion. When attempting to improve communication in the plant, it is best to focus attention on internal barriers.

Perhaps all that is really necessary to improve communication is to get other people in the plant to concentrate on lowering their internal barriers. If only they would encode their words properly and decode our words properly, life would be so much simpler. If only they would stop treating inferences as facts and realize the distinction between the two, we would have fewer problems. If only the other fellow would not let his attitudes and emotions get in the way, it would be so much easier to get through to him. If only . . . but what about ourselves? Isn't there another side to this communication coin? Are people having difficulty understanding us because of our own encoding and decoding process? Are we having a problem getting through to others because we are confusing inferences with facts? Are our attitudes, our emotions, influencing how others get through to us? For the greatest barrier to communication is the illusion that it has taken place.

RELATIONSHIPS BETWEEN LINE AND STAFF IN MANUFACTURING OPERATIONS

By JOHN W. FAUS

All the people, departments, divisions, and organizational segments that are authorized to determine the basic objectives of the business or the company, and make possible their achievement, constitute the "line." The "staff" is that part of the organization which is expected to assist and advise the line in carrying out its duties. It is important to remember that what is line in one type of enterprise can be staff in another. Every company is organized for a specific purpose, and this purpose determines who is line and who is staff, provided that there *is* a line–staff organization. There almost always is, although frequently it is not clearly defined.

If the objective of the business is to make and sell a product or a group of products (whether a basic material like steel or a complicated electro-mechanical device), the line functions are usually manufacturing and sales. If the company designs the product as well as makes it and sells it, engineering becomes a line function. In an oil company the development of sources for crude oil could be line. In a freight-forwarding company, transportation is line. In a chemical company the research department may be line. American Cyanamid, for example, feels that in the chemical industry techniques and new products change so fast that a steady stream of products is essential to staying in business; hence it identifies research with one of the basic objectives of the enterprise, and research is therefore part of the line organization.

Although all large manufacturing organizations—and, for that matter, practically all large organizations regardless of primary objective—have a line and staff form of organization, some organizations can be considered as essentially

JOHN W. FAUS is Plant Manager for the Remington Rand Office Systems Division of the Sperry Rand Corporation in Marietta, Ohio.

line only. All their departments from top to bottom are operational components. Certain staff work is nonetheless performed, even though it may not be identified as such. The point is that each operational or line group—sales, manufacturing, finance—does its own staff work; that is, each group hires people, trains them, pays them, sets work standards, plans and schedules the work, and so on. Each line department head is fully responsible for everything related to getting his work done to the satisfaction of the next higher level of line authority.

Without question the biggest single advantage of an all-line organization is the elimination of buck-passing. No doubt can exist about who gets the credit if things turn out right and who takes the blame if things go wrong. Moreover, this type of organization certainly allows decisions to be made quickly unless the line men are so bogged down in detail that they don't get around to decision making.

This last statement hints at the disadvantages of an organization consisting entirely of operational units:

1. It overloads executives with too many duties and too much detail.
2. No one can be expert at everything, but the all-line organization apparently assumes otherwise.
3. It is hard to keep company policy consistent.
4. Labor troubles are more likely to arise.
5. Morale, because of pay inequities, is likely to decline.

FUNCTIONAL ORGANIZATION

The word "function" has at least two different meanings in business organizations. It is often used to mean a specialized activity, such as sales, engineering, or personnel. It is also used frequently to refer only to staff departments. The term first came into use in a business organization context with Frederick W. Taylor, who seems to get credit or blame for many of the expressions and practices observed in modern business. He believed that the best way to organize a business was to make a specialist of everybody. He eliminated the foreman in the shop and divided the supervision of the workers among eight specialists:

1. Time and cost clerk.
2. Instructions card clerk.
3. Order of work and route clerk.
4. Disciplinarian.

    5. Gang boss.
    6. Speed boss.
    7. Repair boss.
    8. Inspector.

He called this division of supervision a "functional" organization. He had the
germ of a basically good idea, but this particular plan didn't work out very
well. With eight bosses, not only did the workmen get pretty frustrated, but
the enterprise simply didn't produce. He was on the right road, though, and
probably can be credited (at least in part) with developing the line–staff idea
now so common in business.

Taylor's functional organization appeared just when business was starting
to recognize the need for a line–staff concept. His refinement of the functional
specialist idea developed into a line–staff form of organization which enjoyed
the advantages of utilizing specialists without the handicaps of employing nothing but specialists.

HISTORICAL BACKGROUND

Business began to feel the need for the line and staff form of organization
in the early 1900's. However, it would be inaccurate to say that the concept
originated in America. Regardless of what it is called, the idea has been used
by the military for centuries. Good staff work and, even more importantly,
good line–staff organization and working relationships have been essential to
the success of every military group from the days of Alexander the Great and
even earlier. Hannibal, Attila the Hun, Genghis Khan, and Napoleon, as well
as other generals and strategists, observed the distinction between action and
advice. Determining exactly when or by whom the idea first was brought into
use is of little or no importance; what matters is *why*. The basic objective
of military organization is to seek out and destroy the enemy, to win the battle
or the war. Decision making therefore must be positive, must be fast, and
had better be right at least more often than the enemy's.

How many times was it said, after both World Wars, that Germany had
an efficient military establishment because it had a good general staff. The
staff men in an army, who are specialists in all the problems related to a
war machine—logistics, armament, food, transportation, ammunition, training,
pay, clothing, and so on—not only are expert but are organized to provide
the facts needed to make the decision and then help the line execute it. Without this staff type of work Attila would never have scourged Europe and Asia.

Not only did his staff know the best routes, the best time of year for travel, the food, shelter, and clothing available for money or for the taking, but it also knew how the crops were faring at a particular time and what livestock could be eaten, moved, or used for hauling or for riding. Beyond all these things it had a shrewd idea about what kind of reception the army would get from the people: whether it would be welcomed, accepted, or fought bitterly and, if so, with what weapons and on what terrain.

GROWTH AND INCREASED COMPLEXITY OF CORPORATIONS

The importance of making good decisions and executing them quickly caused the military to use line and staff. Speed induced by competition, the added pressures of governmental red tape, the growth of labor unions, the increasing complexity of taxes, legislative restrictions, bureaucracy, the need for research and development and for improved techniques in handling men and machines, the advent of electronic data processing—all the other complications arising from an expanding and maturing business environment made some form of line and staff a necessary ingredient in doing business successfully.

The old days when the bosses were expert at everything, when they were all things to all people, disappeared with the horse and buggy. In fact, the man who buried the horse and buggy—Henry Ford—is often thought of as the best example of a boss who knew everything about everything and needed no staff. Really, however, he used a staff organization in a truer form than did any other big industrialist of his time. He may not have liked it, but he was smart, and he liked making money more than he disliked leaning on experts in certain fields.

MODERN CONCEPT OF LINE AND STAFF

Just as what is line in one organization can well be staff in another, the same type of activity, the same "function," if you will, can be both line and staff within a given company. For example, in many large corporations where sales, manufacturing, and engineering are the principal line functions, staff people at the corporate level advise the president or chief executive officer about these line functions. This is particularly true in a decentralized corporation where each division is a fairly autonomous unit under its own general manager who reports in a direct line to the president and is responsible for the design, manufacture, and sale of his divisional products. At the corporate level of such an organization, a staff man (or a group of staff men) frequently advises the president on engineering, sales, or manufacturing problems even though he has no authority over the line engineering, sales, or manufacturing personnel in each division. On the other hand, within a staff group or department, the people reporting to the department head are the line organization even though the department itself is a service group.

These variations on the main idea are neither surprising nor difficult to understand. They exist because they are necessary. Many areas of the modern business organization require expert help, and staff men provide it so that the line men can devote their time and energy to the company's basic objective, whether it is producing automobiles, selling soap, designing anti-missile missiles, packing horsemeat, or prospecting for new crude oil sources.

A MATTER OF CONTRASTING VIEWS

The line man is characterized by his direct tie-in with the basic objectives of the company, but he is also characterized by his relationship to staff. Too frequently he has an understandable but not quite realistic viewpoint of the staff. He is prone to feel that staff—

- Tends to assume line authority.
- Frequently offers unsound advice.
- Tries—often successfully—to steal credit.
- Is unable to see the whole picture.
- Simply doesn't understand operating problems.

Perhaps nowhere are suspicion, frustration, and even bitterness more likely to manifest themselves than in labor relations, particularly at contract negotiation time. The animosity between line and staff results from not thinking fairly enough about the other fellow's job. Not that it isn't aggravating to have the staff claim all the credit when it's finally over. Not that it isn't equally annoying for the staff to be blamed for all the things that later prove to be not too smart in the final instrument. The point is that labor relations or the negotiation of a new contract is almost certain to turn out better with a good line–staff working relationship than it ever would if one or the other tried to handle the job alone.

The line people, if allowed to negotiate without staff, would almost certainly be inclined to frame the agreement around the local plant of their particular division. This attitude too often leads to trouble in another plant or division where conditions are different and where the union is strong enough to use the previous pattern to its advantage.

From a staff man's viewpoint the line man—

- Seldom or never makes proper use of staff.
- Resists new ideas or even minor changes.
- Refuses to give staff any authority.
- Is reluctant to give staff any credit.

The line man or the staff man who worries about what he does; how he fits into the organization; how carefully his duties, his responsibilities, and the limits of his authority can be classified and codified; who gets the credit and who takes the blame for specific results; who is the more important; and so on is indulging in a word game, an exercise in semantics, a time-waster yielding little or no profit. In the final analysis the good men, both line and staff, will find a way to get along and get the job done or eventually they will be moved up, down, or out.

The key to cooperation between line and staff is understanding how to make the best use of all the tools, mechanical and human, which are available to accomplish the corporate objective. This objective almost always is making more money for the owners, not just this month or this quarter or even this year, but steadily and, if possible, increasingly! Peter Drucker has a good final word in this argument. He reminds us that there are really no line functions or staff functions—there are only management functions.

THE ORGANIZATION CHART AND ITS LIMITATIONS

The bookshelves are crowded with treatises on business management, and most of them devote a great deal of time to the importance of good organization. And rightly so. It is certainly basic to good management. The more we read, however, the easier it becomes to get so wrapped up in drawing an organization chart that the business itself is disappearing down the drain of uncontrolled costs. The establishment of reasonable lines of authority, the elimination of overlap, the fixing of limits of authority, the functional relationship between people and organizational segments are all fundamental to good organization. Putting these principles on paper in nicely balanced boxes with everyone from president to assistant foreman in his proper place in the chain of command does very little to make the organization structure work. It's a good beginning but a futile exercise if the proper people are spotted in the right places and then not inspired, taught, trained, encouraged, and allowed to operate together in the direction of a better-looking profit and loss statement.

Organization charting often complicates the line and staff relationships, but good relationships cannot be insured by an organization chart anyway. However, they can be roughly indicated. What should be remembered is that the position on a given chart does not necessarily indicate the importance of the job. The staff assistants to the president are usually placed directly under him on the corporate organization chart, but seldom do they have the great responsibilities or draw the high salaries of the line or operating people who are shown at a lower level.

These matters are all related to the type and size of the business, the degree to which it's centralized or decentralized, the philosophy of the owners, and even the whims of the chief executive officer. There are assistants to presidents who are at the top of the chart and do nothing but open the mail, arrange luncheon dates, and keep the switchboard operators on the ball. There are also assistants who wield tremendous influence and power not only because they are cloaked with the same authority as the boss but more often because they are strong and competent and are obeyed as much out of respect as they are for their position at the right hand of the top man.

With line and staff organizations now almost universal, the differences among them are basically those of degree, depending upon company size. The variations in relationships are practically unlimited. A company of 500 or 1,000 people will have a fairly straight line organization from president to foreman with very little opportunity for misunderstanding the chain of command. The giants like General Motors Corporation, General Electric Company, U.S. Steel Corporation, and International Business Machines Corporation have organizations so complex that it takes a Ph.D. to understand them. The point is that the staff of experts helping the president has the same relative relationship to him and the line organization that a plant's staff has to its manager and line organization.

General Electric has a staff department at the corporate level known as Employee and Community Relations Services, and the Remington Office Systems Division of Sperry Rand Corporation has a personnel department in Marietta, Ohio, that does the same basic job on a smaller scale. The corporate service group on industrial relations, whether in General Electric, Sperry Rand, or the Woolworth chain, provides expert advice and help on all vital matters that affect the people in all its plants: pensions, insurance, workmen's compensation, unemployment benefits, sick leave, hospitalization, contract interpretation, grievances, arbitration cases, labor negotiations, and so on. At the corporate level or at the plant level, the staff people are specialists in a very complex function, and the only thing worse than letting them run the operation would be to fail to solicit their help or neglect to give careful consideration to their advice. Staff people can *only* advise, counsel, suggest, and help. They dig up the facts, analyze them, and recommend how to use them.

ADVANTAGES OF LINE–STAFF

One famous definition of line and staff goes like this: "Line men try to make products; staff men try to keep them from doing it." It isn't true, of course, and no one seriously believes it. Line men *act;* staff men *advise.* The staff says, "When you do it, you should do it this way." A modern business can't be successful without good staff work, and the bigger the enterprise, the more staff men are required and the greater the need for experts in various functions. Just as in the successful army, planning is vital, and planning to a great degree is the responsibility of the staff. In fact, it belies to some extent our notion that staff men only advise. Planning—or any other form of staff work, for that matter—can be and often is the hardest kind of work.

The big corporation executive's need for expert staff help is obvious. But what about the small plant manager, the middle-level manager, the department head, the foreman, or the supervisor? The need for staff is there, but how does it really work?

The staff work in a small organization frequently falls to a person who also has certain line responsibilities. The industrial engineer, for example, has to plan the shop work, set the standards and rates, and work out new methods, and many times be his own tool design engineer. In that respect he is a line man. Yet he must also serve as staff to the line foreman. The industrial engineer is usually overworked and understaffed, but the plant that stifles its foreman's initiative is not going to compete successfully in the long run, and normally the foreman gets his staff assistance from the industrial engineer, just as he does from the plant accountant and the personnel manager.

What about the general foreman or superintendent who doesn't take kindly to the foreman who goes to industrial engineering for help on a new idea? In a small plant the good manager will soon catch up to such a person and either replace him or move him out. Usually, however, the problem can be traced to the foreman and his lack of tact. He should be taught the old trick of letting the boss share the credit; it is still one of the best ways to get around or through him.

But what about the industrial engineer himself? He gets pretty fed up with listening to crackpot ideas, most of which he has tried before. The foreman must rely upon his persistence, his patience, and his judgment in not espousing impractical ideas. The industrial engineer must listen to each new idea with the knowledge that one in 50 may be worth the time wasted listening to the other 49.

Line and staff cooperation on a small scale, in the small operating group, is just as vital as it is in the highly formalized top echelons of big corporations. The Remington Office Systems Division makes every supervisor spend one hour each month with the industrial engineer airing his problems, expounding his ideas, and offering his suggestions. It takes time, and it inconveniences the industrial engineer, since he frequently has to deviate from his schedule; but sooner or later every man at least gets the opportunity—and knows he will get another—to suggest and receive credit for improvements. The staff assistance in this case is listening, evaluating, analyzing, and, if necessary, preparing cost figures, accumulating related data, perhaps making time studies, designing a tool, or preparing justification for a capital expenditure.

Nor is the industrial engineer the only line man with staff duties. The plant accountant, for example, must discharge his line responsibilities of setting budgets, accumulating cost figures, preparing payroll, issuing financial reports, and so on and still perform many staff services for the other line departments. He must guide production control in such matters as determining the proper inventory levels by breaking out the elements that make up inventory carrying costs. He must advise the superintendent and the personnel manager on the true costs of hiring people for short periods as opposed to the cost of overtime. He must constantly break down and analyze figures to assist other people in operating more efficiently, regardless of whether these costs relate to material, fringe benefits, the influence of special taxes, the costs of insuring, or the rate of depreciation. The smaller the organization, the greater the necessity for incorporating both line and staff responsibilities *and understanding* among the operating people.

Use of staff within the group is largely a matter of the climate created by the head man, but even a reluctant chief can be made to listen by smart, aggressive, and tactful subordinate supervisors. If the boss thinks a suggestion will improve his cost picture, help his quality, speed up delivery, or make him a hero, he will buy it, especially if he can be induced to think it is *his* idea.

Use of the staff at higher levels is basically no different, but it varies according to overall corporate policy. Some top staff people operate with a heavy hand and modify their "advice" with words that imply, "This is just a suggestion, but bear in mind who is making it." There are times when it is wise to follow advice of dubious merit to avoid rocking the boat. This is not to say that bad advice—advice that can cost money, lose business, or damage customer relations—should be accepted to keep the staff happy. The point is not to waste energy complaining about staff suggestions that don't do too much harm. The line man should bear with the staff; and, when he really needs help, the chances are the staff can furnish it, for staff people have at least three big advantages over the local operating man:

1. They usually have a good knowledge of their specialty.
2. They are situated at headquarters and so can exert pressure where it counts.
3. They usually have access to (and time to study) technical data that will help explore an idea or justify an expenditure.

LINE–STAFF RELATIONSHIPS IN PRACTICE

One of the hazards of a line–staff organization is the danger inherent in having more than one boss, or "duality of command." No matter how clearly company policy states that staff can only advise—not order—the problem remains. The stronger the staff man (and, conversely, the weaker the line man), the more likely "advise and consent" is apt to become "do or else."

Staff work, particularly the kind that requires high-priced experts at headquarters, can and often does lead to political maneuvering that is both frustrating and damaging. Internal politics usually flourish most when line and staff men are not making an all-out effort to work together. Politics can be held to a minimum if just one party makes the right effort.

The staff man should bear in mind that he is just as important as the line. His first objective should be to find a way to make the line man trust him, seek him out, ask for his help, and give careful consideration to his suggestions, and he must do all this without ever being disloyal to his job or his boss. It's not so difficult as it sounds. The staff man can keep these suggestions in mind:

1. Try to avoid sounding like a know-it-all.
2. Try to consider the operating man's daily pressures.
3. Don't say, "In my last job we did it this way." Nothing can slow down acceptance faster.
4. Bend over backward to give the line the credit. It often pays dividends and even gains the staff more credit than it deserves on some occasions.

5. Always try to visualize the situation that would arise if suddenly the staff man and the line man he is working with were to trade jobs—it has happened.

Let the line man bear these thoughts in mind:

1. The staff man is painfully aware that the line need not take his advice. However, if it's good advice, it's better to take it now than to have it come down later as an order from the boss.
2. The old idea about who gets out the product and makes the money is worth remembering. A great many profitable ideas come from the staff. Credit also goes to the line man who can install them and make them work.
3. A little confidence in the staff men can pay big dividends in expert help when it is needed and in a good word at the right place and the right time.
4. There's a big difference between not letting a staff man give orders to line men and stifling his efforts to help. One should be a little forbearing—and, if he gets out of control, chat with him tactfully in private. The line may gain a helper in this way without any increase in overhead.
5. Again, it pays to remember that the line man and the staff man may be switched about unexpectedly.

SOME FURTHER COMMENTS

The basic principle of hiring specialists—staff men—to help the operating man do his job better not only is sound but represents one of the most important elements in the organization and management of a business or any segment thereof.

The need for one person to perform each specialty is not vital. Recognition of the necessity of employing specialist *knowledge* is the important thing, even in a two-man operation. Common sense tells us it is advantageous to both and to the enterprise if each is a specialist to some degree in a different function. Illustrations of this abound: the engineer and the salesman who successfully run a small shop; the accountant and the mechanic who run a garage; the lawyer and engineer who have formed a partnership to provide patent services; and so on. Each is both line and staff.

The mistake of having too many purely staff people is frequently perpetrated by consultants. Consulting firms consist of professional staff men for hire, and they sometimes tend to encourage overstaffing. Not only is this foolish and costly, but it has given staff work an unfair reputation in many places. The idea is prevalent that staff men always "have it good": short hours, high pay, liberal expense accounts, fancy hotels, all the credit and none of the blame. It just isn't so, as any staff man can quickly point out. Good staff men are hard to find because staff work is difficult. The hours are frequently rough, and more blame than credit is likely to be the rule.

Having too few staff people is not so common as failure to recognize the need for making someone the equivalent of staff, if only as part of his line job. In the small plant or even in the small operating department, it's not only good business, it's a good morale builder to make everyone an expert or a "specialist" at something. Let's take the small shipping department supervisor. Even if everyone but the foreman is a union man, working under a job classification covered by a contract, it's not difficult to apply the staff principle to the regular workers. One man can be the expert at where the packaging is stored (many shipping departments waste a lot of money looking for the right-size carton); another can be the specialist in watching the supply of tape, strapping, and so on; another can make sure that the electric trucks are charged. These examples are extreme, perhaps, but the point is that "staff" work at lower levels is actually a matter of assigning responsibility to gain greater efficiency and better control. The principle can be applied to any group, and the benefits accrue in proportion to the judgment used in specializing to a *practical* degree.

Good relations between line and staff at any level are not difficult to maintain and can be pleasant as well as profitable. The easy way to keep working well together is to remind ourselves consistently that we can be asked to swap jobs. It's amazing how easy the other fellow's job looks until we give careful thought to how it would be if we had to do it. The staff man must lean heavily on persuasion, on the weight of his arguments, and on his tact. Patience, persistence, and careful timing are all-important. The line man can normally issue an order and get it done, but the line man who issues orders without judgment or operates in a vacuum will be ineffective. So, too, will the staff man who gets his work done by veiled threats, by "ratting" to the boss, and by claiming credit where he should at least share it. The good man will get the job done without disrupting people or plans, regardless of whether he's line or staff.

MAINTAINING SOUND
RELATIONS WITH UNIONS

By RICHARD F. POWELL, JR.

Labor relations is a dynamic aspect of business life with serious cost implications that arise not only in the negotiated package but also in the administration of contracts. Mistakes in other areas of business can generally be rectified. For example, an erroneous sales forecast can be updated by correction and production schedules can be adjusted accordingly; there will be temporary disruption and possibly some financial loss, but the damage can be repaired before it reaches disastrous proportions. This is not so in labor relations, where a mistake can have repercussions throughout the life of the enterprise, or at least until the next period of negotiations. Even then it may take a strike to rectify the mistake, because negotiation is primarily compromise. Through proper administration of the contract and knowledge of how to make it work, such untenable and costly mistakes can be avoided.

One cost, although hard to measure in dollars and cents, results from the effect that poor labor relations has on employee morale. Not only does poor morale lead to an unsatisfactory work environment, but it also has a serious and deleterious effect on costs because of lower production, poor quality, and general inefficiency.

Labor relations is generally divided into two major areas: contract negotiation and the daily administration, interpretation, and application of the agreement. Negotiation seems to many people the more important of the two areas, probably because it makes the headlines and in general is in greater public prominence. However, the key to good labor relations—and truly its heart—is the daily dealings with the union. This day-to-day administration of the contract is primarily the function of the manufacturing manager, either through personal control or through delegated authority to his supervisory staff.

RICHARD F. POWELL, JR. is Labor Relations Advisor for Johnson & Johnson in New Brunswick, New Jersey.

DIFFERENCES BETWEEN UNION AND INDUSTRY OPERATIONS

A union is essentially a political organization. An understanding of this basic fact helps a manager—especially a first-line supervisor—to understand why a union's officers and stewards behave the way they do, and why a logically sound argument does not always prevail in settling grievances. To illustrate the difference between the viewpoints of management and the union, let's analyze the ways in which a manager and a union officer or steward obtain and hold their jobs and the consequences of unsatisfactory performance in each case.

Before a manager is hired by an organization, he submits a résumé, undergoes interviewing and testing, and describes his academic and work background. A union official, on the other hand, is elected to his position by a majority of the members of the union. The manager is generally hired for an indefinite length of time, whereas a union official is elected for a specific period—normally only one or two years. At the expiration of his term of office the union official envisions re-election; his chance of success is determined primarily by an evaluation of his past performance by the membership which he represents. His existence is therefore dependent upon political considerations.

If a manager loses his job, he will seek a comparable position with another organization. He probably will be successful in his quest for a new job—he even may be able to obtain a higher-level position than the previous one. But what happens to a union official if he is not successful in seeking re-election? Undoubtedly he rose directly from the ranks to his present position in the union. Let's take the hypothetical case of a union member who is a material handler and who runs for the union presidency. If he wins the election, one day he is a material handler and the next day he is the union president. This type of elevation has no counterpart in managerial promotion. Similarly, if a union official is not re-elected, the demotion is catastrophic.

Aside from the monetary rewards which may or may not characterize a union office, it is a position of high status and great prestige. Its loss is a significant one. The union official cannot apply for a similar type of job in another union local or in a different union. He must return to his former position in the bargaining unit. Because his station in life is dependent upon politics, it is natural that his behavior will in large measure be dictated by these considerations.

The difference between a union and a company also can be seen in the objectives toward which they are oriented. The labor relations climate can and does vary in every degree, from extreme militancy and hostility to sophistication resulting in what is frequently termed a mature collective bargaining environment. These two polar positions are light years apart.

A company is first and foremost profit-oriented. Its very existence and ability to grow are determined by its ability to accumulate property. Property in this sense means anything of ascertainable monetary value. An analogy can be drawn between what profits are to a company and what salary is to an individual employee. Salary invariably does not rank first in any survey taken to indicate why a person works or why he likes his job or company. Nevertheless, salary is the most important reason for working—in fact, the sole reason. Take all his salary away and a man would not work. Take away any of the other items listed in a survey, such as long vacations, pension plan, pleasant working conditions and environment, and the like, and he would still work. Salary, therefore, becomes the only indispensable incentive to work. Similarly, without profits, the very existence of a company ceases. Not only does it lack a motive or reason for continuing its operation but also, by the very nature of our economy, it cannot remain in business. While this fact may seem elemental, it is frequently overlooked in endeavors to solve labor relations problems.

The union, on the other hand, is not primarily profit-oriented. A union is "people"-oriented. A union has as its primary goal the preservation and expansion of the desires of its members.

This does not mean that a union is not interested in corporate profits or that a company is not interested in the welfare of its employees. A union is interested in corporate profits, because it is only through an increase in the profitability of a company that a union can hope to achieve additional benefits for its members. Similarly, a company is interested in the good health and welfare of its employees. Both unions and companies have many of the same goals and objectives, but different weights are assigned to them.

The company's basic role in labor relations is to act; the union's basic role to react. This does not mean that a union does not share in responsibility. Unions have responsibility, but their principal role resembles that of a defense attorney—that is, they make a company prove its case. Initiating action, be it in the application of the contract or in discipline, is a right of management that should not be diminished or abrogated.

THE MANUFACTURING MANAGER'S ROLE IN AVOIDING CONTRACT "GIVEAWAYS"

The administration of a labor agreement is ultimately the job of the manufacturing manager. The labor relations environment depends on how he handles this critical aspect of his job. He or his supervisory staff is in close, day-to-day contact with the employees and the union. To them he *is* the company, and their opinion of the company is derived mainly from the relationship that exists between the manager and the employees.

The manufacturing manager must realize the importance of interpretation, application, and administration of the labor agreement, because it is in these areas that contract "giveaways" can occur. Of course, he is accountable for problems in many other areas, such as production and engineering, and consequently he may tend to let labor matters go and give his attention to something that seems more important at the moment. However, he should avoid this tendency because probably no other decision in the course of any one day will have greater significance and impact, not only on the manufacturing department but on the company as a whole, than a labor relations decision.

Most managerial errors can be rectified; mistakes in labor relations decisions cannot be corrected, because answers to grievances are precedent-setting. An arbitrator, normally limited to the confines of a contract, can deviate from it to the extent that the parties themselves have done previously. The rationale that an arbitrator uses, and justifiably, in deviating from the contract is that he is following what the parties want as evidenced by their past acts—they have mutually agreed to the change. No matter how good a contract is, it can be watered down and even abrogated if grievances are handled in a manner inconsistent with the agreement.

Improper grievance handling is but one of the two ways in which contract giveaways occur. The other is loose contract administration. If a contract is not administered firmly enough or if the company's goals are not given proper weight, unintentional contract giveaways can result. For example, let us consider a contract containing a clause which reads: "Leaves of absence may be granted to employees for personal reasons. The granting or denial of a leave of absence shall be within the sole discretion of the employer." It is incumbent upon management to administer such a clause fairly and with controls. If it is administered haphazardly, the number of leaves granted may be excessive in relation to the number of employees and the proper operation of a department. Proper controls on the number and duration of such leaves must be applied. Too many leaves also can greatly increase the cost of doing business. It may be necessary to hire additional employees as temporary replacements who must be trained and for a period of time will produce inefficiently. The hiring, training, and lower productivity of these employees are cost items. The productivity and quality of a group may be affected if a contractual "bumping" procedure applies or if employees are on a group incentive system.

The manufacturing manager's primary labor relations duty is the protection of the company's rights under the contract. Once lost, a right can be regained at the bargaining table only by giving up another right to recapture the one that has been given away; no benefit is derived from this type of barter.

TECHNIQUES OF GRIEVANCE HANDLING

Knowledge of grievance-handling techniques and conduct is essential to the manufacturing manager's job. A grievance procedure is a negotiated item in a contract and is designed to be beneficial to both the union and the company. It provides a means for the orderly settlement of disputes and a mechanism for enforcing the contract and protecting the rights of the parties involved.

Too often, managers erroneously believe that if grievances are filed against them or their supervisors, they are not properly performing their job. This is not true—in fact, the case is just the opposite. It is only human nature that whenever two or more people are together constantly, conflicts and differences of opinion result. Hence, grievances are a normal, natural product of a work environment. Grievances are actually a safety valve. If employees feel free to file grievances and if their problems are resolved as they arise, grievances generally will not become major disruptions. If they are not properly aired, they build up and multiply, and eventually they cause a violent eruption which is disadvantageous to both the company and the union. It is analogous to a boiling pot of water; if the steam is not allowed to escape, there will be an explosion.

No optimum number of grievances should be expected from any group, but from a historical analysis of a department it can be determined what a reasonable number is for a certain period of time. An investigation should be made if too many or too few are being filed in any given area of the company, because either can indicate the existence of a problem. Too few grievances could be the result, for example, of a supervisor's yielding on points on which he should remain firm. An increase in the number of grievances can usually be traced to a cause such as the installation of new incentive rates or the introduction of new methods or equipment. Reaction in the form of grievances is natural under such circumstances. However, the cause could also be a breakdown in the relationship between the supervisor and the employees or their union steward. Any deviation from the normal pattern should be investigated, its cause ascertained, and corrective measures taken if the cause so indicates. It must be borne in mind that the grievance load will fluctuate greatly at certain times of the year; for example, immediately before the vacation period it usually decreases greatly.

Grievances can also be used as a barometer of morale. Through careful analysis and study of grievances a manager is able to keep his finger on the pulse of his employees. An analysis of grievances has the further advantage of enabling a company to anticipate contract demands and hence prepare for negotiations well in advance of the actual expiration date of the contract.

Certain rules should be followed in preparing for a grievance meeting. In summary fashion they are as follows:

1. Get all the facts. Emotion must be put aside in order to achieve a purely objective appraisal of the situation. To obtain the facts a manager must talk to those people who have any knowledge of or relation to the problem. Where relevant, a visual survey of the area should be made, documents relative to the grievance studied, and past history scrutinized to determine if any similar case has occurred and to uncover anything else that may apply to the grievance at hand. Adequate investigation and preparation have no substitute.

2. Communicate beforehand. There are two parts to this pre-grievance-meeting communication. The first is communication with other managers to see if they have or have had similar problems. If so, discussion before the meeting will enable a company to be consistent in its approach and to avoid perpetuating an erroneous decision. Such advance communication helps to avoid what is commonly referred to as "whiplash"—a situation in which a manager's decision on one grievance is used to management's disadvantage by a grievant in another case in a different section or department.

   The other part of communication can be referred to as "role playing." The manufacturing manager should relate all the facts to another manager; then they should enact a debate as it might occur at the grievance table, one arguing from the union's point of view and the other arguing from the company's point of view. Role playing has a twofold advantage: first, it aids in determining the type of case the union will present, and, second, it shows weaknesses and missing elements in the company's case which need further investigation and preparation. Communication of certain facts and information to the union in advance of action the company plans to take can frequently prevent grievances. We must remember that a union is a political organization. If, for example, a steward knows about a future action on the company's part, when consulted by a union member he may be able to avoid a griev-

ance; however, if he does not know of the company's plans, a grievance may result for no other reason than to save face.

3. An elementary, but essential, prerequisite for participating in the grievance meeting, and one that is frequently overlooked, is a thorough knowledge of the contract, its meaning and intent. In addition, knowledge
   of the grievant and the steward and any idiosyncrasies they have is
   helpful in planning the approach to be used in arriving at a solution
   of a particular grievance.

In the actual conduct of a grievance meeting the manufacturing manager
must follow certain actions and steps. They are:

1. The union steward or officer should be treated as the manager's equal.
   He is. Generally he is extremely knowledgeable about the contents of
   the contract and the conduct of a grievance meeting. Union officers
   are usually quite capable and should never be underestimated.

2. A rule that should be strictly followed is to be firm but fair and consistent in dealing with the union and employees. If dealings are carried
   out in this manner, the employees and the union will respect the company—and respect is the key to maintaining sound relations with
   unions.

3. It is imperative that the meeting be confined to the actual issue or
   issues covered in the grievance; the manager should avoid hypothetical
   discussions. He can be lulled into a false sense of security when discussing
   a hypothesis because it appears to be an aside from the problem at
   hand. The danger here is that he may "philosophize." He must stick
   to the facts; an answer to a hypothetical question can be used against
   him.

4. A grievance should be processed promptly. Procrastination has a tendency further to alienate the grievant because he may feel that he
   is being deliberately ignored. Furthermore, if the steward surmises from
   the delay that the manager has a weak case and is afraid to answer
   the grievance, he may present a stubborn front at the meeting, thus
   making resolution of the problem more difficult.

   Although grievances should be processed promptly, snap judgments
   must be avoided. Don't answer a grievance or hold a meeting until
   the problem has been thoroughly investigated and all the necessary facts
   have been obtained.

5. Be objective. Rule out emotion. If the manager is wrong, let him not
   be afraid to admit it. Admitting a mistake will gain respect.

6. It is advantageous to settle grievances early, preferably at the first step.

As grievances go up the line, the positions of both union and company tend to become hardened and more difficult to resolve.

7. During the grievance meeting, be a good listener. Let the employee talk. Frequently a grievance will be settled merely by giving the grievant an opportunity to be heard. This is known as "letting the employee blow off steam and talk himself out of it." But in listening, be sincere and don't just feign interest.

HANDLING DISCIPLINE PROBLEMS

Many of the principles of handling grievances are also applicable to the successful handling of discipline cases. To begin with, in matters of discipline, the burden of proof is upon the employer. Therefore, it is incumbent upon the employer to develop a set of rules and regulations applicable to the employees and to assure that they are aware of them. This is generally accomplished by giving a list of regulations to each new employee as he is hired and by posting the regulations in a conspicuous place.

The rules must be public knowledge, but the appropriate penalties for infractions are preferably not provided with the rules. This is a matter within the purview of management. Rules should be audited periodically and changed when circumstances warrant. The issuance of rules and regulations should be within the control of management; the union should be granted only the right to contest the reasonableness of the rules, not to challenge the company's right to prescribe rules.

Discipline is necessary to maintain good order and conduct among employees; chaos would result if certain standards of conduct were not prescribed. There are essentially two kinds of discipline, punitive and corrective. In corrective discipline the primary emphasis is placed on correcting an employee, whereas punitive discipline is negative and has the sole purpose of punishment. Punitive discipline such as penalties and dismissals should be used only when an employee has been given an opportunity to correct his shortcomings and fails to do so.

Management has a moral obligation to inform employees when their actions are not in accordance with the prescribed company standards. This is the very essence of corrective discipline.

Corrective discipline for infractions of the rules and regulations follows prescribed steps. After the first violation, the employee is spoken to and a record is made of this conversation. After subsequent violation, a written warning is issued to the employee, and a copy of it is sent to the union. If another breach occurs, the employee is suspended, the duration depending upon the severity of the offense. At this time or after further infractions a recommendation of dismissal may be made if deemed necessary. At each of these steps the manager must make an effort to correct the employee, for a great deal more is accomplished by correction than by dismissal. However, if an employee does not respond, discharge will ultimately result. For more serious offenses the procedure may be expedited and, in extreme cases, discharge recommended for the first offense.

It is preferable for a company to structure its disciplinary procedure on a cumulative basis—that is, to create a system in which progressive steps are taken for subsequent violations of the same or a different rule. The rationale behind such a system is that the employee's total conduct must conform to a prescribed standard.

Management is responsible for maintaining discipline and initiating disciplinary action. Again, it is the company which acts and the union which reacts. The rules of discipline must be enforced uniformly and consistently. A rule unenforced is not a rule. Every breach of a rule must be called to the employee's attention promptly, but the penalties imposed can vary. In determining the penalty the employee's total record should be evaluated. The penalty can be imposed later after the manager has had a chance to investigate the employee's file and analyze other relevant data. The corrective discipline approach has the added benefit of giving the union notice of problem areas, and it gives the steward the opportunity to help alleviate the situation. It does not, however, relieve the manager of his responsibility for initiating action. Arbitrators, in deciding a discipline case, will be favorably disposed to uphold an action where the steps of corrective discipline have been fairly and consistently applied.

The techniques mentioned here are predicated on full disclosure to the union and a fair and consistent approach to all labor relations problems. If they are consistently followed, sound relations with the union will be the reward.

DEVELOPING AND CARRYING OUT MANUFACTURING POLICIES

By WALTER R. OLSON

Manufacturing policies are developed to assist in solving the customers' delivery needs and wants, to attain the lowest possible product cost, and to achieve the highest degree of quality while using the available machinery, equipment, tools, facilities, and manpower. The manufacturing executive must, however, first understand the company's overall policies which necessarily limit or control his programs. Some that he must consider when he is developing manufacturing policies are:

- Sales forecasts.
- Research and development projects.
- Inventory investment.
- Possible mergers or acquisitions.
- Capital and expense funds.
- Consolidation or expansion of existing facilities.
- Addition of a new manufacturing facility.
- Company organization.

THE EFFECT OF COMPANY POLICIES ON MANUFACTURING POLICIES

Let us take a short look at the effects of these overall corporate policies on manufacturing before we proceed to examine specifically manufacturing policies.

The manufacturing manager needs a sales forecast of one to five years to

WALTER R. OLSON is Director—Manufacturing for Remington Rand Office Systems, Division of Sperry Rand Corporation, New York City.

develop policies covering financial and cost budgets, inventory requirements, anticipated direct and indirect labor requirements, fixed costs, overall manufacturing organization, cost reduction programs, and planning for the expansion, consolidation, or construction of manufacturing facilities. In addition, manufacturing policies are affected by new products whose introduction may influence future plant capacity requirements, methods of manufacturing, expansion or consolidation of facilities, or type of manufacturing organization (for example, increased or decreased requirements from the quality control and inspection departments depend upon the type and quality of the new products).

The amount of inventory to maintain depends not only upon the extent of the customer service required but also upon the lowest possible production costs that can be achieved without jeopardizing the company's ability to hold its share of the market. After a practical inventory level has been determined, policies and targets must be established to insure that it is maintained. It may be important to build up finished-goods inventory at the sacrifice of raw material in order to comply readily with the customers' delivery requests. If so, this policy must be established so that the direction and method of inventory control are clear.

Limitation of the inventory investment governs in part the size of production runs. If production planning reduces lot sizes below the calculated economical level because of tight inventory policy, product unit costs will rise. It is important to establish manufacturing policies that guide and direct production control, purchasing, and other departments in controlling inventory to attain minimum unit costs which are consistent with the company's inventory policy.

Anticipated mergers or acquisitions can have a serious effect on manufacturing policies, since they may cause radical changes in capacity, methods of manufacture, organization, inventory, delivery requirements, and so on. A manufacturing plant acquired through merger, for example, could increase manufacturing capacity beyond total volume requirements. There may in turn be a need for consolidation of facilities. Excess as well as new equipment, which could change the capital expenditures in the existing plant, may be available.

Management's limitations on overall capital and expense spending have a significant effect on policies in terms of payback on capital investments, extent of investments for improving systems, personnel policies where they effect increases in wages and fringe benefits, the type of equipment replacement programs, the extent of expenditure for tools on new or existing products, improvement of existing facilities, and so on.

Consolidation or expansion of existing facilities or construction of a new facility is governed by management's decisions in such areas as sales forecasts, acquisition or mergers, and research and development programs. If, because of an anticipated increase in sales volume, it is necessary to expand the existing facilities or build a new facility, changes in policies must be developed accordingly.

Changes in organization structure can have definite effects on established policies not only in the need for a change but also in the method of implementation. In a large corporation, for example, if a manufacturing service section is added to group or division headquarters to assist in improving the techniques and effectiveness of plant departments such as industrial engineering, production control, and quality control, there will be changes in flow of information, techniques of control, and possibly plant staffing.

The effectiveness of established policies depends on the strength of the executives involved and on the organization structure required to implement the policies. If authorities and responsibilities are changed within the organization, the implementation of existing policies could also change, resulting in the need for their revision.

Management policies should be clearly understood because of their controlling influence on the policies of subordinate departments. If no clear statement of direction is given by the senior executive, there will be constant confusion, which may lead to a less profitable business.

DEVELOPING MANUFACTURING POLICY

Since constant change must take place in order for a business to remain competitive, it is essential that the manufacturing executive be represented in general management planning and thinking and that he have a voice in top management decisions. It is, in fact, important not only for the manufacturing manager, but for the managers of marketing and engineering to participate in all phases of planning, whether it be dropping a product line, acquiring a new product, reorganizing the overall company structure, or any other change—regardless of the *extent* of its effect on manufacturing. Manufacturing will then have firsthand knowledge of top management's intentions, as well as those of other departments, and can adjust its own plans quickly to suit the overall program.

Constant changes in top management policies can of course result in constant changes in manufacturing policies, and it is difficult to maintain and execute any kind of plan under such circumstances. While vacillation may be necessary in a rapidly moving situation, with better long-range planning many of the radical changes can be eliminated and the existing policies be made more effective.

Once overall company policies are understood, the manufacturing department can proceed to establish its own. There are overall manufacturing department policies as well as manufacturing executive policies to be determined. Moreover, the production, production control, industrial engineering, quality control, plant engineering, personnel, and accounting departments all must develop their policies within the framework established by manufacturing management. Thus, in developing a policy or program for manufacturing, detailed research must first be conducted on all factors in the particular area under study. All departments involved in the study should be contacted and everyone's point of view analyzed.

One factor that often results in malfunctioning of a policy is incomplete communication within the organization. To assist in overcoming this problem, most policies and procedures should be put in writing. They will be more thoroughly thought out before issuance and reach their proper audience if they are committed to paper.

The following example shows how a manufacturing policy is developed into a workable program. Inconsistency both in the routing and handling of capital requisitions and in determining adequate "payback" was apparent in this company. Initially the manufacturing manager gave the chief industrial engineer the assignment of developing a procedure which would solve the problem. He limited the maximum dollar authorization for each supervisor and, working with the plant controller, used the proper tax provisions to determine the difference between capital and expense expenditures.

The chief industrial engineer made a complete study and established a capital requisition policy in writing. In developing this policy he discovered that other departments were involved; and, before he proceeded further, he knew he had to discuss his program with the managers of engineering, plant control, quality control, production control, plant engineering, personnel, shop supervision, and anyone else who requested capital items.

After each department head had been consulted and the written policy modified to incorporate practical suggestions, the engineer presented his proposal to the manufacturing manager for final analysis and approval. The heads of the major departments involved—marketing, engineering, accounting, manufacturing, and particularly the treasurer of the corporation—met to discuss and revise this policy until there was complete understanding by everyone concerned. Finally, the revised policy was published. The example is hypothetical and does not necessarily reflect any existing procedure, but it does indicate the extent of the information required in a written policy.

XYZ Company

Policy and Procedure Instruction

Number A-1   Effective Date: October 1, 19—
To: All Department Heads   Issued By: John Jones
Subject: Approval and Processing of   Issue Date: September 1, 19—
    Capital Requisitions   Reference:

I. Policy. Authority is defined and delegated by the manufacturing manager to areas of manufacturing management to acquire, within the limits established in this policy, capital assets, special tooling, test equipment, and associated items of expense.

II. Purpose. Establishes the approval authority of capital requisitions.

III. Applies to all manufacturing departments.

IV. Procedure. Each requisition requires a minimum of two signatures—one the plant manager's and the other the plant controller's. Financial justification is required on all requisitions over $XXX.

V. General

  A. Purchases or commitments may not be made until the approved copy of the capital requisition has been received by the originator.

  B. The following items must be capitalized:

    1. The acquisition of fixed assets, such as land, buildings, machinery, furniture, appliances, and school assets or permanent additions thereto.

    2. Improvements to fixed assets which increase their value, productivity, or usefulness.

    3. Replacement of complete units or equipment other than tooling or test equipment.

    4. Rebuilding major items of equipment if XX percent or more depreciated and if the equipment is completely rebuilt and is equivalent in production performance to new equipment.

    5. Improvements to or alterations in leaseholds. Acquisition of items costing less than $XXX is ordinarily charged to expense. However, permanent items of office furniture and appliances such as desks and chairs are classified as capital expenditures, even when their cost is less than $XXX.

       Expenditures for some items (such as minor additions or changes to buildings) costing more than $XXX may be charged to expense. The controller will rule in questionable cases.

  C. Requisitions for items included in the facilities budget.

    1. Each capital expenditure item or project on an approved

budget must be covered by at least as many capital requisitions as there are general types of assets (machinery, land, buildings, etc.) listed for that item. The number of capital requisitions submitted should be kept to the minimum consistent with this requirement.

2. Each capital requisition must be approved and an authorization number assigned before any material is requisitioned, work performed, or purchase commitment made.

3. For miscellaneous capital expenditures of $XXX or less, a single capital requisition may be prepared for each such budget reference number. Upon approval of these requisitions, expenditures for the miscellaneous items under $XXX may be made without further approval.

   D. Requisitions for items not included in the facilities budget.

1. Such requisitions *must* be considered for approval on the basis of the substitution or the deletion of specific aggregate dollar items contained in approved facilities budgets. The requisition must identify the item or items in the current budgets that are being replaced by the higher-priority item or items.

    Substitutions must be made within the asset classifications except that no substitution is permitted in the categories "Land and Land Improvements," "Building and Building Improvements," and "Airplanes."

    When the item requisitioned is a substitution, regardless of the dollar amount, it must have the approval of the manufacturing manager.

2. It is possible that no funds will be available for a substitution to handle an unbudgeted item as noted above. In all such cases, the following procedure pertains: The originating location will prepare the requisition, clearly labeling it "non-budget" in the "Budget Amount" blank. "Requested to Date," "Balance," and "Budget Reference Number" will be left blank. "Budget Classification" and "Asset Classification" must be completed. One copy is retained locally, and all other copies must be approved by the manufacturing manager.

  VI. Overruns and Underruns

   A. Overruns or underruns on an approved requisition shall decrease or increase the total facilities budget funds available for future appropriations.

   B. Preparing capital requisitions for overruns.

1. When actual expenditures or estimated completion costs exceed the amount authorized by less than $XX or X%, whichever is greater, no additional authorization or requisition is required.

2. When actual expenditures or estimated completion costs ex-

EXHIBIT A

CAPITAL REQUISITION FORM

REQUISITION NO. _____

AUTHORIZATION NO. _____

LOCATION - DIVISION _____

DATE _____

BUDGET PERIOD FROM _____ TO _____

BUDGET
CLASSIFICATION _____

BUDGET
AMOUNT $ _____

BUDGET
REFERENCE NO. _____

REQUESTED
TO DATE $ _____

ASSET
CLASSIFICATION _____

BALANCE $ _____

DESCRIPTION:

REASON: (STATE INCREASED OUTPUT OR SAVINGS TO BE EFFECTED.)

	ESTIMATED COST
MAKING: MATERIAL	
LABOR	
BURDEN	
PURCHASE PRICE	
TRANSPORTATION	
TAXES	
INSTALL: MATERIAL	
LABOR	
BURDEN	
TOTAL	

	COST OF PROPERTY OR INVENTORY OBSOLESCENCE (IF NONE, STATE SO)		
PROPERTY	ORIGINAL VALUE	DEP'N. RESERVE	SOUND VALUE
INVENTORY			
TOTAL			

RECOMMENDED ①	LOCAL APPROVAL - TITLE ③	DIVISION OR GROUP APPROVAL - TITLE ⑤	EXECUTIVE APPROVAL
PLANT CONTROLLER ②	WORK ORDER NO.	PUR. REQ./ORDER NO.	PRESIDENT ⑦
			GROUP BUDGET DEPT. ⑥
ACCOUNTING DISTRIBUTION		DIVISION CONTROLLER'S DEPT. ④	

ceed the amount authorized by more than \$XX or X%, whichever is greater, authorization must be requested on a supplemental requisition.

After local approval by the originator, the requisition will be processed for approval as a nonbudget item.

VII. Emergencies. Certain expenditures may be made on an emergency basis to protect life or property or provide for fire damage, damage by the elements, unexpected breakdown of production equipment, etc. When immediate action is necessary in emergency situations, the plant manager may act on his own authority within the limits of the manufacturing manager's maximum authority, securing the necessary approvals on or after the fact.

	Maximum
VIII. Authorizations and Limits	
Manager Production Control	\$XXX
Plant Controllers	\$XXX
Plant Managers	\$XXX
Division Production Manager	\$XXX
Director of Manufacturing	\$XXX

NOTE: A minimum of two signatures is required on all capital requisitions.

IX. Exhibit A: Capital Requisition Form

The cooperation of all departments, divisions, and sections is requested in order to make this procedure operate effectively.

IMPLEMENTING MANUFACTURING POLICY

No policy will produce the desired results without follow-up and enforcement. Determination and strength on the part of the manufacturing executive help keep it in force and effective. It is important that each individual understand his duties and responsibilities. If there are no clear lines of responsibility and authority, then there may be misunderstood, overlapping, or void areas of activity.

The line and staff relationships in any organization must be well defined to insure follow-through on manufacturing policies. The staff departments usually develop the policies and procedures, and the line carries them out. The line man may issue an order and get the job done, but if he issues orders without judgment, he will be ineffective in the long run. The staff man who gets his work done through coercion, who always claims credit for what he considers his accomplishments, will seldom obtain the desired results from any established policy.

Reports assist the managers in following up on an established policy. They should be periodic, but they may vary in frequency with the areas being checked. Some typical manufacturing reports that can be used as a check on progress by departments are:

1. Industrial engineering
   a. Cost reduction program results. Actual savings compared to established cost reduction goals for direct labor, indirect labor, material, and other fixed costs.
   b. Percentage of incentive coverage by department and plant.
   c. Variance on estimates for special orders.
   d. Actual unit costs on key products.
   e. Indirect labor to direct labor ratios.
   f. Anticipated savings on capital investments compared to actual savings.
   g. Number of employees by departments.
   h. Actual cost of tooling versus estimate both on new and existing products.
   i. Performance against cost budgets on indirect labor, indirect material, and other expenses.
   j. Temporary versus standard rates.
2. Production control
   a. Percent of orders shipped as scheduled.
   b. Broken promise reports by orders.
   c. Inventory status reports.
   d. Analysis of status of economic lot sizes.
   e. "Perpetual" inventory checks.
   f. ABC inventory program analysis.
3. Purchasing
   a. Progress of value engineering program against established goals.
4. Quality control.
   a. Plant waste (total scrap and rework dollars).
      (1) Purchased material.
      (2) Finished parts.
      (3) Final inspection.
   b. Field quality reports.
5. Plant engineering
   a. Machine down time.
   b. Maintenance inventory investment compared to budgeted amounts.

6. Personnel
   a. Absenteeism.
   b. Tardiness.
   c. Accident frequency rate.
   d. Labor turnover rate.
   e. Number of third-stage grievances.
   f. Job classification changes.
   g. Results of training programs.

Again, it takes strongmindedness and positive action by the executive upon receipt of these reports to move quickly in areas that are not meeting established goals or are slipping away from established procedures.

Because of the complexity of most manufacturing organizations and operations and because of the myriad changes that occur constantly both inside and outside the company in products, methods, and procedures, it is important that policies be constantly checked and reviewed for consistency with current overall corporate thinking and practices. Where there are no obvious methods to determine the effectiveness of policies the established program should be audited continually to assure compliance. Management auditors may be used, but many policies can be checked by the manager himself. If auditing is not done and corrections are not made when necessary, no written policy will ever be fully effective.

Manufacturing efficiency can no longer be judged by labor productivity alone. It is still a major factor, but modernization and technological advances have reduced labor cost in most industries. In analyzing the manufacturing department's performance against established policies we cannot overlook the effect the other departments, such as sales and engineering, have on their workability. They may not have fulfilled their responsibilities. Sales must be supported by adequate and timely production, but sales must also be responsible for meeting forecasts or notifying manufacturing when changes are anticipated. Engineering must be practical in designs, specifications, and production drawings, for that department can make it impossible to produce a product at the desired costs by insisting on impractical tolerances and specifications. Many other interdepartmental relationships should be studied as a part of the audit in order that all factors are evaluated in determining why a particular policy is not effective. If policies are allowed to deteriorate, the organization can quickly become ineffective.

LONG- AND SHORT-RANGE PLANNING

By JAMES G. EVERHART

In the free enterprise system the motivation underlying the activities of the usual manufacturing concern is a desire to make a profit. Years ago, profit may have been a somewhat vaguely understood force; profitable results were largely occasioned by chance. Not so today!

As our knowledge in the field of business has grown, we have seen an intellectual awakening, giving rise to an increasing awareness of the principles of economics and leading to the realization that making a profit need not and cannot be left to chance. Out of the thinking and actions of many have come the principles of management which already form a large body of specialized knowledge.

The widespread acceptance of formalized management principles and techniques is due in part to their overall applicability and to their basic, common-sense nature. Thus, in considering the manufacturing function specifically, we accept almost automatically the premise that profitability should always be uppermost in our minds.

Just the realization of this fact leads inevitably to the first of the five basic functions of management, which are generally recognized as planning, organizing, directing, coordinating, and controlling. Of these, planning is the keystone. It is essentially intellectual in character and requires careful and analytical consideration of the many alternates that can be considered in the areas of corporate objectives, policies, procedures, utilization of resources, and timing. It is the one facet of management that of itself has the greatest influence on the other four in the process of reaching the common objectives.

THE CHARACTERISTICS OF PLANNING

Planning is the conscious process of selecting and developing the best course of action to accomplish some objective. It is a reasoned and systematic ap-

---

JAMES G. EVERHART is General Manager, Porcelain and Fibre Products, Line Material Industries, of McGraw-Edison Company in Macomb, Illinois.

proach to the solution of business problems and is the basis from which future management actions spring. Progress, without planning, is only accidental. Planning is essential for good supervision and is absolutely necessary to achieve good morale within the organization.

In view of this, the manager must budget (we may say "plan") his time to allow for planning and replanning. How much time he must so allocate is closely related to his level in management. The ultimate responsibility for planning lies at the top, from whence the delegation of its various phases comes.

Thus a president may spend less than 10 percent of his planning time thinking about today and the period one month ahead, 60 percent on the period two years and beyond, and 5 percent or more on the period five to ten years ahead. The factory manager, who is more concerned with operational details, may spend 30 percent of his planning time on the immediate one-month period, concentrating about 40 percent on the three- to six-month period and 15 percent on the two- to five-year period, probably spending no time at all on the "beyond five years" period. In contrast, the manufacturing foreman, who is concerned with translating overall management plans into worker action, may spend 40 percent of his planning time on today's business, 40 percent on the week ahead, and 20 percent on the period one month to one year ahead.

The areas requiring manufacturing planning are almost without limit. Paramount among them is production planning with its emphasis on scheduling and control. Because of its importance and complexity, production planning is often regarded as a separate activity.

Other major planning efforts that find application to many phases of manufacturing result in budgets of all kinds. The preparation of worthwhile budgets, which are primarily used for control purposes, takes a great deal of study and thought. Good budgets contribute much toward related planning, coordinating, controlling, fixing of responsibility, and stimulating better performance.

Specific manufacturing objectives and plans are desirable in establishing the quality level, controlling scrap, reducing costs and expenses, controlling and improving breakeven point, determining economic ordering lots, and controlling inventories. They are also useful in connection with the many facets of product, processes, equipment, and facilities.

Good planning requires knowledge, foresight, judgment, experience, and, above all else, conscious effort. The difference between good and bad planning is the difference between confusion and order . . . things done on time and not done on time . . . cooperation and conflict . . . pleasant working relationships and intolerable friction.

Planning takes many forms and spans varying periods of time. Some plans are inevitably complex and detailed, others are simple and uncomplicated. Plans may cover periods of many years or of only the next few minutes. They may be, in the light of future experience, good, bad, or indifferent, but in any event plans represent proposed courses of action.

Because of the interaction of the plans of one segment of the business with all others, it is essential that planning exist for, and in, all phases of the business and be coordinated through the efforts of central management. Since, in short, managers must not be complacent but must make things happen, they need good plans as roadmaps to successful performance.

MANUFACTURING'S RESPONSIBILITY FOR PLANNING

Good sense dictates that the result desired should be determined before any action is taken to achieve it. The establishment of objectives is thus the fundamental first step in planning. Consequently, manufacturing must consider what its reason for being is. It is to make profit. The prime goal of profitability demonstrates the interrelationship of, and need for, carefully defined objectives. The key factors relating to manufacturing and affecting profitability can be readily identified. Among them are:

1. Productivity—the percentage increase of output over input.
2. Manufacturing resources—trained manpower, effectively organized and controlled; efficient productive capacity, available at the right time; unity through proper planning and coordination in a consciously directed effort to reach the specified objectives.
3. Manpower resources—their effectiveness implemented through careful selection, programed development, and deliberate efforts to develop a desirable employee attitude and motivation toward planned company objectives.
4. Innovation—the planned development of new equipment, new methods and processes, and new products which will directly contribute toward profit.

It is easy to see that the effectiveness of these factors is basically dependent upon the establishment of interrelated objectives and upon the resultant planning. If left to chance, manufacturing profits over the years will be minimal, fleeting, and uncertain. Thus, in striving for profitability, good management

will, first of all, plan in depth and over a broad front to determine the answers
to these questions:

- What is the existing situation?
- What should be done or accomplished?
- Why should it be done?
- When is it to be done?
- How is it to be done?
- Who is to do it?
- Where should it be done?
- What is its cost?

Thus we see that the actual planning process is by no means fragmentary
and elusive but can be expressed in practical, common-sense questions.

Whether free-wheeling, conservative, down-to-earth, or fanciful, planning
reflects the personality of the company and its stated or unstated policies. Ordinarily, manufacturing represents a substantial portion of a company's resources,
and it is imperative that a major part of the corporate master plan deal with
manufacturing. The springboard for manufacturing objectives must therefore
be the short- and long-range goals and objectives established by the board
of directors. Only through these means can the unified effort of the company's
total resources be marshaled and directed toward common objectives. To fail
to have corporate guidance is to nullify the best efforts of individual
departments.

Also influential to manufacturing planning is the effect of product planning.
It is reflected not only in short- and long-range market forecasting but also,
most importantly, in the actual character of the product. In today's market,
obsolescence is a prime factor in production, since product life is becoming
shorter and shorter. Faced with this condition, product planning often dictates
making in the future what today is a purchased component, or perhaps making
that product which utilizes the currently manufactured item. This is the "make
or buy decision" discussed more fully elsewhere in this book.

Characteristically, new products for the existing market offer a relatively
low return and long life, while new products for new markets generally offer
a high return and a relatively short life. The implications for manufacturing
in its planning for profit are readily apparent.

Whether it be caused by changing products or optimistic marketing forecasts,
redirection or expansion of manufacturing capacity requires substantial physical facilities, manpower, and money. Appreciable lead time is necessary as
well as a large measure of forecasting and planning, involving all segments
of top management in a cooperative and unified effort.

EFFECTS OF MARKET FORECASTS

Market forecasts have such a profound influence on manufacturing planning that further consideration is worthwhile. Long-range sales forecasts of five or ten years are essential to plan adequately for the large expenditures that will be required to provide the physical resources—buildings, special equipment, trained technical and managerial manpower—to support vastly different or expanded product lines. The lead time is of further importance in training and developing the required manpower and in implementing decisions through the design of equipment, the planning of plant layouts, the development of process techniques, and so on. It is of course essential that long-range forecasts be periodically reviewed and revised.

One-year forecasts are necessary to plan intelligently for coming production requirements. The short-range forecast should be more specific, more detailed, and much more nearly accurate than longer-range forecasts.

It is essential to translate marketing forecasts, which may be expressed in dollars or quantity, into units and factors that are significant to manufacturing. For example, the marketing information may be converted into capital requirements specifically covering buildings and equipment. It then may be evaluated in terms of inventory requirements, both work-in-process and finished goods. The further impact of the forecast on the organization structure and on the types, numbers, and specific characteristics of manpower should also be considered.

Certain financial aspects of the forecast may have serious implications for manufacturing. What is the forecast selling-price level as compared to the present? Is the proposed current standard cost to shipment sales dollars ratio favorable, judging by past experience? Do other factors predicated upon the forecast indicate a satisfactory product profitability? Manufacturing planning will be greatly influenced by the answers to these and other pertinent questions.

Shorter-range forecasts (for less than one year) are commonly useful in an operational sense. They find their greatest worth in production planning, which is a specialized application of general planning principles.

THE EFFECT ON PLANNING OF RETURN-ON-INVESTMENT FIGURES

An important factor of both long- and short-term planning of particular interest to manufacturing management is the amount and rate of return on investment. It joins the factors of profit, product, and facilities in the concern of manufacturing planners.

For many years "percent return on sales" was a magic phrase representing the most important criterion by which a business was judged. However, return on sales was not particularly helpful as an operational tool to pinpoint management's needs and guide its action.

The profit concept should imply the realization of the maximum net income possible from the capital invested in the business. As management has become a more conscious and deliberate process, the profit concept has come in for more searching analysis. Thus return on investment, often expressed as a percentage, has emerged as an invaluable management tool.

When a corporate objective as to the desired return on investment is determined, an important guide for all levels of management is established. Products providing an inadequate rate of return can readily be spotted. Management effort can then be concentrated either to bring about improvement or to reach a decision to drop the product from the line. The worth of proposed new products can similarly be evaluated. In either case, manufacturing can alert itself to the need and, through study and planning, may make an important contribution to profit.

In an operational sense the return-on-investment concept offers an important method by which many manufacturing decisions can be evaluated. The desirability of new equipment or a new process can be taken out of the realm of opinion and put on a profit-dollar basis. Similarly, with technological advances coming at an explosive pace, manufacturing management must be alert to the profit potential obtainable through obsoleting a perfectly good piece of equipment. Make or buy decisions, economic order quantities, inventory requirements, and questions of new or expanded facilities are other manufacturing decision areas where consideration of return on investment may play an important part in guiding management actions.

The modern manager, facing the increasing scope and complexity of manufacturing operations, can be expected to make ever increasing use of the return-on-investment concept in both short- and long-range planning.

THE ROLE OF OBJECTIVES

To this point, we have drawn the broad outlines of manufacturing planning for profit. When performed in depth and suitably integrated with overall management planning, manufacturing, in common with any other functional planning, requires detailed agreement throughout the several levels of management involved, often embracing many with interests in a wide range of functional areas.

Long- and short-range objectives are established by manufacturing management, marketing, engineering, the president, and the board of directors, each participating to the degree that each is interested in, or affected by, particular manufacturing objectives. These objectives, by conscious effort, confirm and implement company goals and policies and are designed to contribute to the basic soundness of operations.

Guided by well-stated, specific objectives, the manufacturing manager can ascertain the scope and nature of the job to be done. He examines and appraises the strength and weakness of existing capabilities. He evaluates other key factors such as economic conditions, competitive factors, and governmental influences.

When he has evaluated all of the circumstances, he establishes the general procedures required to reach the objectives and assigns specific responsibility for them. These assignments or delegated responsibilities should indicate the desired time schedule affecting both segments of the project and the whole.

Within the framework of major plans must fall many implemental decisions and supplementary plans concerning such practical factors as men, money, materials, equipment, facilities, and time. Here the responsibility and the control should be placed as close as possible to the point of execution. Ideally, these plans should be broken down and divided so that they are simple and easy to understand, have maximum flexibility, and are economical.

When the operational plans are completed, it is desirable to proceed with establishing the standards by which the accomplishments under these plans will be judged. It is advisable to build into the plans and procedures such measurement indicators and self-operated controls as are practical.

Control is a basic managerial function. Since the success of the manufacturing operation depends upon its plans and their implementation, it is axiomatic that sound plans will allow progress to be easily measured. The decision to put the plans into operation completes the planning process.

Planning is often complex and demands careful and clear thinking. Whatever the degree of confusion or difficulty faced, it is always necessary to include all the fundamental steps in arriving at a good plan. Simply stated in terms of action, they are:

1. Define objectives.
2. Obtain the facts.
3. Develop a course of action.

4. Evaluate the course of action.

5. Assign responsibilities.

6. Establish the criteria for satisfactory accomplishment.

7. Initiate the course of action.

Since the establishment of objectives is so essential to planning, it is helpful to consider certain necessary characteristics and results of sound manufacturing objectives.

Ineffectual planning would certainly result if it was based on objectives that were carelessly conceived and expressed in ineffective generalities. Extra time and effort are easily justified in order to crystallize and sharply define the objectives. They should be put in writing to avoid misinterpretation and to assure complete understanding by all concerned.

It is not enough that specific objectives be established by the planners. The success of any plan is dependent upon those who must carry it out. Because of this, it is an essential characteristic of sound objectives that they be reasonable and acceptable to those who must successfully meet them.

Sound objectives, accepted as such, provide a common goal throughout the organization. Line and staff and all levels of management become jointly involved in a common cause which provides them with a unity of purpose that raises their level of accomplishment.

RESPONSE TO CHANGE

No discussion of this facet of planning would be complete without recognizing that objectives and plans must be changed continuously as conditions change. It is impossible to anticipate with complete accuracy all of the varied circumstances that can affect the future. The most careful planning is clearly affected by both external and internal happenings and is very much subject to the limitations of human foresight and analysis.

It may be almost impossible, particularly in long-range planning, to arrive at specific plans without facing a number of important "ifs." When these factors are beyond any reasonable ability to control or foresee, alternate plans should be prepared with the same care and attention to detail as the primary plan. With such planned flexibility, managers can pursue their long-range plans with an assurance that otherwise might not be justified.

Whether the plans are short- or long-range, objectives must not be considered sacred. Planners must be observant and flexible enough in their thinking to adjust their objectives quickly to meet changing circumstances, altering or completely revising their plans as may be required by the situation. Once changed, the revisions must be communicated to all concerned. Similarly, the results of implemented plans must be continuously appraised and plans and objectives adjusted as indicated.

The company in which every level of management is alert and responsive to changing circumstances will unquestionably enjoy an advantage that may significantly affect its competitive standing and assure more rapid realization of its objectives. Conversely, blindly to pursue plans made for circumstances that have seriously changed is to lose ground in the competitive race and may lead to future disaster. In fact, rigorous adherence to plans made obsolete by changing events is probably worse than having no plans at all.

WHAT TO TELL THE OPERATING SUPERVISORS

It should be apparent that effective planning is truly a joint effort encompassing every level of management, with every member of the organization having some responsiblility for developing plans or for making them work. It may be useful to explain to the operating supervisor in manufacturing, who must both help develop plans and make them work, how objectives can be interpreted and related to his own sphere of operations.

The objective should first be broken down into its component parts and the relationship between the components should be clarified. Each component may then be analyzed in terms of what is necessary to achieve it. Specific tasks are thus identified.

This type of analysis should be continued through successive stages, finally reaching the level of specific jobs and clearly showing their relationship. For this type of analysis, we ask the *what, why, when, how, who,* and *where* questions mentioned earlier. These steps allow the supervisor to visualize the succession of steps in an operation and the interrelations among them. The completed plan can be seen as a "build-up" of the specific operations.

In relating the objectives to the existing situation, it is beneficial to utilize all available knowledge and experience. Past, present, and future circumstances should be appraised in terms of available resources. Likewise, the supervisor's relationships to other groups, established policies, and working procedures should be evaluated. His possible impact on other operations should not be overlooked, and he should be encouraged to establish liaison with such other groups as may be interested or affected. In doing so, the supervisor will be urged to consider how these operations may assist or contribute to the fulfillment of the objective, affect the timetable, or otherwise have an effect on the overall corporate plans.

In implementing the objectives, there are usually innumerable combinations of factors in the existing situation which permit the formulation of many courses of action. By application of knowledge and experience through the medium of the question technique, the supervisor can test possible courses of action for their suitability, feasibility, adequacy, acceptability, and timeliness. The best course of action, in the supervisor's judgment, is then selected.

*   *   *

Planning should be imaginative yet realistic, challenging yet possible. It should be dedicated to improving and sustaining the basic strength of the company. The manufacturing manager, within the framework of overall objectives, must stimulate his subordinates to plan and perform with ever increasing skill.

New techniques and new applications of old methods combined with tough-mined appraisal of all cost factors make today's manufacturing world a highly competitive battleground. The quality of planning, with all that it entails in subsequent execution and appraisal, is the key to good management and profitability.

TYING THE PLANT TO THE OFFICE THROUGH ELECTRONIC DATA PROCESSING

By ARTHUR B. TOAN, Jr.

Nothing is new about the idea of tying the work of the plant and the office together, for plants have been dependent on forms, reports, and records for hundreds of years. Even a simple plant cannot operate effectively without a substantial amount and variety of information. In most companies, as a matter of fact, manufacturing creates and needs more information than any other part of the business. It is probably even true that, since the accompanying paperwork mirrors to a major degree the production processes it controls, a good information system is one of the major determinants of how complex the manufacturing organization itself can effectively become.

THE INTERRELATIONSHIP OF PLANT AND OFFICE

Some indication of the extent of the reliance of manufacturing on the work of the office can be obtained from the accompanying table, which lists in one column the major actions in the process of manufacturing and, in the other, some of the principal documents and records which are used or created in connection with these manufacturing processes.

The clerical and administrative process which produces the information and documents shown in the table is performed partly in what can be described as, for want of a better term, "the office." It is carried out also to a very substantial degree in a variety of other offices of varying sizes located within the plant itself. In fact, one of the striking characteristics of many plants is the amount of clerical work which takes place within them—work done by clerks, by foremen, by timekeepers, even by direct production workers.

ARTHUR B. TOAN, JR. is a Partner of Price Waterhouse & Co. in New York City.

MANUFACTURING IN TERMS OF ACTIONS	MANUFACTURING IN TERMS OF DOCUMENTS AND RECORDS USED OR CREATED
1. Determine sales requirements by periods from forecasts or orders.	Sales forecasts and analyses, orders, order status records and reports.
2. Determine new manufacturing requirements and reschedule old.	Inventory records, existing and revised production schedule, commitments, forecast/actual orders.
3. Issue new manufacturing releases and reschedule old ones.	Manufacturing releases, production schedules.
4. Break down manufacturing releases to determine component and material requirements.	Bill of materials, where-used lists.
5. Compare new and revised manufacturing requirements by periods with items on hand and on order.	Inventory records, outstanding purchase and manufacturing orders, commitments.
6. Issue purchase requisitions, purchase orders, and manufacturing orders.	Purchase requisitions and orders, manufacturing orders.
7. Schedule production.	Production schedule, machine-loading schedule.
8. Schedule manpower.	Same or with addition of manpower schedule.
9. Manufacture parts, assemblies, products.	Manufacturing orders, operations sheets, material requisitions, production reports, quality reports, time tickets, move tickets, inventory records, status reports.
10. Store and ship.	Inventory records, shipping tickets, invoices.
11. Measure and control costs.	Cost reports, standards data, time records, requisitions, etc.
12. Follow progress, correct, expedite, etc., throughout process.	Status reports, "hot" sheets, etc.

Thus, when we talk of tying the plant to the office through electronic data processing (EDP), we are not really discussing an attempt to do something which has never been done before. We are rather talking about utilizing the capabilities of EDP systems to perform this function more effectively than has been possible in the past. We also are talking, not about utilizing EDP equipment to the exclusion of manual work, but rather about finding the best balance of manual and electronic data processing in the light of the relative capabilities of each and the requirements of the plant.

BASIS FOR JUDGING VALUE OF ELECTRONIC DATA PROCESSING

The clerical systems which have supported manufacturing in both the pre-electronic and the present electronic eras have had their strengths and weaknesses. However, they did make possible large and complex manufacturing activities. It is only right, therefore, that the proponents of increased EDP should have to make a satisfactory case for its increased use and that in so doing they should consider a variety of factors, which in total determine the overall contribution of increased mechanization to the effectiveness of the company's operations. Of these factors the following are the most important:

1. The impact of manufacturing costs, customer service, product quality, and so on.
2. The effect on the investment required to handle a given volume of business, in terms of the degree of utilization of manufacturing facilities, amount and balance of inventories, and the like.
3. The impact on management decisions in manufacturing and other major functional areas—design, marketing, finance, and the general management of the business.
4. The effect on clerical and administrative expenses.

In some areas of a business the major objective sought by the application of EDP systems may be reduction in clerical and administrative expenses. As the foregoing list amply indicates, however, this is usually only one, and perhaps a smaller one, of the major objectives sought through the application of EDP to the clerical and administrative work supporting manufacturing. The fact that it may be hard to identify the impact of EDP on some of these areas and to assign monetary values to the impact may make it more difficult to determine the value of EDP to manufacturing. This should not, however, lead to an evaluation based solely on factors such as clerical cost savings which can be more readily and clearly isolated.

PROGRESS TO DATE

The progress made to date (early 1966) in applying EDP to the clerical work supporting manufacturing has been uneven, with some companies having made substantially greater use of electronic methods than others. In a number of instances EDP methods have been applied in connection with sales forecasting, order entry and other status systems, the determination of production requirements, the establishment of purchase requirements and purchase order status, production scheduling, machine loading and manpower scheduling, inventory status, cost information, CPM, PERT/Cost, and so on. Generally, however, progress has been much slower in applying EDP equipment in manufacturing areas than in those relating closely to finance and often to marketing as well.

Many reasons can be offered in explanation; one of the most important must obviously be the difficulties of mechanizing the administrative work of manufacturing. The demands of manufacturing personnel for accurate, detailed, and current data are well known, and the very substantial difficulties which can be encountered when plants do not have proper information can easily turn potential advantages into manufacturing problems. Accuracy, detail, speed, and availability are necessary in any kind of a clerical system, from the most manually oriented to the most highly mechanized. No system has ever fully served these demands, and probably no system ever will. Mechanized systems—with work being performed in machine centers on equipment with characteristics that strongly influence if not determine the way the clerical work is to be done—have both increased and decreased the ability of the clerical process to meet the requirements for accuracy, detail, and currency.

Consider the causes and effects of delay as an illustration of one of the difficulties. Prior to at least some of the more recent improvements in EDP and communications equipment, the mechanized record-keeping process was in most companies characterized by a series of seemingly inevitable delays of varying duration. These delays were caused by the facts that—

1. Since the computing facilities were not adjacent to the several manufacturing departments, there was a delay in getting the information to the center where the record of what was produced would be brought up to date. The same, of course, applied to new orders, shipments, receipts of materials, in fact to almost everything connected with the manufacturing or any other mechanized clerical process.

2. Since the computing facilities were, to a major degree, restricted both

physically and economically in what they could do at one time, work was forced to "stand in line" and "take its turn," thus bringing about a further delay even after the data to be entered reached the processing center.

3. Since the computing facilities could not be constantly interrupted to report on the current status of a given item, reports were printed periodically, and they were expected to be useful and meaningful until the next set of reports was available. If these reports were not actually out of date when prepared, they usually were soon thereafter.

EDP was consequently most successful in dealing with that portion of the manufacturing process in which delays could be tolerated (such as planning production, purchasing, and reporting costs) and least successful where current information (like the current position of an order on the manufacturing floor) was necessary. For the latter kind of information more often than not manual records, posted in the manufacturing departments themselves, were usually necessary and were kept, whether they constituted "bootleg," unauthorized records or not.

The amount of detail which a machine system could handle also was limited, primarily by the availability of storage. One of the results of this limitation has been, for most companies which have utilized EDP equipment in connection with manufacturing, to do so in relation to individual areas of clerical work. Thus electronic methods were used for order entry, the maintenance of inventory records, or the preparation of production schedules, but primarily as individual tasks or as tasks in a partially integrated system rather than as part of an integrated whole. This approach has made the application of EDP more manageable, has reduced the risks involved, and has more nearly matched the capabilities of machine systems with the difficulties encountered. It has also, however, reduced the opportunity to make major advances which could come from using detailed information about several of these areas in an interrelated manner.

The point, of course, is that there was and still is and always will be a direct relationship between the role which can be played by EDP equipment in handling the clerical work associated with plant operations and the technical capabilities and cost of that equipment.

INDICATED FUTURE DIRECTION

In recent years, particularly during the last one or two, EDP's role in tying together the plant and the office has been growing as a result of the rising pressure of four forces: (1) the advent of more powerful data processing and communications equipment, (2) the emergence of ideas and of concepts pointing in the direction of a "total information system," (3) the development of more manufacturing and warehousing equipment which is intended to be data controlled, and (4) the greater experience of methods analysts and programers and the increased expectations of management. It would be well, therefore, to consider each of these factors at greater length, while fully recognizing that much of what is discussed lies more in the future than in the present.

EDP equipment. Recent (so-called third generation) changes in EDP equipment which have particular value in relation to manufacturing-oriented office work are (1) the substantial increase in the amount of low-cost, high-speed, readily accessible storage, (2) the increased ability of communications facilities to link computing facilities to both nearby and remote plants and offices, (3) the increased ability of computers, through time-sharing and monitoring features, to perform a variety of tasks virtually simultaneously, and (4) a further decrease in the cost-performance ratio of computers themselves.

While the advantages of these changes are by no means limited to manufacturing, they do hold particular promise for this type of work, primarily—

- By making "electronic information" more readily and more continuously available to the user.
- By making it possible to keep this information more "up to the minute."
- By making it possible to link more locations in a single network.
- By making it possible to have together, as part of a larger system, information which was previously available principally or only in relatively isolated, smaller systems.

These changes will not eliminate all the difficulties created by equipment limitations, but they should lessen substantially the difficulties of accuracy, detail, speed, and availability.

With these changes it is much more practical to consider the development of a system under which (1) data can be sent rapidly, often virtually instantaneously, by wire from the point at which it originates in the plant to the data processing facilities, where (2) it can be processed and recorded virtually upon receipt, where (3) it can be held in a form of quickly accessible storage which (4) will make a substantially updated record available at all times for questioning by wire by a remote user. In their most complete and fastest form these systems are often referred to as "real time" systems. However, systems which fall technically short of qualifying as real time can also be altered and accelerated by means of some of the features discussed above, and others not mentioned, to accomplish many of the same results.

The total information system. The concept of the "total information system" also merits attention since it is a powerful and useful idea, in spite of the fact that, taken literally, it is quite unlikely even to be approached, let alone achieved. The term "a lot more information system" is probably more appropriate, for a "total information" system usually turns out, on close examination, to mean either a rather complete information system about a limited area or a limited amount of information about several large, interrelated areas. It also usually turns out to be based on encompassing in one area information which had previously been largely handled as two, three, or four separate areas.

The total information system tends to put in one larger electronic "record" those data which were formerly contained in several electronic and manual records. As such, it both integrates electronic records and moves the compromise between manual and electronic data processing further in the direction of the latter.

As an ultimate goal "the total information" system would encompass all information about orders (customers, manufacturing, and purchase), inventory status, production schedules, project status, commitments, prices, costs, control items, and so forth. This is clearly a mammoth idea of great complexity. While some may decide to attempt to move directly toward a highly integrated, sophisticated total information system, it seems more likely that most companies moving in this direction will do so by a series of individual, carefully planned steps aimed both at accomplishing results in the particular area with which they are concerned and moving in a purposeful fashion toward accomplishing the desired ultimate result.

Data-controlled equipment. While the office has been moving in the direction of processing data electronically, the plant has been moving in the same direction—creating machines and processes which are controlled by data generated within the office and often also producing a substantial amount of data which must be rapidly handled so that this can be done. The numerically controlled tool is a simple illustration of this trend; it is simple in the sense that the manufacturing operation involved is largely self-contained or confined to a machine which is required to follow a largely or completely predetermined pattern of actions, as is described elsewhere in this volume. It is perhaps more properly an example of tying in engineering and the plant, while reducing the amount of paperwork required to carry out these manufacturing operations, than a pure example of data controlled equipment, but it is a trend of great significance.

A second area, somewhat more complex and with many variations, is often referred to as "process control." Under the simplest form of process control, data about machine settings, temperature, pressure, and other specifications of either the process or the material being processed are correlated with the quality and quantity of the product being produced in order to learn more about the effectiveness of the manufacturing process. At a second level, process control uses this basic knowledge in conjunction with information obtained about current processing by means of sensing and recording equipment or other devices, not only to record and analyze the effectiveness of current operations but also to compute the adjustments in temperature and pressure which should be made in them. In a still more advanced version of process control often referred to as "closed loop," the instructions by which the machine changes its method of operation are both determined and transmitted direct to the machine without human intervention. For the most part, computers performing the more advanced aspects of process control have not been used to perform other clerical and administrative work in connection with manufacturing or other operations. They have been and will surely continue to be used for some of the less advanced forms of it. There is, however, a strong possibility that with the increased capabilities of future data processers both clerical and process control functions will be performed more frequently on the same equipment.

A final and probably more direct merging of plant and office is found in the automated warehouse. There the order picking, order assembly, packing, shipping, and billing operations have become far more integrated than ever before, and the punched cards or tapes created for the (physical) purpose of directing the operations of the automated warehouse often serve another (clerical) purpose as well. There is reason to believe that this integration too will become more frequent and more complete.

Thus, while the office has been moving toward the plant, the plant also has been moving toward at least one part of "the office."

Experience of methods analysts and programers and the expectations of management. The increased experience of methods analysts and programers is also a major force pushing in the direction of more sophisticated and more widely inclusive electronic procedures for use in connection with manufacturing. It is logical that those tasks should have been undertaken first which were easier, had a history of prior mechanization, and were not accompanied by a fear of dire consequences if unsuccessful. In most companies this stage of automation has passed, and both the staff charged with electronic development and the managerial group which uses the results have gained broad experience. Both groups are, therefore, able and willing and often have the time to undertake more difficult problems. As a matter of fact, many of the most experienced men in this field have become more or less bored with routine work and actively seek the greater challenge of plant-associated clerical work.

The greater experience of methods analysts and programers has been accompanied by an increase in the expectations of management about the assistance which can be provided by utilizing EDP to solve plant and companywide problems. Many plants have been under severe pressure for a number of years as a result of the high level of their operations, the rapid pace of technological change in manufacturing methods, the more stringent requirements established by customers for products with higher specifications, customer demands for more rapid service, and so on through the roll call of progress. At the same time they have felt a pressure to reduce inventories and to make maximum use of company investment in equipment and other facilities for productive purposes.

Management has developed an awareness of the importance of fast and responsive administrative systems in helping to realize these objectives. As the pressures of these objectives expose to view the inadequacies of existing systems, we have witnessed a natural tendency to seek at least part of the solution through further utilization of EDP. This, in turn, has brought about pressure on methods analysts and programers to devote more of their attention to the clerical and administrative problems associated with manufacturing. The fact that new or improved equipment has come along which has made it possible to do things which were more difficult, if not impossible, several years ago has permitted methods analysts and programers to think in bolder terms. The fact that the administrative problems of manufacturing have become more difficult has also made management more willing to invest in communications and data processing equipment in an effort to solve them. This combination of greater experience on the part of methods analysts and programers and greater expectations on the part of management has been a very significant force in the developments which have been and are now taking place.

THE IMPORTANCE OF FUNDAMENTALS

The clerical work associated with manufacturing has always contended, with varying degrees of success, with one fundamental problem: the accuracy of the original data it is given to process. We can develop a highly efficient system which will faithfully record the data with which it is supplied, but if the data are incorrect in any substantial way, the results are of dubious value. With a manual system it is often possible for clerks who are aware of what is taking place, because of their proximity to the manufacturing operations, to make whatever corrections are required. On the other hand, a mechanized system relying essentially on remote processing has less opportunity to insure the accuracy of the originally recorded data. If the bills of materials are not correct, if the material-coding structures are inadequate, if production is poorly or incorrectly reported, if scrap, rework, and quality rejects are not accurately handled, information may be made quickly available, but it will not reflect the situation and thus cannot be utilized to anything like its full potential.

The more highly mechanized systems are developed with the expectation that the information with which they are furnished will be sufficiently accurate for their intended purposes. There is also no question that through more automatic recording devices, through machine and programed checks of the validity of the recorded data, some improvement can be made in accuracy, or at least in the detection of inaccuracy, through the machine processes themselves. However, the fundamental responsibility for a major portion of the improvement in accuracy which is required still must fall on individuals in the sales, engineering, purchasing, manufacturing, stores, and other departments. Since many of the individuals in these departments have neither the training nor a prime interest in clerical work, this problem can never be fully solved but can only be lessened—and then only by the constant emphasis of supervisors and departmental managers, and at times even by the higher levels of management, on the importance of accuracy.

Most companies which embark upon a more extensive program of applying EDP to manufacturing operations will find that a substantial portion of their efforts must be directed toward improving the fundamentals on which any system, particularly a sophisticated one, must rest.

*   *   *

Tying the plant and the office together is a process which has been an integral part of manufacturing for many centuries. The increased use of EDP equipment for this purpose in most companies is in the early stages of development. Increases in equipment capabilities, in management expectations, in the experience of methods analysts and programers, and in the idea of a total information system will push toward greater mechanization at an accelerated pace in the years ahead. Moving directly into anything approaching a total information system will probably be more than most companies dare to attempt; to move toward this goal in careful steps, each of which has its own advantages, would seem to be the proper approach.

The advantages of improved clerical and administrative work in support of manufacturing extend far beyond the possible clerical cost savings; as a matter of fact, it would not be too surprising to find that clerical cost increases are accepted in order to accomplish greater results in other areas.

At the same time that great potential advantages seem to exist, there is also a great potential for harm if the new EDP methods are not well conceived and carefully developed and if proper attention is not paid to meeting the fundamental requirements of promptness and accuracy which underlie any satisfactory administrative system.

PART TWO

Various Aspects of Control

BUDGETING AND FINANCIAL MANAGEMENT

By HARRY S. MANN

The education, training, and experience of manufacturing executives have conditioned them to look upon their responsibility as that of managing "men, machines, materials, and methods." Indeed, the successful manufacturing executive is one who is able to properly coordinate and place relative emphasis on "the four M's." Most manufacturing executives think of financial management as a separate activity under the direction of such other executives as the controller and the treasurer. However, underlying each of the manufacturing executives' four "M's" is a fifth "M," money, which in fact is the common denominator of all business transactions. Although it is true that controllers and treasurers have some specialized areas of financial management for which they are solely responsible, the manufacturing executive plays one of the most important roles in financial management in industrial organizations. With few exceptions the largest amount of money is expended under the direction of the manufacturing executive, who is therefore responsible for the control of the largest segment of a company's funds.

Manufacturing executives have a tendency to think of physical things as ends unto themselves. This is natural because of their preoccupation with the development of physical things, using physical facilities in the process. As a result, executives in this group often are misled into believing that their operations are well under control if the physical plant is in good working order and appears to be functioning well and the finished product meets specifications. As important as all these things are, they must be looked upon only as symptoms and as means to an end. The backbone of our capitalistic system is the profit motive. Satisfactory profits are achieved only when a minimum of capital is used to produce the necessary volume of product and at a cost

HARRY S. MANN is Vice President and Controller of Walter Kidde & Co., Inc., Belleville, New Jersey.

which provides an adequate profit margin at competitive prices. Well-kept buildings and grounds, wide aisles, and beautiful machines may give the manufacturing executive a feeling of well-being and a conviction that the business is under good control, but if his competitor can produce as good a product in a loft building with secondhand machinery, skimpy aisles, and lots of ingenuity, the manufacturing executive is suffering from a false sense of well-being. He may have achieved a good control of physical things but has lost sight of his primary goal—fiscal responsibility.

Budgeting is a universal control technique which has been developed and refined over many years by many companies. In attempting to do a better job, industrial managers have experimented with and introduced many different types of systems and procedures. None of these has better withstood the test of time or gained more universal acceptance than budgeting techniques. The vast majority of industrial enterprises handling a volume of business of $1 million or more a year use some form of budgeting. When companies are small and rely principally on hand labor, the manager can usually judge his progress by simply counting the cash in the till from time to time and coupling this with his overall impression of the increase or decrease of physical things within his operation. The larger an operation becomes, the less reliable, and in fact misleading, this approach to financial control becomes. It is virtually impossible for a manager to be able to integrate mentally the pluses and minuses of day-to-day events and evaluate the trend of his profits without the aid of detailed and precise accumulations of data and a base against which to compare their findings. Budgeting provides the bench mark against which current data from various sources are compared to determine the strong and weak points of an operation.

CUSTOM-BUILD THE BUDGET

There is a wide range of opinion as to what the term budgeting means. For example, one automobile dealer claims that he operates against a budget. His budget consists in estimating the number of Model 98, 88, and F 85 automobiles he expects to sell each month during the coming year. He does not do any more than estimate because he knows what margins he can anticipate in each class of sale, that he will have to sell two and one-quarter used cars for each new one, and generally what his monthly operating expenses will be.

A vice president for planning of a large national company has budgets which are printed and bound with gold letters embossed on the binder. The figures inside cover a five-year period and detail all types of sales as well as various expenses. Detailed operating budgets for each manufacturing plant and for departments within each plant also are computed, taking into consideration expected changes in material cost levels as well as labor rates.

These two examples cover the extremes of budgeting; each is effective in its own situation, but to reverse them would be ludicrous. They underscore the fact that budgets must be designed for a particular operation. To copy another company's technique without modification would in most cases be a sheer waste of effort and in fact could be very harmful because of the misinformation which would inevitably result.

If the automobile dealer attempted to predict his material costs for five years and to determine how many of each type of automobile he would sell five years hence, his would be a useless exercise. Were he, on the basis of the estimates, to go out and borrow a great sum of money to build a large new facility, the results would be disastrous. In his case it is entirely beyond his control to know whether certain models of the line he is now selling will be dropped or others added, to know what other makes of automobiles will be like five years from now, or, for that matter, even to know whether he will have his franchise five years hence. On the other hand, if the vice president for planning of the large national company did not make a careful study of the trends and attempt to measure his situation five years hence, his company might well find itself with inadequate facilities, improperly located, while its competition would be walking away with the business.

BUDGETS SHOULD BE SIMPLE

When a system of budgetary control is being evolved, simplicity should be the key word. The automobile dealer could produce a very formal budget which would be a good working tool and in no way misleading. Using historical data and trends and planned changes, he could develop expense figures for the new model year with considerable accuracy. He could plot actual expenditures, month by month, against the budget figures and variances. Obviously, this type of budgeting would be more precise than simply estimating car sales, but at the same time it would be significantly more expensive to develop and maintain. The only justification for such refinement would be the realization of savings greater than the added cost of performing the work. Because of the day-to-day intimate personal control exercised by the owner–manager, it is highly unlikely that detailed measurements and comparisons would reveal any information which he did not know long before the figures appeared in the record book. Hence corrective action would have been automatic and not dictated by a budget.

Experts in budgets are like experts in almost any profession. They tend to see their work as an end in itself rather than as a means to the end. The end result of any business is to achieve a satisfactory profit. It is not to produce the most precise and clear budget possible for any given operation.

CONSIDER ALL AVAILABLE INFORMATION

Unlike the automobile dealer's, most manufacturing businesses are complex, and the budget therefore must be prepared in great detail if it is to be an effective tool of management. When carefully prepared, a budget becomes a set of working drawings for the company's activities for the next one, two, or five years. Like a set of working drawings which are reliable only if they are based on many facts previously determined through preliminary designs, qualification testing, and development work, the budget must be derived from many sources of information carefully culled and evaluated. For budgeting, such activities as market research, product planning, historical trend analysis, and economic forecasting serve the same purpose as the back-up work for a final set of drawings. When prepared in this manner, the budget immediately highlights areas of weakness such as dwindling markets and sales opportunities, possibilities of excessive or insufficient capacity, unsatisfactory product mix, and so on. These facts then serve as the guidelines for developing new objectives and plans to bring about proper balances and acceptable profits.

The effort spent in preparing a budget is usually more than compensated even if it is never consulted after its completion, provided, of course, that it is based on studies in depth. With the press of daily problems, managers of all phases of a business, whether of manufacturing, marketing, or finance, too often defer planning for the future until they "have more time." Budget preparation forces these managers to think about the future in a very specific way. It is interesting to see the number of new ideas, changes in plans, and the like that are generated during budget time, while these activities are almost nonexistent during the balance of the year. In manufacturing, the value of such activities is particularly apparent.

The budgeting process normally begins with preparing a sales forecast. To be useful, it must be carried out with considerable care and in painstaking detail. Although it is not always possible to forecast by specific models and sizes, the closer this ideal can be achieved the better. At least, the forecast should be by product class, by geographic area, and expressed in units as well as dollars. The manufacturing executive can be confident of the reasonableness of a sales forecast when prepared in such detail, but he has cause to be suspicious if it is obviously mapped out by the sales executive some evening when he was watching his favorite television program.

Overall volume figures sometimes give the manufacturing executive a new perspective. Often a new product is started off as an adjunct to some existing manufacturing operation. As the volume grows little by little, the upward trend is not recognized. Looking at the budget figures, however, the manufacturing executive may suddenly realize that the time has long since passed when a separate production line should have been established for this product which has now reached maturity.

The costs of labor and various overhead categories are summarized by operating centers as part of the budget preparation. This practice affords an excellent opportunity to gain perspectives on those centers where cost per hour of production is abnormally high. The information gained by the manager during his scrutiny in turn provides a basis for directing his attention toward cost reduction opportunities. In like manner, when costs are summarized by major product groups, those items for which the material content is high and the value added by in-the-house manufacturing is low stand out clearly. This information gives the manufacturing executive a clue to where investment in new capital can produce high returns.

These values can be realized, however, only if sufficient time and effort are spent not only at the clerical level but also at the management level in the preparation of the budget.

SEASONALIZED BUDGETS

Somewhat related to the importance of gathering as much supporting data as possible is the matter of preparing forecasts on a seasonalized basis; that is, showing variations by months or even weeks. At a minimum, the budget should reflect quarterly fluctuations. Variations in sales volume from time period to time period and product line by product line may reveal a substantial swing in total labor requirements. Likewise, overload periods may not be anticipated until too late unless variations in requirements from period to period are spelled out in the budget.

The seasonal variations on a product-by-product basis provide the information necessary to measure the increase or reduction in inventory levels. This information in turn is basic to planning for financing, warehouse space, extra shifts on certain manufacturing lines, and scheduled overtime.

BUDGETING BY ORGANIZATION UNITS

It is clear that budgeting must be done by product lines as well as by time segments. In addition, it is essential to budget by organization units. In other words, the budget finally must become three dimensional: one dimension being product, another time, and the third organization units.

A totalized manufacturing budget is of considerable value to a top management which is constantly attempting to grasp the overall corporate situation. To the manufacturing executive himself, however, a totalized budget, even if subdivided in respect to time and product, is not an adequate operating tool because he in turn has divided his total responsibility and hence, by implication, his financial responsibility among the subordinates reporting directly to him. They in turn have delegated their responsibility to the next tier of supervisors, and so it continues. The number of tiers of manufacturing management is a function of the size of the organization and the complexity of the operation.

The degree to which the budget is broken into small segments should be related to the degree to which expenses and performance in general are delegated within the organizational pyramid. For example, if the superintendent of a shop has eight foremen reporting to him, it may or may not be desirable to develop a budget for each foreman. If the foreman acts principally as a lead man and does not exercise control of all costs within his area, then the effort to develop a budget in eight pieces is unnecessary and, in fact, could be confusing since the superintendent may not see a clear picture of his operation unless he adds together the eight segments. If, on the other hand, each foreman has cost control authority and responsibility, each should have his own budget.

BUDGETING FOR DIRECT LABOR

Some operations are limited to the manufacture of a few items on mutually exclusive production lines. For example, one plant may have an assembly line exclusively for toasters, another line for hair dryers, and a third for electric razors. The budget data in such a setup give a clear indication of the loading on each line. Most operations, however, are far more complex. Different products use different parts of common facilities in differing proportions. Then the sales figures give only rough ideas about loading and must be further analyzed if a true projection of workload by operating center is to be achieved. Unless a fairly accurate estimate of loading by each center is available, budgeting for overhead items, equipment needs, different labor skills, and so on becomes quite inaccurate.

Before the advent of computers such analyses as are necessary to obtain accurate estimates were time consuming and tedious. So relatively few companies performed the work necessary to obtain accurate loading estimates. Now most companies with computers can perform accurate analyses, and budgets for shop operations can, as a result, be greatly improved. We are seeking to obtain a labor load expressed in either hours or dollars for each operating center for each period being budgeted. For example, if we are budgeting on a quarterly basis and there are 30 operating centers, we want to end up with a total of 120 figures. If, in turn, there are 20 product lines which run through the shop being budgeted, we must be able to determine the labor load indicated by the forecast of sales for each of these 120 calculations, making a grand total of 2,400 computations.

Most accounting systems express the relationship between sales dollars and the cost of goods sold as material, labor, and burden by product line. It is seldom, however, that the accounting system further breaks the labor down on a center-by-center basis. Detailed information on such a basis, however, is usually available for individual items within product classes in cost-accounting records. It is therefore necessary to bring these two sets of information together to produce the 2,400 figures.

One way of accomplishing this is to analyze all shipments for a representative recent accounting period by running a special program through the computer. The detailed cost-accounting records are placed in the computer and are extended by the quantity of each of the items shipped during the period in question, and the findings are summarized and printed out. The relationship between direct labor in each cost center to the sales dollar for each product line is thus determined. This knowledge then forms the basis for figuring what sales volume should be budgeted in the future, with adjustments if necessary, whenever a major change in design or a mix of items within a product line is contemplated.

The massiveness of this job is readily apparent, and the need for the computer is inevitable. It is normally necessary to perform it, not each time a new budget is prepared, but only when sufficient changes in relationships warrant a new computation. In smaller companies product lines and the number of cost centers may be considerably fewer than in the example cited and manual processing may be practical, but even if the company has no computer and manual processing is impractical, it will undoubtedly be worthwhile to discover what its direct labor load will be in detail, making use of service organizations which sell computer and punched-card equipment time.

BUDGETING FOR DIRECT MATERIAL

Budget preparation for material expenditures is usually a much simpler task than for direct labor. As we have seen, most accounting systems provide the necessary relationships by product class between sales dollar and material content. These relationships usually can be translated directly to the volume of sales anticipated in each future period being budgeted. Once again, however, it may be necessary to make some adjustment when there are changes of product mix within a product line, when design changes will affect material requirements, or when changes in methods will reduce the material requirements per unit produced.

BUDGETING FOR BURDEN

By far the most difficult of the three manufacturing cost areas to budget is burden. The objective is to determine the total burden for each of the operating centers in a shop, plus a budget figure for each of the indirect centers in the shop. Included among the indirect centers are such departments as receiving, stockroom, packing, production control, time study, and tool design. The total burden figure in each of these centers is composed of numerous small items, all of which must be budgeted. Unlike direct labor, the components of burden cost in each center do not vary directly with changes in volume. Our budgeting procedure consequently must somehow make it possible to calculate a budget figure for each burden component for each center, not only at the budgeted volume of direct labor but also for variations above and below it, so that comparisons of performance against budget can be fairly calculated and the budget kept flexible. The budget should never be viewed as a straitjacket but always as a help in achieving goals and making profits. Any other view of a budget is untenable, and any practice which does not allow for variation is not sound fiscal procedure and is, even, dangerous to company growth.

Historical data showing actual expenditures for each item to be budgeted in each operating center are normally available in the accounting records. An analysis of these data and a relationship between each expenditure and the direct labor employed on a period basis will provide some clue to what can be anticipated for future periods. The first step in preparing a budget for burden items is to summarize and analyze these historical data—which, nonetheless, must be tempered by changes in conditions of manufacturing, by changes in labor rates and in the costs of services and supplies, and by the types of products being processed.

The next step is to arrange meetings with supervisors of the areas being budgeted. The budget director provides the historical data concerning each burden item as well as the anticipated direct labor load for the periods being budgeted. The discussions at these meetings bring out information about significant changes in operations and about other matters of value to the budget director. This step is of great importance because it provides the line manager with a personal understanding of how the budget figures are derived and established as well as with the opportunity to participate in the preparation of the budget for his operation. He does not feel that the budget is something that is arbitrarily contrived and imposed upon him but rather something of which he is a co-author. Such discussions, too, cause the budgeting procedure to become more than a strictly theoretical exercise, to become, in fact, an activity that produces a practical, living document.

After budget data have been accumulated for each cost center, the total budget is assembled and submitted to the chief manufacturing executive for his overall review. Almost always his review discovers the need for reducing budget allowances for certain overhead items in order to achieve the desirable overall cost results. At this point the budgeting process is repeated and adjustments are made in individual budgets in order to bring their details into line with the revised total. All figures, of course, have been arrived at by reference to the anticipated direct labor load previously computed.

Having established the expected expenditure at the expected direct labor load for each burden item in each work center, the budget director is in a position to apply formulas for variations if the volume is less or greater than planned. These formulas are derived from a study of prior variations; no matter how carefully they are derived, however, they are impractical if the variation from the budgeted level of direct labor is more than 15 percent in either direction.

The manner in which overhead items vary with volume is important to know, for only with this knowledge can accurate and fair budgets be drawn up. Some items of shop overhead increase and decrease in direct proportion to ups and downs in the amount of direct labor, and these items are easy to budget once that amount is determined. Fringe benefits, shop supplies, and the cost of electrical power are typical of this class. At the other extreme are items which are fixed in cost almost irrespective of volume, and these, too, can be readily budgeted. Heat, occupancy, and depreciation expenses are typical.

Many items fall in neither pattern, and these are the true obstacles to drawing up a realistic and fair budget for manufacturing. Setup costs are a good case in point. If we assume the increase in volume to require just more of the same items, the setup costs are independent of volume, except for a small amount of extra reset cost. On the other hand, if the increase in volume stems from production of more and different items, the relationship between the increase in volume and the setup costs is entirely changed. Often it is impossible to forecast sales in such a way as to determine how much of which type of setup cost will prevail. Nonetheless, the budget director must make reasonable assumptions in order to complete his work. Historical data will doubtless be useful to him in this instance, too.

CATCHING IMBALANCES

Sometimes during the preparation of a budget or at the completion of its preparation it becomes clear that shop facilities are not adequate to handle the expected sales volume. This condition should be carefully watched for and the sales executive contacted as soon as it begins to hamper operations. The alleged inadequacy of the facilities should be thoroughly examined, and if it is concluded that the sales forecast should not be revised, the cost of increasing facilities and the time required to do so must be estimated. Then top management must decide whether to implement plans to increase capacity. Sometimes it is preferable to discourage the sales of low-priced items in order to remain within the existing plant capacity rather than to make substantial investments for expansion.

The early flagging of imbalanced conditions is one of the great values of budgeting techniques, since vital lead time is gained in taking steps to bring supply and demand into balance. The manufacturing executive should never ignore indicated imbalances on the theory that the sales forecast is wrong.

THE BENEFITS OF BUDGETING TO THE MANUFACTURING MAN

If all the steps outlined above are carefully followed, the manufacturing executive will have a useful budget and a valuable tool. A tool is worthless, however, if it is not used. All too often line managers feel that they are doing the accounting department a favor when they help prepare the budget. Because the final budget looks like a financial statement with everything expressed in dollars, it is easy to think of it as an accounting report. If this attitude prevails, the budget is usually filed and forgotten until the next one has to be prepared.

Although the value of being forced to think about what truly constitutes one's responsibilities stems directly from preparing the budget, a greater value comes from its constant use. If weekly and monthly results are compiled in the same form as the budget and if the variations are noted, the first step in effective financial control is the result. If each level of supervision makes frequent reviews of the results with the next lower level and finds the reasons for variations, a reduction in costs is inevitable. More effective planning for both the short and long term becomes possible when reliable budget figures are available. Disputes with marketing people about performance or excessive inventory can usually be resolved factually and meaningfully, and more accurate cost estimating is possible because overhead can be more accurately predicted. Decisions of whether to take additional work at marginal prices can be made more intelligently when we know the expected level of shop activity.

Even if the manufacturing executive is not persuaded that budgeting will accomplish such benefits, he should consider its importance to his own performance. A company committed to budgeting procedures gives a great deal of weight to variations from budgets when evaluating the performance of its executives. This attitude requires the manufacturing executive to satisfy himself that his budget has been fairly and accurately developed and that variations from it are corrected or satisfactorily explained. Nothing is more frustrating than to be playing in a game in which the cards are stacked against us and the score is not being recorded fairly.

In spite of all these values the manufacturing manager should never become a slave to his budget. If an opportunity presents itself that will enhance profits, improve quality or service, or in some other significant way favorably affect results, the manufacturing executive should not ignore it simply because it is "not in the budget." In the final analysis the budget makes use of the best available information at the time it is developed. As new information, opportunities, or difficulties arise that the budget did not properly anticipate, an intelligent manager will recognize the need for revisions. In order to compensate for such situations the budget program should include extra allowances, if they are approved by proper authorities. By using this simple technique the operating manager will be fairly measured on performance and at the same time not be discouraged from performing most effectively because such a performance would reflect adversely on his variations from budget.

CONTROLLING CAPITAL INVESTMENTS

By RICHARD F. PERDUNN

The ultimate cause of nearly all business failures is incompetence on the part of management. In young enterprises failure is often traceable to lack of know-how or experience on the part of the principals; in old companies, to a feeling of contentment and a desire to ride on past achievements. It is also noteworthy that lack of controls over expenditures for capital investments is usually one of the dominant areas of managerial neglect in a failing company.

Of the two major managerial actions that can be taken to control capital investments, the first is dynamic; it is choosing the right investments. The second is passive; it is tantamount to being put out of business by failing to keep pace with the investments of competitors or with economic and technological changes.

This chapter is primarily concerned with the dynamics of capital investments and, therefore, with an examination of the four steps necessary for proper control. These steps can be summarized as follows:

1. Establishing capital investment policies. Most companies do not have such policies, and those that do have them too often have formulated them so vaguely that they are neither understood nor communicated to those managers who are responsible for making recommendations on capital investments.

2. Selecting projects for capital investments. This is obviously the step that determines success or failure.

3. Estimating return on investment. The mistake most often made in this connection is evaluating only the financial returns rather than considering the overall gain to the company.

4. Accurately measuring returns on investments. Follow-up reports can be

RICHARD F. PERDUNN is President of Stevenson, Jordan & Harrison, Inc., in New York.

valuable information even when reporting on investments which are failures.

Capital investments can be classified as either "front office" projects, involving new business, acquisitions, expansions, and new projects, or "operating" projects, such as the improvement of existing plant and production facilities. While the principles discussed here apply to both classifications, the latter category is more troublesome and will concern us more nearly in the following pages.

Capital investment policies offer unparalleled opportunity for creative and imaginative managerial thinking, planning, and performance, yet American managers express great dissatisfaction about them. Some of the reasons are not hard to uncover. Operating personnel frequently are not stimulated to make a systematic search for investment opportunities. They are too often inadequately informed about management's corporate objectives and plans. True, no one has a surefire, simple method of knowing what the most successful policies should be, and the scarcity of investment capital means that enough money never is available to satisfy everybody's pet project. Little margin for error exists; most decisions are irreversible; and the amount of money invested in a project is usually large enough and mistakes serious enough to hurt both the company and the individual decision-making manager. Yet, while mistakes can be disastrous, the challenge and the rewards of success for both the company and the manager are tremendous.

ESTABLISHING CAPITAL INVESTMENT POLICIES

In formulating its capital investment policies management must take into account many of the phenomena of modern-day business life which have a profound effect on operations. Chief among them is the ever increasing speed of technological and economic changes. New and improved equipment is being developed at a faster rate than ever before. New products are replacing older ones much sooner than was previously true, and the new ones offer wider margins of future improvement. Developments come so fast in some fields, such as electronics, that some plants which were modern three or four years ago are obsolete today.

The rate of obsolescence has a disturbing effect on capital investment policies. It has increased so greatly that we find paradoxical situations in which, for example, plants, products, and processes become obsolete while still only in the process of being designed. Examples can be found in the missile industry, where products and processes are antiquated before the designs are completed.

The steel manufacturing industry, for which plants are still being designed and built along conventional lines in spite of advances in processing that make it possible to eliminate many of the steps in the manufacturing process, is another example of this trend toward premature obsolescence.

The effect of automation on investment policies is undeniably troublesome. The first business computer was installed in 1952; a few short years later third-generation equipment is being utilized in the more sophisticated organizations. However, some large firms are just beginning to consider the installation of tabulating equipment, the forerunner of the computer. Frederick W. Taylor, the grand old sage of scientific management, described the present situation quite succinctly when he noted, back in 1914, that most organizations remain in business not because they are so efficient but rather because their competition is so inefficient.

George Terborgh of the Machine and Allied Products Institute says: "Defects of investment policies stem from two main sources. One is cloudy thinking on basic theoretical or conceptual issues. The other is faulty administration in terms of procedure and practice." Operating personnel must search for meaningful methods improvements, not just for equipment replacements. The dramatic modern-day improvements are in new processes, not in new equipment that can perform the same processes at a faster or cheaper rate. Management policies should clearly state the company's plans and objectives as they concern both the present and the future. These policies must be phrased in terms which lend themselves to an organized search for investment opportunities.

Many dramatic cost reductions and process improvements have been made by re-examining basic objectives. One such improvement made by a cost reduction team at a large oil refinery vividly highlights this type of analysis. The problem was mowing grass on the retaining barricades surrounding the storage tanks. Changes were suggested that would have reduced this maintenance cost considerably, but one analytically minded youngster on the team asked, "Why have the grass in the first place?" This question was answered disdainfully by one of the older men; everyone, he explained, knew that the grass was used as a stabilizer for the dirt and held it solidly in place. The breakthrough in the problem had been made, however, and it didn't take long for these men to recognize that they were working on a secondary problem instead of the major problem of stabilizing dirt in the barricades. Shortly thereafter a new method of stabilization was developed, and there was no more grass to cut. Thus thousands of dollars were saved for the company simply by determining the real objective of the dirt-stabilizing process.

EXHIBIT 1

LIFE CYCLE CURVE OF SALES VOLUME PLOTTED AGAINST TIME

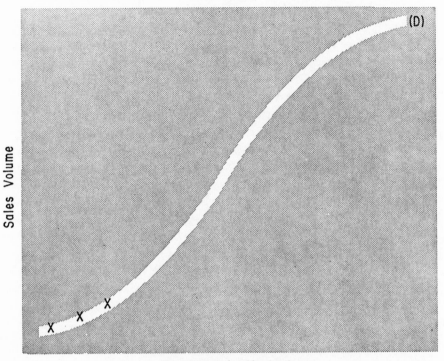

Time (years) Life Cycle

Again, in the course of policy formulation management must take an objective look at all the company's products, markets, and distributor channels. Peter Drucker suggests that products be separated into 11 categories and that policies be developed according to the individual requirements of each classification. His terms for identifying each group are:

1. Today's breadwinners.
2. Tomorrow's breadwinners.
3. Productive specialties.
4. Development products.
5. Failures.

The next six groups Mr. Drucker calls "problem children":

6. Yesterday's breadwinners.
7. Repair jobs.
8. Unnecessary specialties.
9. Unjustified specialties.

EXHIBIT 2

LIFE CYCLE CURVE RESULTING FROM PLOTTING PROFIT
AGAINST SALES VOLUME

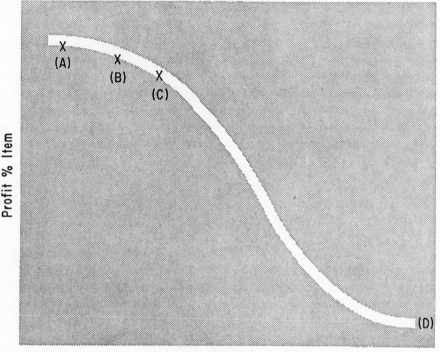

Time (years) Profit Cycle

10. Investments in management ego.

11. "Cinderellas," or sleepers.*

Drucker also suggests that every product has a life cycle and that we should determine where each product lies inside that cycle and the length of time remaining before the cycle is completed at the end of the product's useful life. Of equal importance, however, is the determination of the profit cycle. A fairly accurate estimate of the profit cycle can be made by mathematically charting the contribution to profit, using the principles of direct costing. For instance, if the sales volume were plotted against time for a given product, the life cycle curve would undoubtedly be similar to the one shown in Exhibit 1. If the profit cycle were plotted against sales volume, a curve similar to

* Peter F. Drucker, *Managing for Results*, Harper & Row Publishers, Inc., p. 51.

EXHIBIT 3

ESTIMATED PRODUCT HALF-LIFE

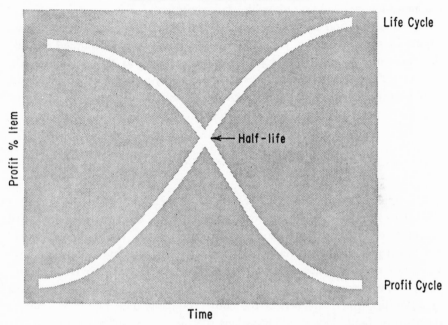

Life Cycle

Profit % Item

Half-life

Profit Cycle

Time

the one shown in Exhibit 2 would result. These curves can be described by the following formulas:

$$\text{Life cycle} = y = \tan^{-1} x$$

Where y = sales volume by year expressed in dollars
    x = time from beginning of product life expressed in most convenient terms

$$\text{Profit cycle} = y = \cot^{-1} x$$

Where y = profit contribution expressed in percent of sales
    x = time identical to that selected for life cycle

Therefore, knowing three or more points such as *A, B,* and *C* and using these formulas, we can easily project point *D* in Exhibit 2. Then, if both curves were plotted on the same grid, the result would be similar to Exhibit 3, showing a fairly accurate estimate of the product's half-life. And, when a product reaches its half-life, serious consideration should be given to major cost reduction or product replacement.

A word of caution, however: We should not try to apply this method to a product or process unless we use direct-costing techniques. Standard- or job-costing techniques will lead to nothing but confusion.

One more caution should be noted in connection with the formulation of capital investment policies. Restrictive policies can greatly discourage risk taking and can stifle many good projects. Policies such as those which rigidly require a 30 percent return on investment or specify a maximum payoff period of four years discourage individuals who might otherwise come up with capital investment projects with prospects of success.

SELECTING PROJECTS FOR CAPITAL INVESTMENT

The weakest aspect of selecting capital investment projects is that the ones offered to management for approval frequently are sifted from a haphazard collection of divisional or departmental projects which various people would like to see put into effect. Each project has fervent advocates, and some have vociferous opposition too. Seldom, however, is management presented with a group of projects resulting from a cooperative, organized search for investment opportunities which will benefit the entire company. This failure is management's own fault since it rarely assigns specific responsibility for such a systematic search. Some steps that can be taken by a progressive management include organizing a formal capital management committee, encouraging attendance at professional meetings and expositions, sponsoring membership and active participation in professional organizations, and requiring reading and advanced education in the various arts affecting the company and its products.

There are some dangers to avoid in selecting capital projects. Frequently, for example, projects are selected for capital investment because the people who sponsor them are powerful or respected, but the strong sponsors often operate on the "squeaky wheel" principle. Divisional interests are sometimes put ahead of company interests, causing the selection of projects to become a field day for company politicians.

Too often capital investments are directly traceable to management ego. For example, a manufacturer of door chimes discovered his competition had captured that market while he had been intent on expanding other parts of his business. Confident that he could still make a better door chime than his competitors, he proceeded to pour enormous amounts of valuable investment capital into an uphill fight to regain lost markets. Meanwhile, he passed up several opportunities for other profitable investments which did not have quite so much appeal for management ego.

Scarce capital funds should not be channeled into products which are nearing the end of their life cycles. A case in point: Mechanical annunciators are still being made instead of electric or electronic types. While one company was continuing to make a personnel locater using coded audible signals on bells or buzzers, the competition had developed a short-wave pocket unit audible only to the person being paged.

Most companies continue to have old equipment cluttering their plants. They seldom seriously consider selling it for whatever price they can get and replacing it with more profitable facilities. Yet it can be proved that the company that does not buy new equipment pays for it anyway indirectly in large maintenance charges.

Management should consciously search for capital which is tied up unnecessarily in "problem children" products and replace these dead investments with ones which can contribute to future profits.

Some capital projects are just not needed. Many "storage space projects" fall into this category. Space devoted to inventory frequently can be reduced when reserve stock is removed to more remote and inexpensive storage areas, thus releasing for more productive purposes the space previously occupied.

Sometimes an opportunity arises to spin off unprofitable operations which are necessary to the company's functions but seem inevitably to produce a loss. One distributor of heavy cranes and construction equipment financed two of its mechanics who set up a business to make repairs which the company had found to be unprofitable and bothersome. The former mechanics are now managing their own profitable enterprise, and the company is happily farming out all its repair business to them.

Sometimes investment opportunities are forced on companies by public or competitive pressure. Philadelphia milk dealers were compelled to invest in equipment for bottling milk in gallon jugs when a competitor from outside the city was able to generate sufficient public pressure on regulatory commissions to make it mandatory for all companies to make milk available in gallon jugs.

Sometimes a profitable investment requires the cooperation of one or more of the company's large customers. A large supermarket chain in Washington threatened to build its own dairy processing plant unless its supplier of dairy products cooperated in developing an extensive program of capital investments and procedural changes. The supplier did cooperate and the new program ultimately resulted in more profitable operations for both companies. Improvements thus were made which neither company could have accomplished individually.

Selection of projects for capital investment, then, requires imagination and creative leadership on the part of both managers and operating personnel. Market leadership will be captured by those companies that can recognize and exploit opportunities which have been conscientiously and systematically sought out. The talent of recognition, one of the marks of leadership in American industry today, is becoming increasingly more important as the rate of change in business continues to accelerate.

ESTIMATING RETURN ON INVESTMENTS

Extensive literature is available concerning the computation of the rates of return on capital investment, for this is an area in which the experts occasionally generate a good deal of disagreement. Five principal methods for estimating financial returns have been developed and are commonly in use:

1. *Accounting method:* To compute the ratio of the first year's savings to the original investment.
2. *Payback method:* To divide investment by annual savings or net receipts, to indicate the time needed to return the money to working capital.
3. *Annual cost method:* To calculate an index of relative attractiveness of alternate investment opportunities on the basis of annual after-tax savings and net investment.
4. *Investor's method (discounted cash flow method):* To discount the cash flowback after taxes using different rates of return on the money invested. Results are expressed as the number of payback years.
5. *Improved MAPI method:* To determine the relative profitability of operating with and without the proposed project, in order to calculate the savings in the next year when the project is in operation. An urgency rating indicates the relative merits of maintaining the project and deferring it for one year.

While each of these methods has its merits, frequently too much attention is paid to the development and use of intricate financial measures and too little to finding and evaluating all the cost considerations of the capital investment decision. For example, if all the company's engineering time and effort in getting a new piece of equipment on site and actually producing are not taken into account, an accurate decision cannot be made. On the other hand, if all the savings in previous and subsequent steps of the project are not included in the calculations, the expected returns may be understated.

It is also important to assign some kind of acceptable measurement to the intangible factors, both favorable and unfavorable. If a new piece of equipment will require a continuous supply of work to make it pay, it is necessary to compute the cost of processing and procedure changes in the prior operations. On the other hand, if the capital investment will improve delivery performance, then this is a "plus" that should be evaluated.

A good example of the failure to evaluate all the factors in bringing out a new product is contained in the following item from *The Wall Street Journal:*

> New products aren't always a tonic for corporate profits. Three out of ten major new products introduced in the past five years failed in some important respect to meet expectations, and one of those three was withdrawn from the market, according to the National Industrial Conference Board, a private nonprofit organization.
>
> More than 50 percent of 87 company executives responding to a recent NICB survey cited inadequate market analysis, product defects, and higher-than-anticipated development and production costs as the major reasons for new product failures. But poor timing, competitive products, insufficient marketing efforts, inadequate sales forces, and distribution weaknesses were also big pitfalls.

Management's dissatisfaction with the data on which it must base its decision to invest in capital equipment usually stems from one or more of the six following basic errors:

1. Placing emphasis on saving money rather than on making money.
2. Placing emphasis on improvement of existing equipment rather than on replacement with better methods and processes.
3. Making an inadequate analysis of all cost factors, both for and against the investment.
4. Disregarding deferred and intangible benefits.
5. Accepting the narrow focus of survey work, or not carefully studying all the implications and effects on other steps in the process.
6. Assembling poor work-sampling data. This error can lead to dangerous assumptions and inadequate, even incorrect, data upon which to make a decision.

A company sometimes gets locked in an undesirable position, and unless some imagination is brought to bear on the situation, it may continue to be regarded as one of the burdens the company must carry. For example, a milk company in Detroit, badly in need of capital, sold its retail routes to the drivers and recovered part of its capital investment by also selling its trucks. As a result, the company is thriving and has practically no labor problems.

New equipment or new methods can sometimes eliminate an entire workshift, including supporting personnel such as maintenance men, nurses, timekeepers, guards, sweepers, material handlers, and truckdrivers. The cost savings in such an instance may far outweigh the necessary investment. Sometimes the introduction of new equipment or methods eliminates the necessity for negotiating with a specialized union and thus avoids all the costs connected with a separate bargaining unit.

Availability of parts or high repair cost is sometimes the deciding factor in making a capital investment. For example, the exorbitant quotations for the replacement of a rope drive on an old-fashioned machine in a Pennsylvania steel mill weighed heavily in the decision to replace the ancient equipment. This factor was important in another case: Stevenson, Jordan & Harrison made an evaluation of maintenance costs for a large public works department. New equipment would have cost $1 million, whereas repairs and maintenance of the old equipment would have cost $1.5 million. Naturally, the authorities chose to invest capital in new equipment.

New equipment may improve quality, permit easier and faster setup, and facilitiate the acceptance of shorter runs with resulting improvements in delivery and customer service. Having production facilities under company control may be a valuable factor. A manufacturer of electrical equipment began making his own steel junction boxes instead of buying them from a subcontractor. He found he was able to make special orders quickly, and buying larger quantities of steel yielded substantial savings. The company greatly improved its customer service and reduced its production delays and bottlenecks.

Timing capital investments also has a significant effect on return. One plant was too small to manufacture the large products demanded by customers, its foundry was not equipped for profitable operations, and its plant and equipment were not up to date. Five years previously the firm could have saved some of the customers which it subsequently lost, and it could have remained an important factor in its markets. As it is, the management of this firm is seriously handicapped by capital deficiencies and is looking for a merger with another company that has the facilities it lacks.

There are, frequently, unexpected benefits in letting subcontractors perform some operation instead of investing company funds for internal manufacture. Subcontractors are often ingenious and able; they may have excess capacity and be anxious to do the work.

Technical considerations frequently affect investment returns. Some products are so difficult to manufacture that it would be a mistake to make any investment in capital equipment. At one time, for example, traveling wave tubes for airborne radar equipment were proving very difficult to manufacture satisfactorily, and only one company continued to struggle with the production complexities. Any prospective competitor would have had to face these difficulties without the previous experience of the original manufacturer.

One consideration which management faces more and more frequently is the risk of having an intricate process stolen by an employee or a competitor. American Cyanamid Company, for one, has recently charged an Italian drug firm with buying stolen data from one of its research chemists. For security reasons, various parts of a process may be kept decentralized, or only certain parts of it may be subcontracted. More than one manufacturer has found himself faced with competition from equipment and methods which he had developed himself.

Another consideration related to capital investment is leasing—rather than purchasing—equipment and plant, frequently with an option to buy at a later date. Similarly, the cost of rebuilding existing equipment may give a greater return on a smaller investment.

MEASURING RETURNS ON INVESTMENT ACCURATELY

The ultimate management control and record-keeping aspect of capital investment—commonly referred to as measurement of return—is the one handled most poorly. It is surprising how many companies do not follow up on performance against the original cost estimates. Or, if they take that elementary step, many do not follow through to ascertain that the expected return on investment is actually attained.

The specific steps taken to measure return and the records kept vary from company to company. However, every such measurement should incorporate the following principles:

1. The complete actual costs of acquisition and installation should be collected and compared with the original estimates.
2. The differences between the estimates and the actual costs should be investigated. This is a valuable way to learn from mistakes and develop estimating skills.
3. Actual operating performance and results should be recorded.
4. Actual operating performance and results should be compared with the original estimates of performance. Then, if discrepancies exist, they should be corrected where possible.
5. The results should be publicized, whatever they may be. If the compari-

sons are bad, it takes courage to publicize them; but others in the company can learn from each communicated experience, whether good or bad.

It is well to remember, when reporting return on investment, that the only relevant figures are those that have changed since the previous returns were reported. Incremental costs and expenses are the true financial barometers of whether an investment is profitable. Many companies fail to follow up adequately the capital investments they make. Others maintain voluminous files purporting to show that this or that investment was a good one. Few companies, however, can show records that reflect the true return on an investment. This failure to include all the costs and benefits is primarily due to the fact that no one person or department is charged with the responsibility for collecting this type of information.

PUT IT IN WRITING

The November 20, 1964, issue of *The Manager's Letter,* in an article called "When Failure Helps," points out:

> Most new-product planners learn little from past successes and failures—because they have no access to that experience, according to J. L. Huck, director of marketing, Merck Sharp & Dohme. Their firms throw away marketing knowledge by leaving it in the brains of executives instead of writing it in company records. Valuable experience vanishes as memories fade and people move to other locations. Write it down—the good and the bad, Huck urges. Don't be ashamed of your marketing failures. Your firm can benefit from them too—if the details are readily available.

The following are typical areas of failure to record capital costs and investment returns for what they truly are.

1. Unforeseen costs such as excessive installation and delivery charges, unanticipated modification of other equipment, overloads of piping or electrical capacities, and additional demands made on other facilities (traffic, material handling, power, drainage, sewage, compressed air, pumps) create major capital costs.

2. Other costs may gradually become excessive beyond the estimates originally made—for example, freight and insurance charges. Buildings may have to be modified to withstand increased floor loads or vibration or to overcome unexpected fumes and noise.

3. Training time may greatly exceed original estimates.
4. Sometimes setup time, down time, spoilage rates, and manpower requirements are far different from the original estimates. Few of the relevant facts, however, are found in company records.
5. Errors in judging the useful life of equipment are common. Frequently, technical obsolescence is underestimated in original presentation, particularly in industries where technical changes are frequent and widespread.
6. Even when new equipment is installed, it is often difficult to break previous work habits and customs, which leads to inefficient usage.
7. Fumes, noise, and waste disposal frequently require additional outlays of capital beyond the expected amounts. For example, because of increased production resulting from a capital improvement, one company found that local water pollution regulations required an expensive program of acid disposal, whereas it had for years been diluting the acid and letting it run into the local river.
8. Because the need for an investment has not been integrated with the whole manufacturing operation, the newly acquired equipment or process, in some cases, turns out to be totally useless.
9. Some investments just do not work out as planned. Certain companies that have relocated their offices to suburban towns to avoid big-city congestion are still running bus service from the downtown areas to provide transportation for employees. Decentralization, however, sometimes brings unexpected benefits. Changing to a satellite system of milk delivery depots in Chicago meant freedom from union delegates and business agents who closely checked the larger depots to enforce specialized restrictive work rules. And other satellite operations—in Baltimore, for example—have experienced the much higher morale and more cooperative working spirit engendered by a smaller work group.

If management has the pertinent information available when it examines past capital investments, it will benefit from hindsight and thus be able to apply this knowledge when new decisions have to be made. George Santayana warns us in *The Life of Reason* that "those who cannot remember the past are condemned to repeat it."

ACHIEVING OPERATING EFFICIENCY THROUGH PRODUCTION PLANNING AND SCHEDULING

By GEORGE W. PLOSSL and OLIVER W. WIGHT

Production planning and scheduling are two functions that logically fall within the broader classification of production control, an activity which can best be understood by thinking about what it is trying to accomplish. Production control deals with three objectives of business organizations:

1. Maximum customer service.
2. Minimum inventory investment.
3. Most efficient plant operation.

These objectives are basically in conflict. It would be easy, for example, to provide excellent customer service if unlimited inventories were carried or if the plant ran small lot sizes, often broke into setups to run rush jobs, and changed production levels frequently as customer demand changed. But no company that wants to remain healthy could ever risk doing all this.

In the small one-manager plant where the man who provided the capital investment is also the sales manager and the plant manager, the need for striking a balance among these objectives is clear. A customer's order which was obtained by promising a very short delivery time might require using oversize stock, working overtime to grind it down, and pushing other jobs aside in order to deliver on time. Plant efficiency would be sacrificed for customer service. On the other hand, raw material might be kept on hand for this customer's product in the mere hope of obtaining future orders, and this would

GEORGE W. PLOSSL is Plant Manager, Stanley Steel Strapping Division, The Stanley Works, New Britain, Connecticut, and Director of Professional Concepts, The American Production and Inventory Control Society; OLIVER W. WIGHT is a Director of the Education and Research Foundation of The American Production and Inventory Control Society.

increase the inventory investment. Under such circumstances the owner–manager sees clearly that he cannot satisfy any one of the three objectives completely without sacrificing the others.

In larger companies the need for balancing these objectives is not so obvious to individual department managers who are thinking only of their own areas of responsibility. Few sales managers, for example, feel responsible for efficient operation of the plant or for inventory levels, yet there is no question that their activities and decisions have a pronounced influence on both. This is also true of other department managers. It is necessary, then, for production control to provide the information, plan the production levels, and do the scheduling that shows manufacturing management how to balance these three conflicting objectives.

The amount of knowledge in the field of production control has been growing at an accelerated pace in the past few years. While the basic techniques of inventory control have been known for many years, the fundamental principles underlying successful production control have been recognized only very recently. A few techniques, such as the use of Gantt charts in planning and machine loading, have been developed and applied without a clear understanding of their place in the overall system. And the recent advent of the computer and operations research (applying science to business management) has increased the need for that understanding without which the most sophisticated techniques will achieve little success.

ELEMENTS OF PRODUCTION CONTROL SYSTEMS

The basic elements of a production control system are these:
1. A forecast.
2. A plan—
    a. To establish the base inventory level.
    b. To set the production level.
3. Control with feedback and corrective action on—
    a. The level of production.
    b. Mix input—the orders for specific items given to the factory or to vendors.
    c. Mix output—the specific products that the factory or vendors complete.

These elements are not all present or of equal importance in each different type of industry. For example, a distributor of automotive parts is not concerned with controlling production levels since he doesn't manufacture anything, but he *is* concerned with generating the right orders (mix input) to his suppliers and with getting the right material in from them (mix output) at the right time. A make-to-order plant—that is, one where no product is kept in stock—is not as concerned with control of inventory levels as a make-to-stock plant which ships all items from finished goods inventory and manufactures to replenish it. Finally, the make-to-stock plant management must concern itself with both production *and* inventory control.

THE FUNDAMENTALS OF FORECASTING

There are many techniques of forecasting, and a detailed discussion of them is beyond our scope here. Some fundamental concepts should be understood by the manufacturing manager, however, because in most plants good planning and scheduling depend on working effectively with forecasts.

The bases for all forecasts are prediction and historical analysis. Prediction can come from market research, from the sales department's ideas of market trends, or from some individual who knows, for example, that a particular customer is going to double his requirements during the next 12 months. It anticipates the future, whereas historical analysis deals with sales, sales trends, and their correlation with outside indicators according to past experience.

There are no foolproof methods for forecasting, and serious problems are encountered whether forecasts are based on prediction, historical analysis, or some combination of the two. Predictions by sales personnel are often overly optimistic. On the other hand, historical analysis, no matter how sophisticated its techniques, is based on the assumption that the future will be substantially like the past.

To be successful, we must devise a formal system which makes use of both types of forecasting. Sales opinion and marketing information should be compared with data developed from historical analyses of sales. Sales and marketing predictions should be combined with statistical analyses made by the production control people.

Cooperation between the marketing or sales department and the production control group is the foundation upon which the forecasting system must be constructed. Some basic relationships must exist between these two, as shown below:

Function	*Responsibility*
1. Making the forecast.	Marketing (with assistance from production control).
2. Basing production plans on the forecast.	Production control.

3. Tracking the forecast and reporting deviations to marketing.	Production control.
4. Interpreting deviations.	Marketing.
5. Revising production plans accordingly.	Production control.

Forecasts intended for the purpose of planning production levels should be made in terms which are *meaningful to manufacturing;* that is, they should cover product groups which pass through common manufacturing facilities and should be expressed in units which can be easily translated into manloads. Reordering techniques for individual items, which sometimes number in the thousands within a product group, can often be based on a simple device like weighted averages; this is usually handled in the production control department by slide rule, tabulating equipment, or computer calculations. The demand for new products or promotion items also can be forecast by the marketing department, but the situation must be watched closely by the production control department since such forecasts are usually nothing more than educated guesses.

Tracking the forecast is the responsibility of production control, which uses its sales history records for this purpose. When deviations from the forecast fall outside acceptable limits, they are reported to the marketing department for interpretation. It is important to determine the limits in advance so as to avoid spending a great deal of time later in trying to decide whether or not deviations are large enough to require interpretation.

As soon as the deviations have been reported to the marketing department, it should decide quickly whether trends are indicated. In a manufacturing organization awaiting interpretation of a forecast, every week that a decision to change the production rate is delayed means that inventory builds up, so that excess costs are incurred, or customer service is jeopardized because inventory is depleted.

Usually, the most difficult step in achieving a more rational use of the sales forecast is getting everyone to understand what it means to manufacturing. A monthly forecast review can be valuable in developing a better understanding, particularly when a company is just learning to use forecasts effectively. The reviewers should include representatives of production control, manufacturing management, and marketing, as well as the general manager or other top executive to whom all these people report.

Most of the mistakes made in designing production control systems can be traced to failure to understand the characteristics of forecasts. Two of these characteristics are practically universal:

1. Forecasts are more accurate for large groups or families of products than for individual items.
2. Forecasts are more accurate when they cover short periods of time than when they extend far into the future.

Production control personnel frequently complain that forecasts are inaccurate. While there is undoubtedly much truth in this claim, improvements usually can be realized through teamwork in making and using forecasts and by designing flexible production control systems that utilize their basic characteristics to the best advantage.

PLANNING BASE INVENTORY AND PRODUCTION LEVELS

When the inventory control system is designed, and when lot sizes and order points are established or a material planning system has been devised, a "base inventory level" can be determined. In an order-point system, for example, this base inventory level is approximately one-half the lot sizes (ordering quantities) plus the reserve stocks that are built into the ordering points or minimums. The base inventory level is the ideal average that would exist if there were no need to level production in the plant, prepare for peak-season sales, provide for vacations, or support sales promotions. For a distributor ordering materials from his vendors, the total inventory should normally fluctuate only slightly above or below the base. In a manufacturing company, however, the average inventory throughout the year tends to be higher than the base, because inventory is used to keep the production facilities operating at a fairly level rate.

Production level planning is the necessary link between the inventory control system and the act of manufacturing. Production plans should not be based on a backlog of orders generated by the inventory control system or on "firm" orders scheduled for an extended period in the future, despite the common tradition which has it so. In the machine tool industry, for example, backlogs of firm orders representing 12 to 18 months' work were not unusual recently, and the production control system was based upon breaking these orders down into components, scheduling them through production to get a firm assembly or machine "erection" date when the product would be manufactured, and immediately shipping it out to the customer who had been waiting some time for delivery.

Backlog planning has become less and less practical as customers have demanded quicker and more frequent deliveries from stock. Some production control systems, however, have continued to handle their production planning in much the same manner even though the "firm forecast" represented by a substantial order backlog no longer exists. Two basic approaches which attempt this are:

1. Inventory control and expediting.
2. The quarterly ordering system.

The inventory control and expediting approach consists in generating and releasing orders to the factory on the basis of order points or minimums. These orders are then broken down by operations and totaled to measure the load on plant capacity ("machine loading"). With this approach, no real production planning is being done to determine the required level of operation. Substantial backlogs usually build up since plant operating personnel have no way of knowing when changes in the production level are required other than by looking for changes in the backlogs. This system inevitably becomes dependent upon expediting. The backlogs make the lead times substantially longer and more variable than planned. Consequently, the scheduled completion dates of orders become meaningless; production control personnel must expend the bulk of their efforts trying to expedite the most urgent jobs to get them completed on time.

The quarterly ordering system is successful only when all the work to be planned for a three-month period is covered by a backlog of firm orders such as many companies enjoyed until about 1953. Since these backlogs disappeared, however, many production control departments have continued to use the system by substituting a forecast of the products to be made each quarter. From this forecast, three-month assembly schedules are made up and orders are issued to the plant to manufacture the various components and finished products. Since they are based upon forecasts, such firm schedules are rarely accurate and have to be revised many times before the end of the quarter. Typically, the quarterly ordering system also degenerates into an expediting and emergency control system.

Both these approaches to production planning ignore the two forecast characteristics we have cited: greater accuracy with larger groups and for shorter periods. Some principles that should be observed in designing a production control system to take advantage of these characteristics are:

1. The production level should be planned by using a forecast for the largest possible product group that is meaningful in terms of manufacturing capacity.
2. The production level should be established with the least possible commitment to mix.

3. The actual determination of the mix input, the *starting* schedules, should be made weekly, or even daily if possible, to generate orders to meet the planned production rate, using the latest possible information on inventory or order status.

MAKING A PRODUCTION PLAN

Starting with the actual inventory, if sales during the planning period have been forecast and we know what inventory we want at the end of the period, we can calculate the weekly production rate by using this simple formula:

$$R = \frac{D - S + \Sigma F}{N}$$

where: R = Weekly production rate to achieve level production over the planning period

D = Desired total inventory at the end of the planning period

S = Actual total starting inventory

ΣF = Total sales forecast for the planning period

N = Number of weeks in the planning period.

As an example, here is the starting information for making a production plan:

$$D = 20,000 \text{ pieces}$$
$$S = 22,000 \text{ pieces}$$
$$\Sigma F = 32,000 \text{ pieces}$$
$$N = 5 \text{ weeks.}$$

Substituting these data in Equation 1:

$$\frac{(20,000 - 22,000 + 32,000)}{5} = 6,000 \text{ pieces per week.}$$

A rate of 6,000 pieces per week will thus give level production over the five-week planning period, and the desired inventory total will be achieved at the end of the planning period if demand equals the forecast figure and production is scheduled as planned.

Exhibit 1 shows a plan with the quantities for production and the resulting inventory level as of each week. Space is reserved to post actual sales, production, and inventory each week for comparison with forecast. (To support this plan, of course, we also must calculate total operation rates at some of the most important machine centers which are making components.) The data in Exhibit 1 are given in terms of total numbers of pieces of all models; whereas

EXHIBIT 1

PRODUCTION PLAN

All Models of Lamps

[All figures refer to number of pieces]

		Sales	Production	Inventory
Week 8 (Actual Starting Inventory)				22,000
Week 9	Forecast Actual	5,200	6,000	22,800
Week 10	Forecast Actual	6,200	6,000	22,600
Week 11	Forecast Actual	6,200	6,000	22,400
Week 12	Forecast Actual	7,200	6,000	21,200
Week 13	Forecast Actual	7,200	6,000	20,000*

* Base inventory level.

production plans are often made in terms of hours rather than pieces. In any case a production plan should be made in the simplest terms meaningful to the manufacturing area for which it is intended.

There are four principal functions of a production plan:

1. To establish the required level of production for a group of products using common manufacturing facilities.
2. To serve as a "budget" against which actual levels of sales, production, and inventory can be compared to determine the necessary corrective action. This is accomplished by posting actual figures on the production plan.
3. To separate the planning and control of production level from the control of mix.
4. To regulate mix input. This is done by releasing weekly or even daily schedules for the starting operations at the planned production rates.

The production plan shows sales, production, and inventory as related parts of a total picture rather than on individual charts kept by sales, manufacturing, and financial managers. This is important since sales, production, and inventory *are* interrelated and cannot be treated separately in planning and controlling production.

EXHIBIT 2

WEEKLY PRODUCTION SCHEDULING REPORT

[All figures in pieces]

Lamps	Weekly Incoming Business	Year to Date Incoming Business	Net Stock Available	Factory Order	Order Point	Weekly Weighted Average Incoming Business	Total Weeks of Stock	Order Point Expressed As Weeks of Stock	Economic Ordering Quantity
# 7W	341	17,933	1,739	3,078	2,730	485	10	5.6	2,250
# 7D	288	9,837	1,224	832	1,436	274	7	5.2	1,500
# 9W	894	35,329	4,007	1,956	4,242	924	6	4.5	2,000
# 9D	251	10,120	2,189	662	1,386	259	11	5.3	1,500
# 9P	1,187	46,690	8,371	—	6,250	1,290	6	4.8	2,500
#11D	1,332	47,078	2,844	7,050	6,768	1,345	7	5.0	2,500
#11P	598	21,896	778	3,302	3,346	639	6	5.2	2,000

The production plan takes advantage of forecast characteristics by setting the level of production on the basis of forecasts for large product groups which tend to be fairly stable. Establishing the production level for the long term without commitment to a detailed item schedule enables the scheduler to establish the starting schedule mix weekly or even daily to respond to the latest sales requirements.

CONTROLLING MIX INPUT: SCHEDULING AN ASSEMBLY OPERATION

The schedule utilizes both inventory control techniques for generating orders and production planning techniques for maintaining an even workflow in the factory. Inventories in a manufacturing facility exist either as a result of production or to support the production rates, and it is necessary to control production in order to control inventories.

Again, simple inventory control systems, when used to schedule production in a manufacturing facility, inevitably result in backlogs which add to lead time and seriously compound the problems of controlling production. Simple techniques are therefore required to generate orders to meet a planned production rate. Exhibit 2 shows an example of a production scheduling report which does this by using an order-point system. It shows the weekly stock status for the lamps covered by the production plan in Exhibit 1. The usual data in a stock status report, such as weekly incoming business, year-to-date incoming business, net stock available, amount on order with the factory, and order point, are included—in addition to information not usually found. A standard feature of this production scheduling report is a weekly, weighted-average forecast of incoming business, and it shows the total weeks of stock for each lamp (the result of dividing the weekly weighted-average forecast of incoming business into the total of the net stock available plus the amount on order with the factory). It also shows the order point expressed as weeks of stock (the result of dividing the order point by the weighted-average forecast of incoming business). This enables the scheduler to select his starting schedule to meet a planned production rate.

For example, the inventories of the lamps shown on the production scheduling report are all higher than their order points. This is normal when inventories are being built up in anticipation of seasonal sales or a vacation shutdown. Nevertheless, the production scheduling report can be used to insure the proper items to meet the planned 6,000-per-week production rate. Those lamps with the smallest stock must be scheduled so that inventories are kept in balance. Three items are down to a six-week inventory level. The first to

EXHIBIT 3

EXPLOSION CHART

(Product-Line—Lamps)

Assembly	Required Quantity	X18 Switch	X27 Switch	Y2L Socket	Shade #7W	Shade #7D	Shade #9W	Shade #9D	Shade #9P	Shade #11D	Shade #11P	414 Hanger	418 Hanger	VT Base	UP Base	#4107 Cord Set
#7 Wall												2				
#7 Desk																
#9 Wall	2000	2000		2000			2000					2 4000				2000
#9 Desk																
#9 Pin-Up	2500	2500		2500					2500			2 5000				2500
#11 Desk																
#11 Pin-Up	2000		2000	2000							2000		2 4000			2000
Total Required	6500	4500	2000	6500			2000		2500		2000	9000	4000			6500
Total Available		7105	15,423	7002			4595		1244		4715	29,531	11,648			6400
To Obtain																

be included on a starting schedule is the No. 11 pin-up lamp, since it is closest to its order point. The next is the No. 9 pin-up lamp and, following that, the No. 9 wall lamp. Scheduling these three, using the economic ordering quantity of each, would release a total of 6,500 lamps for production.

Thus the production scheduling report provides a technique for generating a starting schedule to meet a planned production rate rather than letting order points generate orders at random, regardless of the plant's production ability. It also eliminates the need to recalculate order points when it is desirable to build up inventory levels in anticipation of a high seasonal sales period.

The assembly process for the lamps involves a number of individual components and subassemblies, the requirements for which should be determined from those for finished goods and not, as is frequently the case, from average usages of the parts themselves. To do so means converting the forecast into a "master schedule" which shows when each lot of the assembled product should be needed and then releasing the component orders to the plant and outside vendors on the basis of their lead time. This technique, called "materials planning," is beyond the scope of a discussion of scheduling, but it does attempt to generate orders in the required sequence so that components will be available at the assembly operation when they are needed. Because of changing demands, however, it is usually necessary to check component availability once again before releasing an assembly schedule. If a component can be used on more than one assembly, it is important to know the *total* requirements for it. As in materials planning, this necessitates an "explosion" of assemblies into subassemblies and components. In practice, explosions are often complex and are frequently made by computer.

A simple "explosion chart" which illustrates the technique is reproduced in Exhibit 3. It is a composite bill of materials for each of the items in a product-family group. Its principal value is that it can show the total requirements for any component by summing the individual requirements for the finished items.

In the particular case illustrated in Exhibit 3, the three lamps selected for production have been scheduled. It must then be assured that all the necessary components are available before releasing orders to the production line. The quantity of each component for each assembly is entered in the appropriate column (doubling that quantity where, for example, two units per assembly are used). The total of each component is shown at the bottom of the column and is compared with the total available. The explosion chart shows that the desired starting date cannot be met because there are not enough No. 9P lamp shades and No. 4107 cord sets available. Acting on this information, the production scheduler now determines whether the No. 9P lamp shades can be obtained in time for assembly or whether another item must be chosen. He is not too concerned about the No. 4107 cord sets since he has to schedule only 6,000 lamps to meet the planned rate and he can schedule 6,400 with the cord sets available. He does realize, however, that this vital component will be needed for next week's schedule and takes action to move the next lot into stock.

In making out an explosion chart, the "ABC" principle should be observed. It is not necessary to have tight controls on all items in the inventory; a few important items constitute most of the value and therefore should be controlled very closely. For many items, such as screws, washers, cotter pins, nuts, and bolts, *the inventory levels should be kept high* so that it will take no great effort to avoid running out of stock. An explosion sheet should include all the important "A" and "B" components but need not include the miscellaneous inexpensive hardware.

CONTROLLING MIX INPUT: SCHEDULING COMPONENT MANUFACTURING

The techniques for setting a production level and scheduling to meet it are, then, rather straightforward for an assembly operation, and they also apply to component manufacture. In most companies where work is of a repetitive nature, the same general approach is valid: Production levels can be planned based on anticipated requirements, and orders can be released to meet the latest requirements within the overall production level planned (or, if necessary *and possible,* capacity will have to be changed). Too often production control does not try to coordinate the release of orders to a planned production level. The result is unrealistic schedules that frequently ask the factory to perform the impossible, and the factory's response is to level out the workload by being continually behind schedule.

Scheduling implies more than just the proper release of orders, however. It further implies that a due date will be assigned to each operation so that job progress can be monitored by operation and that delinquencies will not come to light only after completion dates have been missed. Scheduling is often done by calculating the hours required for each operation (hours per piece times manufacturing quantity) and adding an established standard "transit time" between operations.

One advantage of this type of scheduling calculation—there are other scheduling methods which do not calculate the hours required per operation—is that it provides the data needed for a machine load report. Machine loading implies comparing operation times with available capacities. It results in a short-term report that indicates when men must be moved from one machine center to another or work overtime. Unless firm backlogs are maintained far enough in advance to cover the time it takes to hire and train a man plus the time that the company wishes to retain him before dismissal, the machine-load report should be considered, not as a satisfactory production *planning* technique, but only as a method for showing unavoidable short-term over- and underloads.

PROJECT PLANNING AND CONTROL TECHNIQUES

Many companies work on neither a continuous-production basis nor a job-lot basis. They manufacture highly complex products such as aircraft, missiles, and submarines for which the normal problems of planning and scheduling are compounded; in such cases planning and control can be done only on a project basis.

A very simple project planning technique which makes use of a Gantt chart is shown in Exhibit 4. The Gantt chart, developed by Henry Laurence Gantt at Frankfort Arsenal in 1917, is one of the oldest scheduling tools. Its many commercial variations usually involve some form of board with colored paper, strings and pegs, or plastic inserts to make it easier to plot changes in status and to show conditions more clearly. As Exhibit 4 indicates, a simple Gantt chart can be useful in planning a project. In this case the project includes purchasing a motor and frame steel, fabricating the frame and housing, machining a base casting, assembling, inspecting, packing, and shipping.

Schedule dates for each activity, both starting and finishing, are shown by the short vertical lines at the ends of the light horizontal lines. Each activity has its own set of horizontal lines, and the chart shows the full duration of the project from start to finish. The caret above the date headings shows the present time, which is the end of the ninth week; and the heavy horizontal lines representing actual progress show that the motor has been ordered on schedule, that the frame steel has been ordered, received, and fabricated, and that the housing is now being fabricated on the frame. The chart also reveals that base casting has been ordered but not received and is, in fact, behind schedule; thus the desired delivery date is threatened, and corrective action must be taken at once.

Project planning techniques have been developed extensively in recent years.

EXHIBIT 4

GANTT CHART—ORDER NO. 008160

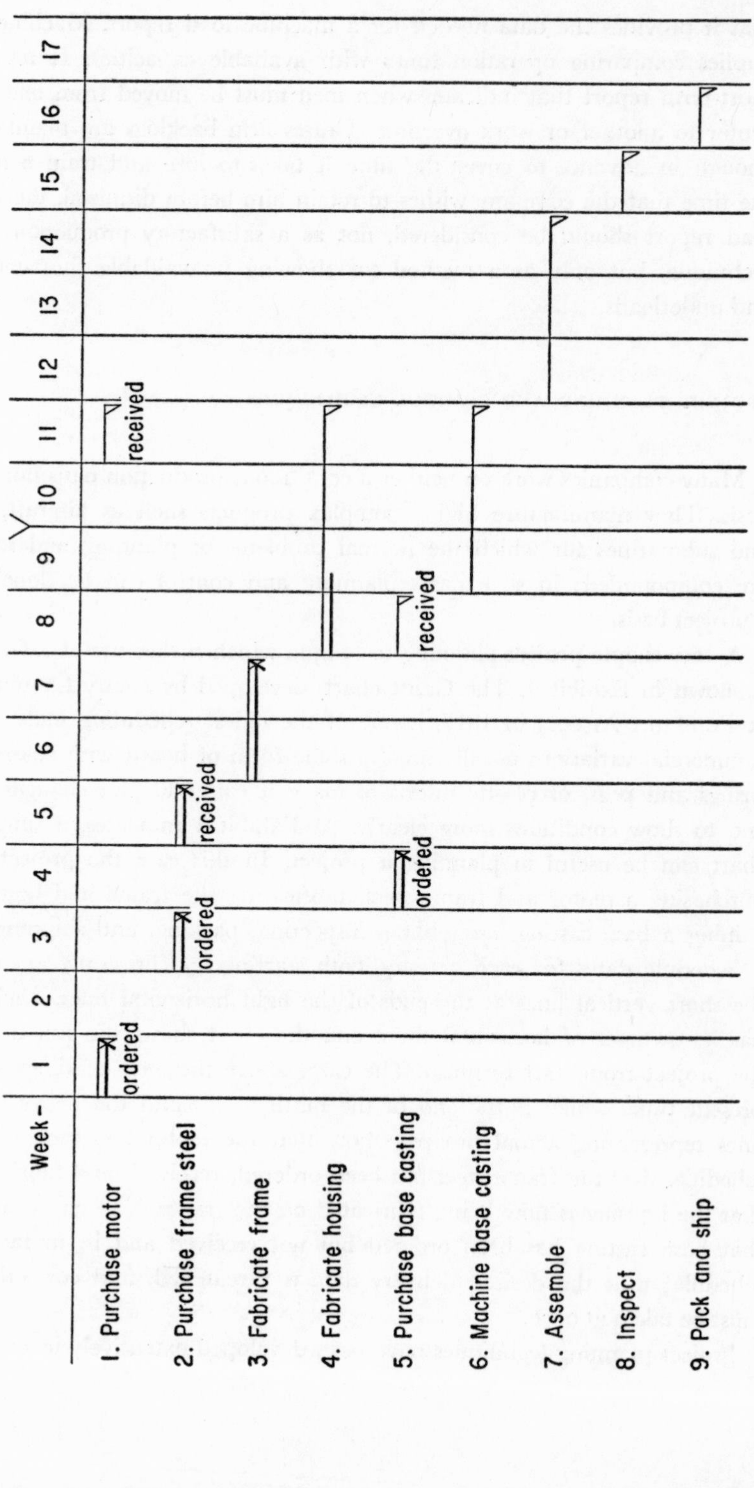

Week — 1 2 3 4 5 6 7 8 9 10 11 12 13 14 15 16 17

1. Purchase motor — ordered — received

2. Purchase frame steel — ordered — received

3. Fabricate frame

4. Fabricate housing

5. Purchase base casting — ordered — received

6. Machine base casting

7. Assemble

8. Inspect

9. Pack and ship

The many varieties have been described in detail in various articles and books. A brief introduction to each basic type is all that is pertinent here:

1. The line-of-balance chart is a refinement of the Gantt chart; it shows the status of individual items within each activity and the percentage of completion for a series of components going into a complex assembly. The Gantt chart shown in Exhibit 4, for example, does not indicate how many frames have been completed; this figure can be included on a line-of-balance chart.

2. The critical path method (CPM) or critical path scheduling (CPS) is a form of network planning. It requires setting up the elements and activities that go into a complex project, showing the necessary sequence and interrelationship of events, and determining the "critical path" or longest sequence of events that determines when the project can be completed.

3. The project evaluation and review technique (PERT) is a refinement of the critical path method and estimates a "most optimistic," "most likely," and "most pessimistic" time for the completion of each element of the project. For a complex project, this information is usually compiled and introduced into a computer, which determines the critical path and calculates the probability of finishing the project by a given date.

4. The learning curve is of value to the scheduler in industries where complex products such as aircraft or missiles are manufactured. The number of man-hours necessary to complete one assembly decreases as workers "learn" their jobs. When they begin a new model run, the components, tooling, and techniques are unfamiliar to them, and they must learn to use them more effectively. There is a mathematical relationship which can be used to predict the rate at which the required man-hours will decrease.

SCHEDULING PRINCIPLES

The basic scheduling principles apply both to complex products that require project planning and to products that can be mass-produced or scheduled by job lot. These principles are:

1. *Schedule to the shortest possible cycle.* Determine the starting mix weekly or even daily. *Don't* put orders into the plant for one quarter or even one month ahead of the starting dates. The reasoning behind

this rule comes from the principles of forecast accuracy: The further out a forecast is extended, the less accurate it becomes; consequently, detailed quarterly or monthly schedules never represent what actually will be required as the month or the quarter progresses. Decisions must be made almost daily as to what items should be started. The starting schedule should be based upon the *latest* sales requirements.

2. *Components must be available.* Never start a subassembly or assembly that can progress only through one or two operations before it must be stopped because parts are not available. It may look good for production control to have such items "on order" with the plant; but if, in fact, a product of this type cannot be manufactured, the orders should be held in production control until it can.

3. *Keep backlogs in the production control office.* Here, again, when production rates are low, it may be comforting to get everything on order with the factory and point to it as the culprit in any failure to meet schedule, but the more work put into the factory, the less control there is over the actual work that the factory does: Production control no longer chooses what is being manufactured daily because the factory has so much choice. When the plant is falling behind in terms of total production rate, extremely tight control over mix becomes most necessary. Releasing more work into the factory as an inducement to pick up the production rate will only compound mix control problems.

4. *Balance the input.* Look beyond the starting department when feeding work into the factory. A day's work in the first department may represent three or four days' work in a succeeding department. For example, a normal quantity of work in a press department may be an abnormal amount of work for the same period in a subsequent jig-boring operation, and serious backlogs will develop here. If the foreman in charge finds that the workload tends to fluctuate widely, he will try to maintain these backlogs at a fairly high level to insure that he always has work for an expensive machine and a highly skilled operator, thus making lead times longer and more variable. Balancing input is one of the most effective techniques available to the production scheduler.

CONTROLLING THE MIX: SHOP CONTROL

These are the principles and techniques, then, for feeding the proper work into the plant—controlling mix input. But an extremely important problem, and the one that determines the ultimate ability to meet schedule dates, is the control of mix output—what the plant produces.

The production plan is consulted in establishing and controlling the overall level of production; prime operation rates for key machine centers should be established to support this level. Scheduling techniques can then be used to feed the right items into the plant. A number of techniques are available for controlling work on the floor so that the right items are completed at the right time.

Perhaps the best-known technique for shop control, the one in widest use today in industry, is expediting, or rushing "hot" jobs through the production facilities by putting them ahead of others competing for the same facilities. The simplest type of expediting is determining which items are out of stock or overdue and getting them through production. It functions *after* trouble occurs, in other words, and cannot truly be called a *control* technique. A more advanced form attempts to prevent trouble by expediting a job when it falls behind at any operation on the basis of due dates established by the scheduler for each operation.

Expediting usually is badly abused. It works effectively only when a few items are put ahead of others. In most companies "rush" tags are put on many items when it is found that they bring results, and it soon becomes necessary to establish "rush rush" and "special rush" jobs so that the really important jobs can be expedited. The entire expediting system may break down when this happens.

Another serious problem with expediting is that it is typically disorganized. There is usually no other man in production control who puts in so much effort to achieve so little as the expediter; his work is almost always haphazard, and he rarely is able to plan his day's activities and follow the plan.

A more sophisticated approach to control is dispatching, which consists in having a production control man in each department who chooses the sequence of jobs to be run. He usually has a file of orders representing the jobs already on hand and those about to come in. When he decides a job is to be run, he issues the necessary order to the factory floor.

Dispatching is plagued with problems. First, it is expensive, since a dispatcher must be placed in every important department. Second, the dispatcher sees the original requested schedule indicated by dates on the orders, but an expediter usually is still necessary to tell him of changing requirements, extremely important jobs, work that is necessary in order to keep other departments operating, and so on. Techniques such as data collection—using an individual tabulating-card-fed machine in each department—have helped to improve communication with the dispatcher and frequently make it possible to move him out of the factory departments and into a central office, thus reducing the number of dispatchers. This type of "centralized dispatching" works well in manufacturing departments where there is little control over the inflow of work and where some formal means of selecting the work to be run from the backlogs in the plant is necessary.

Expediting and dispatching are generally regarded as necessary evils, and most production control departments feel they need more people than they currently have to man these functions properly. In practice, however, adding more people to control operations, particularly expediters, compounds the confusion on the factory floor. Such situations in production control stem from the fact that there has been too much preoccupation in the past with individual techniques and the basic principles of shop floor control have not been sufficiently recognized.

One of these basic principles which is violated in almost every company is this: *Backlogs must be kept to a minimum on the factory floor in order to have effective control of work in process.* Backlogs in the plant have a disastrous effect on lead time. For example, if five jobs are already ahead of every machine center and each takes a day to complete, any new job will not be started for five days. Expediting one or two jobs gets them through more quickly, but others are delayed and the average lead time remains the same. Work on the factory floor is like traffic on the city streets. The time needed to get from one point to another is controlled not by the distance but by the backlogs. In most plants, manufacturing time is a small percentage of the total lead time. The controllable element of lead time is waiting time, which can be reduced only by keeping backlogs out of the *factory*.

Factory backlogs are the principal cause of missing scheduled delivery dates. The more work on the factory floor, the more choice is available to the factory and the less chance there is that any desired job will come through on schedule. Jammed-up factory floors inevitably result in some jobs' getting pushed aside until an expediter starts them moving again. In fact, much expediting is necessitated by excessive backlogs.

Keeping backlogs off the factory floor can result in shorter lead times, less expediting, and more effective dispatching. While expediting may not be completely eliminated, it can be reduced to manageable proportions and can be made considerably more effective. Unfortunately, however, this is easier said than done; the big problem in most companies is *education* of such people as—

1. The foreman who wants to "see" the work on the factory floor before

he adds or transfers manpower, and the worker who slows down as backlogs diminish because he has no confidence in the production control department's ability to keep work flowing in to him.

2. The inventory control man who believes his sole job is to "generate orders" with no regard for planning and scheduling production properly.

3. The expediter who feels that if he had "just two more weeks of lead time" he could get every item completed on schedule.

4. The scheduler who wants to get every job on order with the factory as soon as possible. Even though it isn't needed immediately, he would like to "get a jump on it" and thus insure that it will get through on schedule.

5. The production control man who realizes that the amount of work in process is high but believes that today's problem is trying to get the right items shipped on schedule. He feels that he doesn't have time now to worry about getting his work in process under control.

Unfortunately, such problems of shop control as insuring reasonable lead times, meeting schedule dates, and reducing the number of men required in the production control department are solved only when work in process is effectively reduced. Most plants seem to have very little control over the level of work in process; in very few factories is the available floor space not taken up with this work. Almost any foreman will tell you that he could do his job more effectively if he had "just a little more space." In fact, work in process seems to have no relation to production rate, processing times, or variability of input. It seems to follow a variation of Parkinson's First Law: *The amount of work on the factory floor tends to expand to fill the amount of space available.*

Starting with a major educational program, production control and plant management should make a maximum effort to keep backlogs *off* the factory floor rather than sort out the jobs *on* the factory floor. This desired end comes right back to the need for production planning: When planning has taken place far enough in advance to assure that capacity is available as required, and when production control assumes the responsibility of scheduling to the planned capacity, the plant can become less and less dependent on backlogs in process as a means of leveling out the workload.

Reducing work in process to the lowest level consistent with maintaining minimum down time is a difficult task in most plants, but it will produce concrete results in terms of better delivery schedules, shorter lead times, and reduced in-plant expediting.

FEEDBACK AND CORRECTIVE ACTION

The information generated by production control has frequently been compared to the instrument panel the pilot uses to determine what action to take in controlling his aircraft. Production control is responsible for determining what is happening in the factory, for maintaining levels of production, for getting the proper mix output, and then for calling management's attention to problems so that corrective action can be taken. To achieve all this demands a disciplined approach to developing control information. Haphazard and disorganized information systems are not effective. Production control should prepare a weekly summary of performance against plans for sales, production, and inventory, listing the factory's major problems which require action by those men who report directly to the plant manager. Production control should then review this information and any recommended action with the functional managers who are responsible for reporting exceptional problems to the plant manager.

Control information by its very nature cannot be past history. It's a great temptation to wait for trouble to occur and then try to correct existing problems. Many production control men excel as trouble shooters. "Control" can be exercised only over events which have not yet occurred. The professional production control manager anticipates tomorrow's problems, recommends corrective action, and indicates the consequences and alternatives that face the manufacturing manager. A production control motto and a standard for evaluating the performance of the production control department is:

Good production control means *keeping* out of trouble, not *getting* out of trouble.

QUALITY CONTROL AND PRODUCT RELIABILITY

By R. D. SONDERUP

Quality means many things to many people. To a salesman, it is a magic word to be used as many times as possible in his sales presentation. To the company president, it is a reputation that must be achieved and, once achieved, maintained. To the engineer, it is doing the job as he knows it should be done, without compromise. To the production foreman, it is meeting specifications. To the consumer, quality is that property of a product that creates a desire for continued use or ownership. Advertisement, salesmanship, style, features, and price can all create a desire for ownership, but only quality creates a desire for *continued* use or ownership. Quality control is, then, a control of those characteristics of the product that create this desire.

There are three basic factors by which the quality of a product can be evaluated:

1. Design performance, which is the ability of a product to provide the services for which it was purchased, to the customer's satisfaction.
2. Uniformity of manufacturing, which is the ability of *each* product, turned out by mass production, to provide the services for which the customer bought it.
3. Reliability, which is the ability of this product to continue providing this service without excess cost for its designated life.

As an example of the three basic factors of quality in action, let us assume that a large family in a hot humid climate bought a refrigerator. They filled it to capacity with food, and they placed ice cream in the freezer compartment. Because of its newness, the children were continually going to it for cold drinks,

R. D. SONDERUP is Quality Control Manager, McCall Corporation, Dayton, Ohio; at the time of writing this article he was Quality Control Manager, Philco Corporation, Consumer Products Division, Philadelphia, Pennsylvania.

and so its door was opened and closed an abnormally large number of times. That evening, the housewife found that the ice cream had melted. Her reaction was, "This is poor quality, because my old refrigerator kept ice cream frozen." The reasons for this poor quality reputation may be many. First, the engineering department may have designed this unit with too small a compressor. Second, engineering may have designed adequate reserve refrigeration capacity, but the factory may have installed undersized pistons. Third, on the day this unit was installed a connecting rod in the compressor may have broken, causing the ice cream to melt. In each of these circumstances the responsibility for the poor quality would be with a different component of the manufacturer's organization; however, the result was the same: The housewife complained.

To pinpoint responsibility it is necessary to analyze still further. In the first case did engineering, knowingly under cost targets or unknowingly under timing pressure, underdesign the refrigerator capacity? Or did engineering design the refrigerator to the basic design concept of product planning which specified a low-cost refrigerator that would be completely satisfactory under less strenuous workload conditions? Was the sales department completely aware of the limitations of this model's capacity? In our second assumption we have to ask whether proper-size pistons were specified. If they were, it is clearly the manufacturing department's fault. If they were not, it is an engineering responsibility. In our third assumption, we must ask whether the connecting rod was designed with enough strength to withstand the load, or whether the factory used the wrong or flawed material.

What part, then, should quality control, as a function of the manufacturing department, play in these three assumptions in our imaginary quality problem? In the second assumption, where it was the manufacturer's responsibility, quality control was at fault for letting the unit be shipped, and the same is true in the third example, where manufacturing used defective material. What about the other examples? Should quality control have taken any action in these cases? Here it becomes necessary to understand the function of quality control.

The words "quality control" have become almost a generic term for assurance of conformance to specifications in the manufacturing process. There is nothing wrong with this concept, for it is a job big enough to warrant an independent department. To dilute manufacturing quality control with additional functions and responsibilities usually results in poor overall performance. This does not mean that there is no need for a quality control function in other divisions or departments of the organization. However, to give these groups the title "quality control" results only in confusion when there are such good titles available as "quality assurance" or "reliability."

For clarification of these views, let's start building a quality organization. Let's assign quality assurance to the engineering department; its function is then to evaluate a product to assure its meeting the customer's or product planning's design specifications. Any designs that do not meet these specifications are rejected unless there is a written approved deviation. The value of this group is the same as the value of quality control to the manufacturing group. It guards against designs that do not meet specifications. This group will not invent, suggest, or alter the design in any way. It simply without bias determines whether or not a design meets specifications.

PRODUCT RELIABILITY

There are three basic areas in the overall organization where product reliability can most usefully operate. One is in the engineering department, which is responsible for designing reliability into the product from the start, using all the techniques for testing and proving reliability. The second area is quality assurance, whose responsibility is to audit the product and make certain that the reliability which the engineering group has achieved meets the specifications of the design concept. The third area of reliability belongs to the manufacturing group and can be considered as a part of quality control. Its function is to assure that the manufactured products meet the reliability specifications.

Our imaginary organization now has control of all three phases of quality. Quality assurance, as part of the engineering department, audits the product for design performance and design reliability. It passes only those designs which meet its concept specifications. Quality control, a department in the manufacturing group, then audits the product for conformance to all engineering specifications including reliability, passing all products that meet these specifications and rejecting all that do not.

In order to keep these groups from drifting apart and overlapping in their performance and duties, we need an overall coordinating head. Let's place a director of quality at staff level having functional control over all phases of quality. The quality assurance manager will then report up the line to the chief engineer and functionally to the director of quality. The quality control manager will report up the line to the plant manager and functionally to the director of quality. In this way our total quality concept has been achieved, and it becomes the responsibility of the director of quality to assure control of all characteristics which create a desire for continued use or ownership of the product.

MANUFACTURING QUALITY CONTROL

The manufacturing quality control organization has three basic areas of responsibility: (1) surveillance of the incoming material, (2) control of in-process quality, and (3) evaluation of outgoing products for conformance to specifications and accepting or rejecting them.

Surveillance of incoming material is usually accomplished by one of two methods. The first is receiving inspection, whereby samples of material are selected in accordance with a predetermined sampling plan and inspected for conformance to specifications. A method of rating vendors also is usually adopted. The better-quality vendors are sampled less frequently. Material that is rejected is returned to the vendor for correction, sorted or reworked in the plant, or deviated for use as is, provided that the end product will meet specifications. Deviation should be determined only by the organization that creates the specification in the first place, which is usually the engineering department.

Another method of watching over incoming material is source control; that is, the manufacturer observes the vendor's control methods and accepts or rejects material in accordance with the vendor's quality control evaluation of his own product. Initial sample approval is granted in the same way. The quality control representative visits the vendor's plant to observe his measurements and tests and to assure that the product meets all engineering specifications.

This method of surveillance has many advantages for the manufacturer:

1. It prevents shipments by the vendor of defective material which would be rejected in the manufacturer's plant.
2. It assures that the vendor understands the manufacturer's specifications and can confirm that his product meets them.
3. It saves much time, for defective material is caught long before it reaches the plant.
4. It affords only one quality standard (the vendor's), for the manufacturer has determined through observation of the vendor's organization and operation that his standard is what is wanted.
5. It is less costly, for it results in a steady flow of good material into the plant.
6. It eliminates the necessity for costly space and extra handling of material in the plant.

The U.S. Government for several years has utilized a similar method of overseeing incoming material. Many leading manufacturers in this country are now controlling quality at the source, for experience has shown that most poor quality received from vendors is traceable to misunderstanding of specifications rather than to any unwillingness to provide the quality level desired. This fact should be obvious, for who will deal more than once with a vendor he cannot trust or whose products are faulty?

ZERO DEFECT CONCEPT

The zero defect concept for vendor's material is catching on throughout industry. This concept is simply that the purchaser does not contract to accept any defects and the vendor does not knowingly ship any. When a vendor scrupulously abides by this concept, his operation is improved as well as the purchaser's.

There must be a clear understanding and definition of specifications if the plan is to work. There must be clear-cut agreement that parts meeting these specifications are good and the ones that do not are defective. The vendor must be capable of producing parts to specifications and keep the process under control at all times. If probems develop, the operation must be corrected at once; the vendor must not rely on inspection to catch defective material. The managers as well as the employees of both the manufacturing and the vendor's organization must accept this concept wholeheartedly and conscientiously. Finally, the quality control group should accept or reject each lot of material on the basis of a sampling table with zero as the acceptance level. Exhibit 1 shows the sampling plan used by Philco Corporation in achieving zero defects with vendors.

IN-PROCESS QUALITY CONTROL

Quality control has three basic responsibilities in controlling a manufacturing process:
1. In-process inspection.
2. Analysis.
3. Quality costs.

In-process inspection. It is the responsibility of quality control to provide adequate inspection during the manufacturing process to assure a flow of only

EXHIBIT 1

Sampling Table for Lot Inspection

LOT OR SHIPMENT SIZE	MINIMUM SAMPLE SIZES				DEFECTIVE PIECES ALLOWED
	TABLE A	TABLE B	TABLE C	TABLE D	
1 TO 149	15*	30*	75*	Inspect 100%	0
150 TO 499	30	50	115	150	0
500 TO 7,999	50	150	300	300	0
8,000 AND OVER	115	300	500	500	0

MINIMUM REQUIREMENTS

Major Characteristics:
- *Reduced Inspection*....................*Table A*
- *Normal Inspection*......................*Table B*
- *Tightened Inspection*..................*Table C*
- *Critical Characteristics*.................*Table D*

*When lot size is less than minimum sample size, inspect 100%.

Quality Control Office
Manufacturing Staff

good material. This can be accomplished in two ways: (1) by 100 percent inspection in strategic places along the production line or (2), when the process has proved to be capable, by a lot-sampling inspection system. Too often, both these methods are misused. It has been wisely stated that "quality cannot be inspected into a product, it must be built into it." When a lot-sampling inspection plan is utilized with a manufacturing process incapable of turning out a product which meets quality requirements, something must suffer: The outgoing quality will be bad, costs will be too high, or production will be lost. The only correct way to remedy this condition is to analyze it, find the cause of the defects, and make corrections in the process to eliminate it. If the defects are caused by a buildup of human or mechanical errors and the efficiency of either the workers or the machines cannot be improved, the only answer is 100 percent inspection to sort the good from the bad.

It has been proved that an in-process inspector, even with 100 percent checking for given quality characteristics, will not assure a defect-free product. The ratio of the number of defects found to the actual number in a lot is known as "inspection efficiency." This efficiency varies with individuals, type of inspection, fatigue, and type of working conditions. Our experience shows that an inspection efficiency of 80 percent to 85 percent is average.

One experiment that can demonstrate and prove this contention is to have a group count the number of "E's" on a page of written material and determine the average number found by this group, then compute the ratio of this average number of E's to the number that is known to be on the page. To determine how much individuals vary, an average and range can be easily determined. Similarly, in-process inspection efficiency can be determined by dividing the number of defects in a lot found by 100 percent inspection by the total defects in the lot found through careful screening with several inspections. Once efficiency is determined for a given product and process, it can be used to predict the outgoing quality level. As an example, a process that is producing a 5 percent defect rate and which has been 100 percent inspected with 80 percent efficiency will result in an outgoing quality level of 1 percent defects.

In-process inspection falls into two groups: (1) quality control inspection and (2) production inspection. Quality control should provide all departmental quality "buy off" inspection and now allow rejected material to flow into the next operation. This can be accomplished either by 100 percent inspection or by lot-sample inspection. Production should supply any inspection that is simple and routine, such as checking a part with a "go/no go" gauge, provided that this part is bought off by quality control prior to leaving that department. Exhibit 2 shows one method of determining whether inspection should be carried out by the quality control or the production department.

Each inspection operator should have in view a written instruction or check-off list of the inspections to be performed and a clear definition of the specifications to be met, along with a designation of the proper gauge or test instrument he is to use. The inspector will soon go through the procedure automatically. However, the mere presence of this document will increase his efficiency by several percentage points. The same is true of having him put his stamp or a sticker with his personal identification on the product that he approves. The very fact that the inspection is routine and becomes automatic requires as much subconscious stimulation as possible.

EXHIBIT 2

Procedure for Establishing Minimum Requirements
for In-Process Inspection

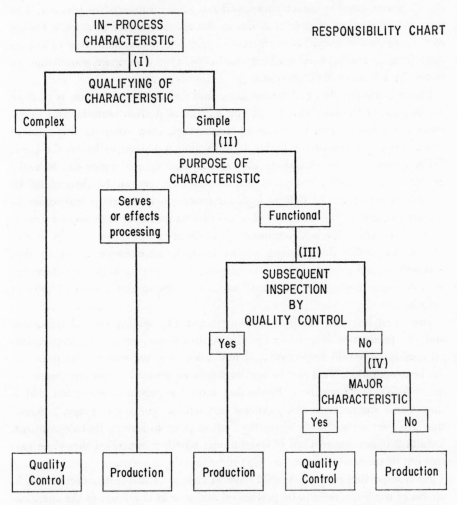

IN-PROCESS CHARACTERISTIC

(I)

RESPONSIBILITY CHART

QUALIFYING OF CHARACTERISTIC

Complex   Simple

(II)

PURPOSE OF CHARACTERISTIC

Serves or effects processing   Functional

(III)

SUBSEQUENT INSPECTION BY QUALITY CONTROL

Yes   No

(IV)

MAJOR CHARACTERISTIC

Yes   No

Quality Control | Production | Production | Quality Control | Production

Analysis. Defects can occur for a number of reasons; however, correction or prevention of defects cannot be accomplished without knowing what the cause is, why it occurs, and who is responsible for correcting it. Although this function can be, and often is, assigned to other manufacturing organizations, there are several good reasons why it should be assigned to quality control.

1. Quality control can assign responsibility for correction without having

to make the corrections itself or trying to shift the blame to some other department.

2. Quality control has access to all the facts and can proceed without interruption or concern for having to keep other departments going.

3. By analyzing and knowing why the problem exists, quality control people are in a better position to know when it has been corrected and thus can truly carry out their responsibility of accepting good material and rejecting bad.

For this analysis function a group completely apart from inspection should be assigned to quality control engineering. This group should be technically competent and equipped with the necessary analytical measuring equipment to confirm its findings.

The quality control group should also be on the alert to detect potential problems. It should gather pertinent data, plot process trend charts, and alert the organizations responsible for correction before the potential defect becomes an actual one. Developing key checkpoints and gathering data that will detect trends early are prime requisites in this responsibility.

It is a function of the quality control engineering group to conduct process quality capability studies. For, if the process is not capable of turning out products that meet specifications, it had better be rejected and corrected.

Quality control engineering should write all inspection instruction sheets, basing their contents on an analysis of engineering specifications. Operator inspection instruction sheets should be living documents. As feedback from the customer, final quality evaluation, or in-process reject data indicate a characteristic that is missed at a given inspection, the instruction sheets should be updated to cover it. At the same time, other characteristics may be so well under control that they can be left to sampling or be checked further along in the process. The right balance between the number of characteristics that an operator has to inspect and the time he has to do so will give maximum inspection efficiency. Deviation in either direction will reduce efficiency.

Quality costs. Quality control is concerned with two cost areas: One is the normal departmental budgeted cost which the quality control manager must administer, and the second is the overall cost of quality, which we shall call total quality cost. While this subject is discussed at length elsewhere by Chester Gadzinski, a brief review and a few comments pertinent to our present purposes are perhaps not out of place here.

The most important point about budgeted cost is to get a workable budget. A lot of thought, experience, and a clear definition of responsibility are essential to preparing a budget proposal. We don't put in too many contingencies, for the experts will surely spot these. On the other hand, we don't shortchange our operations. We ask for what we need and then stand up and fight to get it. If the facts are presented properly, all the reviews in the world won't back it down.

Of course, we must live within the budget. If we start going in the red, we analyze the situation, as Harry S. Mann explains elsewhere in this book. If it is our fault, we correct it immediately. If it is due to an unforeseen change in operations, we present the facts to management and get approval before going any further.

Total quality cost is the sum of all the product quality costs. These costs do not all occur in the quality control department, and so it is not solely responsible for their control. However, quality control is responsible for analyzing them and making recommendations to management for their reduction.

Quality costs are usually divided into three categories:

1. Appraisal or detection cost, which is the cost of inspecting, evaluating, or auditing to detect defective material.

2. Costs, due to product failure or defective components or materials, in handling the defective products or in repairing or scrapping them; loss of production due to the removal of the defective material from the process; and warranty costs because of failure after delivery to the customer.

3. Prevention costs, which include the costs of gathering data to predict potential problem areas, of changing processes to reduce the chance of failure, of establishing and maintaining training programs for improving operator efficiency, and of adding to the product itself some device which will provide a greater safety factor against failure.

No one department can determine the total cost of quality. Each must contribute accurate information to be judged by management. The degree of accuracy with which a company balances these quality costs determines success or failure in the world of competitive manufacturing.

PARETO'S ANALYSIS

One of the most useful tools in quality cost control is Pareto's analysis, which advocates the concentration of the most effort where it will do the most good. Pareto divides costs into categories of causes according to the order of their severity: the highest-cost causes first, the second highest second, and so on. Invariably, the majority of costs result from only a few causes and the majority of causes cost very little. This fact is often referred to as the "vital few and the trivial many." Corrective action obviously should be concentrated on the vital few.

Pareto's analysis can also be applied to different types of defects, to determine which, if corrected, will give the greatest reward. Then, too, the causes of defects can be listed in the order of the percentage by which they can be eliminated. Regardless of the nature of the improvement program undertaken, Pareto's analysis will determine where the greatest gain can be made with the least effort.

IMPROVING OPERATOR EFFICIENCY

One approach to reducing in-process operator errors is to tabulate and post them hourly. Data are gathered from the in-process inspection points and translated into defects per operation. A card is then placed over each operation, and the number of defects contributed to that operation is marked on it each hour. The defects are charged to the operator regardless of whether they result from his error or from the failure of equipment or material. One of the fastest ways to get equipment or material corrected is to charge the operator with defects. You can be sure the foreman will not be left alone until he corrects whatever is wrong.

The card should indicate figures for several days' work so that trends are noticeable at once. Posting hourly defect rates immediately shows the foreman where to concentrate his training efforts. The operators will naturally want to keep to a minimum the number of defects charged to them and will ask for help if they know they are charged with defects but do not know how to prevent them. Consistent bad operations should be investigated by the quality control analysis group to determine what actually is going wrong and to assign responsibility for its correction.

QUALITY EVALUATION OR AUDITING

Quality control is responsible for evaluating the finished product. This is the last chance to decide whether it is ready to be shipped to the customers. The degree of assurance wanted determines the sampling plan to use. More than likely, a reduced sampling plan will be chosen as long as the process is under control.

If defects are found, the entire lot must be reinspected. Quality evaluation should be above and beyond normal in-process inspection and should include inspection, measurements, and tests for all characteristics, including shipping. Evaluation should not be part of in-process quality control but should be a measure of its efficiency and a "go/no go" for control of shipment.

QUALITY FUNCTIONS

All the functions that the quality groups are responsible for should be listed and numbered. A typical function list is reproduced as part of Exhibit 3. For example, it is obvious that functions 7 and 13 are performed by different groups. An organization chart should be drawn up showing the names of the various departments, their relation to each other, and the numbers of the functions for which any particular part of the organization is responsible. If one department requires assistance from another, the numbers should be assigned to both, with an asterisk and a note at the bottom of the chart indicating which department has basic responsibility and which is assisting.

Exhibit 3 shows a chart of the theoretical quality and reliability organizations described in this article. The numbers in each block refer to the functions described in the supplement. This chart is not to be construed as a complete summary of functions performed by the quality group but only as a graphic illustration of functional responsibility.

The names and descriptions of the departments and functions that are used are by no means universal, so it is important that an organization develop a common terminology and that everyone understand it.

A procedure should be established for the implementation of all functions. All departments should thoroughly understand the functions they are responsible for and the procedure for carrying them out. When a problem develops, the manager should be more concerned with what function failed, and why, than with the problem itself. It is only when all functions have been properly assigned and are carried out that the manager's job is complete.

BASIC RESPONSIBILITY OF THE QUALITY GROUPS

The basic responsibility of the quality groups, whether in engineering or manufacturing, is rejecting all material that does not meet specifications and passing all material that does. The quality function is a police force in the

EXHIBIT 3

ORGANIZATION CHART
OF QUALITY CONTROL FUNCTIONS

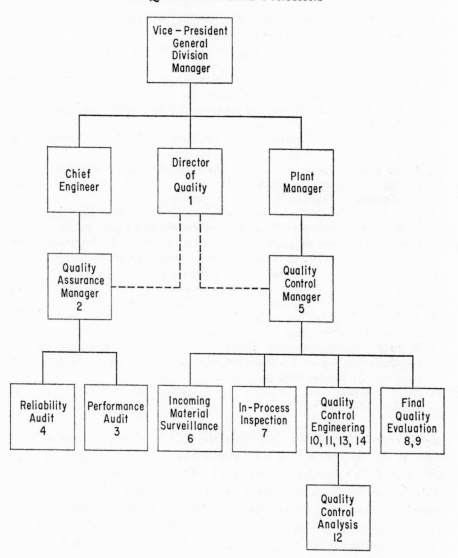

SUPPLEMENT TO EXHIBIT 3

TYPICAL QUALITY FUNCTIONS

1. Assure that all characteristics of a product that create a desire for continued ownership or use meet specifications.
2. Accept or reject all engineering designs on the basis of design concept specifications.
3. Test all engineering designs for conformance to performance design concept specifications and report results.
4. Test all engineering designs for conformance to reliability design concept specifications and report results.
5. Accept or reject all manufactured products on the basis of engineering specifications.
6. Assure that all incoming material meets engineering specifications.
7. Inspect and accept or reject all in-process material for conformance to specifications as listed on the inspection instruction sheet.
8. Inspect and test finished products for conformance to engineering specifications in accordance with sample procedure and report results.
9. Conduct simulated or accelerated life tests to confirm conformance to reliability specifications in accordance with procedure and report results.
10. Write quality evaluation sampling procedures.
11. Write quality evaluation life test procedures; establish method of test, specifications to be met, and number of units to be tested.
12. Analyze and determine cause of in-process defects, assign responsibility for corrective action, and report results.
13. Write inspection instruction sheets for all in-process inspection and list all characteristics to be inspected, specification limits to be met, and gauges and test equipment to be used.
14. Assist manufacturing engineering in conducting in-process capability studies and report results.

overall organization. It does not make the laws but interprets and enforces them. If the company is to be successful, it must back these quality organizations in achieving their basic responsibilities. Quality groups must not be overridden except by the organization which originates the specifications. On the other hand, the quality groups should not become lawmaker, judge, and jury. The only question for quality is, "Does the product meet specifications or fall within authorized deviations?" If not, it is to be rejected. If it does, it is to be accepted.

CONTROL OF QUALITY COSTS IN MANUFACTURING

By CHESTER GADZINSKI

The functional work of a manager has often been defined as planning, organizing, integrating, and measuring. Planning is setting goals and objectives; organizing is husbanding resources to accomplish the objectives; integrating is guiding and directing human resources; measuring is determining whether the objectives have been met. A diagrammatic way of explaining these functions is as follows:

$$
\begin{array}{ccc}
& \text{COMMAND} & \\
& \nearrow \qquad \searrow & \\
\text{MEASUREMENT AND} & \longrightarrow & \text{ACTION} \\
\text{EVALUATION} & &
\end{array}
$$

Command can thus be thought of as intelligence directing action; action as performance of work; and measurement and evaluation as analysis and appraisal of the work performed. Quality costs, in this scheme, are a measure of the effectiveness of the quality strategy of a business.

A business has many strategies, the most obvious being price and service. The quality of its product is also a strategy. Quality strategy can be defined in terms of the product's design (Cadillac or Chevrolet, with all that the quality and status of these two makes of car imply); of its performance (customer satisfaction, five-year warranty, hit probability, mean time between failure, mean time to repair); and of manufacturing costs (yield, scrap rate, rework, and so on). The importance of this concept of strategy and costs is to make possible a better evaluation of the resources required to achieve and maintain quality.

CHESTER GADZINSKI is a member of the Management Services Division, Ernst & Ernst, in New York.

The strategy, of course, is determined before commencing production and not afterward. When the strategy has been set, the total resources required to meet it are measured in terms of quality costs, which consist of quality expenses and quality losses. Quality expenses are costs incurred in implementing quality strategy. Quality losses are costs incurred by failure to meet the strategy's goals, and they include scrap, rework, maintenance during the warranty period, downgrading, and customer complaints. It is generally agreed that it is worthwhile to evaluate and report such losses even if quality costs, as such, had never been thought of.

The sum of quality expense and quality loss represents the total quality costs and varies from one business to another; it has been found to fall somewhere between 7 and 25 percent of sales, depending on the degree of quality required. Such a large percentage obviously means that the control of quality cost, as distinct from manufacturing cost, calls for a definite commitment by management.

In accumulating or assembling quality costs the following conditions, then, are necessary: (1) The costs of doing quality control work, whether it is carried out by the quality control or by any other department, are included in a classification called "quality expenses"; (2) the costs of all defect-caused losses are included in a classification called "quality losses"; (3) "quality cost" is defined as the sum of "quality expenses" and "quality losses."

To explain "quality control work" a carefully defined list of work elements is reproduced in Exhibit 1. One way of viewing this checklist of the elements of quality cost control is as the major part of a quality cost control manager's job description, for it covers all the principal duties he and his staff would be expected to perform. This checklist has achieved simplicity in an otherwise difficult area. With it we can evaluate quality expense with comparative uniformity from one operation to another, regardless of where the elements of this expense originate. The list cuts across functional lines in an endeavor to pinpoint items of expense and suggest a means of controlling them.

HOW QUALITY COSTS ARE DETERMINED

The distribution of quality costs varies between a defense-oriented business and a commercial business. Quality expense is greater than quality loss in the defense-oriented business; in commercial business the opposite condition is found. Four main reasons account for this difference in cost distribution:

1. In the defense-oriented business a product usually has less contributed value than in the commercial business.

2. The defense business, because of its cost-plus-fixed-fee charges, can afford more engineering application than the nondefense business, thus giving rise to higher quality expenses.
3. The lack of long plant runs and the presence of engineering applications in the defense business do not readily create conditions in which chronic underlying losses develop.
4. The need for reliability—process definition, stability, and control—is greater in the defense business.

(*text continues on page 196*)

EXHIBIT 1

QUALITY CONTROL WORK ELEMENTS CHECKLIST

Work Elements	*Definition*
1. Planning and administration of the total quality control system	Planning and administering the activity of reliability engineering, reliability assurance, quality engineering, quality assurance, and associated activities.
2. Appraisal of the total quality control system	Evaluating the total quality control system to determine its adequacy in meeting customer reliability and quality requirements at minimum cost.
3. Reliability and quality studies for bid proposals	Writing proposals for attaining and assuring reliability and quality objectives at minimum cost.
4. Review of customer reliability and quality requirements	Comparing specified or implied customer reliability and quality requirements with the available physical, organizational, engineering, and manufacturing capabilities.
5. Reliability engineering	Evaluating and improving the reliability of materials, components, processes, assemblies, circuits, and complete designs by planning and conducting tests and experiments, providing, analyzing, and interpreting pertinent data, recommending design changes, and monitoring improvement activity.

EXHIBIT 1 (*Continued*)

Work Elements	*Definition*
6. Reliability assurance	Verifying by observation, review of specifications, drawings, and other documents, and interpretation of pertinent data from tests and other sources, that a design compatible with the finished product reliability objectives has been achieved.
7. Writing of reliability manuals and instructions	Initiating and revising documents that describe reliability policies, reliability assurance procedures, and reliability engineering techniques.
8. Tolerance review	Reviewing tolerances on the specified quality characteristics of materials, parts, assemblies, and finished products to determine whether they genuinely represent the limits of acceptability.
9. Establishment of appearance standards	Specifying, by means of documents and physical specimens, required appearance characteristics of finished prototypes and finished products and the materials, parts, and assemblies used therein.
10. Inspection planning	Determining the location of inspection points, the kind and amount of inspection to be performed, the procedures to be followed, the characteristics to be measured, the equipment to be used, the forms to be used, and the records to be kept.
11. Test planning	Determining the location of test points, the kind and amount of tests to be performed, the procedures to be followed, the characteristics to be measured, the equipment to be used, the forms to be used, and the records to be kept.
12. Design of inspection equipment	Planning the construction of gauges and fixtures to be used for measuring dimensional, physical, and visual

EXHIBIT 1 (*Continued*)

Work Elements	Definition

<table>
<tr><td></td><td>characteristics of finished prototypes and finished products, and the materials, parts, and assemblies used therein.</td></tr>
<tr><td>13. Design of test equipment</td><td>Planning the construction of apparatus to provide required environments and inputs and measure resulting outputs of finished prototypes and finished products and the materials, parts, and assemblies used therein.</td></tr>
<tr><td>14. Construction and/or procurement of inspection equipment</td><td>Making or procuring gauges and fixtures to be used for measuring dimensional, physical, and visual characteristics of finished prototypes and finished products and the materials, parts, and assemblies used therein.</td></tr>
<tr><td>15. Construction and/or procurement of test equipment</td><td>Making or procuring apparatus used to provide required environments and inputs and measure resulting outputs of finished prototypes and finished products and the materials, parts, and assemblies used therein.</td></tr>
<tr><td>16. Calibration of inspection equipment</td><td>Comparing and adjusting or correlating dimensional, physical, and optical measuring devices to standards.</td></tr>
<tr><td>17. Calibration of test equipment</td><td>Comparing and adjusting or correlating input–output measuring devices to standards.</td></tr>
<tr><td>18. Maintenance of inspection equipment</td><td>Keeping dimensional, physical, and optical measuring devices in working condition.</td></tr>
<tr><td>19. Maintenance of test equipment</td><td>Keeping input–output measuring devices in working condition.</td></tr>
<tr><td>20. Training of inspectors</td><td>Training inspectors in the techniques of inspecting finished prototypes and finished products and the materials, parts, and assemblies used therein.</td></tr>
<tr><td>21. Training of testers</td><td>Training testers in the techniques of testing finished prototypes and finished</td></tr>
</table>

EXHIBIT 1 (*Continued*)

Work Elements	*Definition*
	products and the materials, parts, and assemblies used therein.
22. Controlling of quality of information to vendors and subcontractors	Verifying the adequacy of drawings, specifications, and quality assurance provisions for transmittal to vendors and subcontractors.
23. Vendor and subcontractor reliability and quality evaluation	Evaluating the reliability and quality capabilities of vendors and subcontractors from past performance and reviews of their facilities, capabilities, and procedures.
24. Inspection of incoming and subcontracted materials	Verifying that materials, parts, and assemblies procured from outside the facility for inclusion in or for sale as finished prototypes and finished products meet required dimensional, physical, and visual characteristics.
25. Test of incoming subcontracted materials	Verifying that materials, parts, and assemblies procured from outside the facility for inclusion in or for sale as finished prototypes and finished products meet required input–output characteristics under the required environments.
26. Contacts with vendors and subcontractors on reliability and quality problems	Working with vendors and subcontractors in eliminating nonconformance to required reliability and quality characteristics of supplied materials, parts, and assemblies.
27. Inspection and test of processing materials	Verifying by means of visual, mechanical, chemical, physical, electrical, and other inspections and tests that processing materials not included in finished products meet specifications.
28. Inspection of work in process	Verifying that parts and assemblies produced within the facility for inclusion in the finished prototypes and finished products of the facility meet

EXHIBIT 1 (*Continued*)

Work Elements	*Definition*
	required dimensional, physical, and visual characteristics.
29. Test of work in process	Verifying that parts and assemblies produced within the facility for inclusion in the finished prototypes and finished products of the facility meet required input-output characteristics under the required environments.
30. Inspection of finished prototypes and finished products	Verifying that finished prototypes and finished products meet required dimensional, physical, and visual characteristics.
31. Test of finished prototypes and finished products	Verifying that finished prototypes and finished products meet required input-output characteristics under the required environments.
32. Disposition of discrepant material	Making decisions whether to rework, screen, use as is, scrap, downgrade, or otherwise dispose of finished prototypes and finished products and the materials, parts, and assemblies used therein.
33. Troubleshooting reliability and quality problems	Investigating the causes of defects, deviations, and failures and recommending corrective action.
34. Follow-up on corrective action	Monitoring and reporting progress in the implementation of solutions to reliability and quality problems and measuring their effectiveness.
35. Inspection of product packing	Verifying that prototypes and products intended for delivery to customers are complete and are identified, packed, loaded, braced, and routed as required.
36. Test of product packing	Verifying that containers and packing materials protect the product adequately against damage and deterioration.

EXHIBIT 1 (*Concluded*)

Work Elements	Definition
37. Appraisal of reliability and quality of finished product	Evaluating finished products to determine how well the products being shipped meet the specified and implied reliability and quality requirements of the customers.
38. Field failure analysis	Determining and classifying the modes of failure of prototypes and finished products which have been delivered to customers.
39. Customer contacts on reliability and quality problems	Working with customers and their representatives in eliminating nonconformance to required characteristics of finished products.
40. Maintenance of reliability and quality records	Collecting, sorting, summarizing, filing, and maintaining reliability and quality data from all sources on finished prototypes and finished products and the materials, parts, and assemblies used therein.
41. Processing and reporting of reliability and quality data	Planning and performing the analysis and synthesis of reliability and quality data from all sources on prototypes and products and the materials, parts, and assemblies used therein.
42. Writing of quality manuals and instructions	Initiating and revising documents that describe quality policies, quality assurance procedures, and quality engineering techniques.
43. Quality cost analysis	Breaking down reliability and quality costs into meaningful classifications and pointing out areas of maximum potential reduction.

These two different patterns of quality cost require different approaches to control. In the defense-oriented business, consequently, the challenge is expense control; in the nondefense-oriented business the challenge is loss control.

Expense control is perhaps more easily understood by citing a few examples.

Case 1. Quality cost studies in one plant pinpointed the receiving inspection activity as being excessively expensive; it employed 265 inspectors. Work sampling revealed that the inspectors were "doing" inspection work only 25 percent of the time. The rest of their time was spent in make-ready and put-away.

Through a better preplanning of the inspection activity, 85 inspectors were removed from the payroll.

Case 2. Quality cost studies in another plant indicated that administrative expenses were too high. An investigation uncovered the fact that this plant, a new one, was purposely overstaffed when it was activated three years previously but that no one had taken a second look to see if all the staff members were still necessary. The result was that ten supervisors were removed from the payroll.

Case 3. Quality cost studies in this third case showed a life test to be a high-cost operation. Tradition had established a four-hour motor test. A review of the test data revealed, however, that motors either failed in the first minute or didn't fail at all. The motor life test was eliminated.

HOW QUALITY LOSSES ARE DETERMINED

Quality losses are broken down by—
- Product line.
- Part.
- Manufacturing area.
- Manufacturing sequence.
- Defect type.

Ranking these cost categories in descending order and making an accumulative distribution will reveal that most costs are concentrated in a very few areas. We call this process the separation of the vital few from the trivial many. This simple procedure is the application of Pareto's economic analysis to quality loss. Once the problems are isolated and defined, we discover that 90 percent are amenable to ready solutions; the remaining 10 percent require sophisticated approaches. Two examples of quality loss reduction will perhaps clarify this discussion.

Case 1. In a plant which manufactured receiving tubes five types and five defect types represented 90 percent of the losses. By concentrating on these ten tubes an $800,000 cost reduction was possible.

Case 2. In a cable manufacturing plant three defects represented 80 percent of the losses. A redesign of a die head produced a $175,000 cost reduction.

WHY QUALITY COSTS ARE NOT REDUCED

If reductions in costs can be made with readily available knowledge, the question arises as to why they aren't more often achieved throughout industry.

We find two answers. First, the principles of corrective action are not being followed. These principles include, in order of their execution,

- Problem definition.
- Problem presentation.
- Problem acceptance.
- Commitment to solution.
- Follow-up.
- Evaluation.

Too often the responsibility for corrective action follow-up has not truly been delegated. Also, too often requests for corrective action deteriorate into an ineffectual paperwork mill. How many times does someone who discovers a problem write a memo with a distribution of at least 20 people! The recipients all conclude that it is addressed to someone else on the distribution list, and no action at all is taken.

One example of corrective action failure may be cited. An electronic navigation system had an achieved mean time between failure of one and one-half hours. (Mean time between failure is the ratio between the total number of operating hours of a piece of equipment and the number of failures it experiences. For example, if a machine operates for 1,000 hours and fails 10 times, its MTBF is 100 hours.) The *specified* MTBF was 36 hours. Many meetings were called and many hypotheses were advanced about the cause of the poor performance, but no action plan was developed and hence no action was ever taken. To correct this situation a "score card" was designed which provided columns for problem definition, the assignment of responsibility, a description of the action plan, the date the action was to be completed, and evaluation. Evaluation was necessary not only to determine whether the problem was solved but also to determine whether its resolution created new problems.

The second reason that a quality cost reduction potential is not realized is more subtle but every bit as current. It arises through failure to separate the short-term from the long-term problems, today's fire fighting from tomorrow's planning. A good bit of energy is expended in just maintaining the status quo, in fighting the sporadic problems as they arise. Consequently, a company may be expending so much energy in this direction that it doesn't have time to look at the longer-range opportunities or the chronic underlying problems. Identifying and outlining an action plan for the vital few, that is, may be forfeit because it spends too much time on the trivial many. The remedy is simple once the problem is recognized. If we have a fire-fighting activity, as we all do, we must organize a group of fire fighters. But we must remember also to organize a group of fire preventers.

QUALITY RISKS

The accumulation and evaluation of quality costs must be balanced against quality risk, which can be defined as the probability that failure to inspect, test, or properly specify a manufacturing process will adversely affect a product's performance. This concept may become more meaningful after considering Exhibit 2's example of a manufacturing plan for making a martini.

EXHIBIT 2

THE MANUFACTURE OF A MARTINI

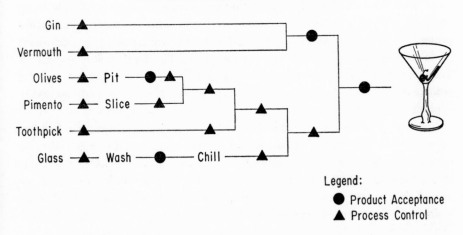

Legend:

● Product Acceptance
▲ Process Control

Let us consider the problem of inspections for product acceptance after pitting the olive. We may wish to X-ray the olive to determine that no residual pit remains because of our concern about the adverse affect it may have on our customers, whereas gauging the size and the depth of the hole in the olive is done only to permit ease of assembling the sliced pimento. In short, the underlying principle of a quality risk analysis program calls for properly categorizing and relating all inspections and tests.

REPORTING QUALITY COSTS

It is desirable to simplify the regular periodic reports of total quality costs as much as possible in order to prevent any significant additions to them from being caused by the work of measurement. For this reason the regular periodic reports are broken down only by the elements required to build them up. Thus, for instance, no attempt is made to separate detail inspection from sampling inspection; they are both included in "inspection," which is one of the elements of quality expense. If this element is subsequently disclosed to be reducible, as it frequently is, it can then be broken down into sampling and detailing or into whatever other subclassifications seem most promising in the search for potentially significant reductions.

The introduction of a report form which does not contain fine subdivisions has proved to be a fortunate breakthrough in the simplification and consequent universal acceptance of the principles of quality cost. The reason for the simplified form lies in the fact that the work elements defined in Exhibit 1 are a description of the functions of an "idealized and integrated" quality control department. If they are the work elements of any actual quality control department, then the operating expenses of that department, which are already being reported by regular accounting procedures, constitute the total "quality expenses." Since part or all of various work elements will normally be performed by other departments, their costs are estimated. The total quality expense is thus the sum of the operating cost of the quality control department and the estimated cost of those work elements which are performed by other departments.

The economic aspects of achieving and maintaining quality and reliability do not cease with the accumulation of quality costs and the evaluation of risks. Maintenance during the warranty period must also be considered in commercial business. Quality costs do not include maintenance in the defense business. This does not mean that customer complaints do not exist in the defense business; it means that the supplier's liability is limited.

AN ANALYSIS OF THE QUALITY COST REPORT

The items to be covered in the regular periodic quality cost report are shown in Exhibit 3. While many are self-explanatory, the following clarifying comments are offered to aid in complete comprehension of the others.

- *Adjustments.* Their purpose is to take any oddities into account. For instance, if safety engineering is a function of the quality control department, its expense is credited. If, however, some inspection work is charged to no specific department but to general overhead, the expense of this work is debited.

- *Special materials and equipment.* Here are listed the other departments, such as production and factory engineering, which do some of the work described in Exhibit 1. The cost of work performed by each of these departments is estimated and debited, as we have aready seen.

EXHIBIT 3

QUALITY COST REPORT FORM

1. Reported quality cost
   Departmental expense ———— ////////
2. Adjustments ———— ————
3. Adjusted quality cost departmental expense ————
4. Special materials and equipment ————
5. Quality expenses, other departments
   5.1_____ ———— ////////
   5.2_____ ———— ////////
   5.3_____ ———— ////////
   5.4_____ ———— ////////
   5.5 Total quality expenses, other
       departments ————
6. Total quality expenses ————
7. Scrap ———— ////////
8. Rework ———— /////////
9. Downgrading ———— ////////
10. Downtime ———— ///////
11. Total internal quality losses ————
12. TOTAL INTERNAL QUALITY COSTS ————
13. Warranty costs ————
14. TOTAL QUALITY COSTS ————
15. COST OF MANUFACTURE ————
16. SALES ————
17. PERCENT ITEMS 12 to 15 ————
18. PERCENT ITEMS 13 to 16 ————
19. PERCENT ITEMS 14 to 16 ————

- *Scrap.* Scrap costs are figured as net. For example:

  Cost of material and labor of substandard quality to point
  of manufacture $10.00

  Plus salvage labor and material 2.00

  Total cost of item 12.00

  Minus value of salvaged part 6.00

  Scrap loss 6.00

  Minus junk value .... .60

  Net scrap loss .... $ 5.40

- *Rework.* Rework is the cost of repairing a defective part and includes
  the charges for both labor and materials.
- *Downgrading.* This is the loss incurred by having to sell the product
  at a reduced price because of failure to meet one or more specifications.
  The amount debited is the price difference.
- *Down time.* This is the cost of idle time of machines, processes, and

operators caused by the fact that the machine or process has been making a defective product and has been shut down for adjustment or repair. It does not include regular maintenance, nor does it include down time caused by lack of good material from a vendor or previous process.

- *Percent of items 12 to 15.* This is the ratio of total internal quality costs to cost of manufacture. It is the measure watched most closely, since it reflects accurately the immediately controllable quality costs.
- *Percent of items 13 to 16.* This is the ratio of warranty costs to sales. It provides some measure of quality assurance, although it may be greatly influenced by market conditions.
- *Percent of items 14 to 16.* This is the ratio of total quality costs to sales. It is the ultimate measure of quality costs, but it is a statistic in which the time factor causes instability. Internal quality costs are incurred during the period being reported. Warranty losses and sales, on the other hand, frequently result from events which occurred earlier.

THE BENEFITS OF REDUCING QUALITY COSTS

The cost of achieving and maintaining quality and reliability must be carefully evaluated. In commercial business a reduction of quality costs by 10 or 20 percent can spell the difference between profit and loss. The May 1962 issue of *Fortune* reported that the 500 largest U.S. industrial corporations showed an increase in sales of 2.2 percent over 1960, whereas the median return on sales slipped to 4.2 percent from 4.4 percent the previous year. A reduction of quality costs, which, as we have seen, vary between 7 and 25 percent, by the 10 or 20 percent here advocated would have caused the return on sales figures to read as follows:

PROFIT CONTRIBUTIONS BY QUALITY COST REDUCTION

Sales 1960 (Billions)	Quality Cost As % of Sales (Estimated)	Quality Cost % Reduction (Potential)	After Tax Quality Cost Profit Contri- bution (Billions)	Median Return on Sales Reported (%)	Return on Sales Potential (%)
209.1	7	10	.68	4.2	4.5
209.1	7	20	1.36	4.2	4.8
209.1	25	10	2.4	4.2	5.3
209.1	25	20	5.0	4.2	6.6

From these figures it is apparent that the control and reduction of quality-oriented operations which do not truly contribute to the value of a product—whether in its design or in its utility—should be a vital management concern if the fullest profit potential is ever to be realized.

A CONTROL SYSTEM FOR MAINTENANCE OF PLANT AND EQUIPMENT

By JAMES F. COLLINS, JR.

Proper maintenance of modern plants and their equipment means providing the right amount of competent maintenance service, and at the right time. The rapid pace of increasing technology in manufacturing, service, and office and administrative operations has resulted in a skyrocketing rate of mechanization of facilities to keep up with demands for more output, improved quality, and reduced costs. Efforts to meet these demands must be applied to successful existing products as well as to all new products.

Greater mechanization requires more and better plant engineering and maintenance service in installations, adjustments, changeovers, repairs, replacements, preventive maintenance programs, and just plain line upkeep of the production facilities. Mechanization has resulted rather generally over the past few years in higher maintenance costs. Sometimes the costs have been justified by the increased output's reducing the direct labor costs so much that there was an overall reduction in unit cost.

Then, too, the increased capital investment in the new and expensive machinery has itself often justified the increased technical service costs. The complexity of the equipment, with its self-sensing and feedback controlling features, has also pointed up the need for more mechanical service and its attendant greater portion of the total cost of operation.

But, even with all these justifications, the suspicion remains firmly implanted in the minds of a very great many production and general managers that maintenance costs are too high. They must be, for they have been rising steadily each year. The maintenance manager swears that his costs cannot be reduced because they barely provide for the upkeep of the plant and of production lines, service, and utilities for the projected production schedules and rates of output. It consequently has been rare indeed for a maintenance manager

---

JAMES F. COLLINS, JR. is Chief Engineer for Johnson & Johnson, Chicago, Illinois.

or plant engineer to submit a budget that is lower than, or even the same as, his previous one. Labor costs are up, and material costs—which reflect other companies' increased labor costs—are also up. Furthermore, all manufacturing superintendents and foremen want more attention paid to their production lines.

THE MANAGEMENT ELEMENTS OF MAINTENANCE

What every general manager, production manager, or engineering and maintenance manager really wants to achieve is the correct amount of maintenance service. The current cost may be too high, or it may be too low. What is needed is the right amount of mechanical service to provide the most effective production operations. This optimum amount of service will then make possible optimum production and thereby the lowest unit cost.

Unfortunately, we have no button to push so that we can obtain the answer to our question of what *is* the optimum maintenance rate or cost. There is no single thermometer, barometer, or easy-to-read gauge to tell us whether we have exactly the right amount and proper quality of maintenance service. Instead, we must realize that the concerns of maintenance management are precisely those of manufacturing management and all other areas of management where the elements of money, men, materials, time, and equipment must be organized and administered to produce an economical product, whether goods or services.

First, there must be an effective *organization*. Personnel with the appropriate skills, education, background, experience, interests, and personal characteristics must be organized into effective subgroups with specifically designated tasks and responsibilities. Their supervision must be the direct responsibility of competent leaders, skilled not only in the technical specialties to be performed by their men but also in managerial techniques. Each manager must insure the necessary job training and communications within his own group, with other service groups, and with the line personnel to whom he will supply his services.

Second, there must be planning, which is in fact essential to the management of any type of operation. This is the outlining of a course of action to achieve a desired objective. Planning and scheduling must be carried out for every maintenance job. Of course, there are varying degrees of formalized and systemized planning, ranging from the very simple to the complex. At one end of the scale the craft foremen handle this function as well as simplified records and paperwork while supervising their men and performing their own assigned jobs. At the other end there are staff planning departments to aid and advise the maintenance supervisor. Some long-range maintenance planning departments are so elaborate that they must use electronic data-processing machines in their calculations.

Third, the *control* element of management must be taken into account. The work must be done as planned, efficiently, within the proper time, and with a reasonable expenditure of hours of labor and units of material. Progress must be reported and evaluated, and deviations must be examined carefully so that out-of-line conditions can be improved. Changing conditions must be reported back so the proper adjustments in job content, procedures, or timing can be made.

Doing the right job at the wrong time or at the wrong place, or continuing to do a job exactly as it was planned and prescribed *after* changes have occurred, must be avoided. Reactions can be noted and judgments made only if there is an efficient system aimed at obtaining information on work performance, relating it, analyzing it, and reporting it to the responsible supervisors.

These elements in performance evaluation constitute control by the supervisors. They improve overall performance by analyzing costs in time, labor hours, and materials so that planning, scheduling, supervision, and administration can be even more effective in the future. They realize that problems that can be averted and changes that can be anticipated need not continue to occur each time the same job is performed if control information is available. Their control procedures range from the most elementary observations of the responsible foreman to systemized tabulations from the accounting department using electronic data processing for rapid collating of data which are printed out in usable form.

THE ROLE OF SUPERVISION

Frankly, the most effective way to assure high standards of maintenance in a suitably small operation—one in which the same type of equipment performs the same tasks and is manned by a small group of employees with approximately the same skills or training—is to select a foreman who is well trained, experienced, and technically competent. He must be told what should be done, how it must be done, when it should be done, and how much it should cost before he can be expected to run the operation efficiently.

However, since this type of management is so successful, the operation soon is swamped with orders. Success thrusts upon it the opportunity to expand, furnish more goods or services, and increase the product line. Suddenly, instead of a readily controlled one-room plant with a group of similar machines turning out the same product, and with the operators all in full view of the supervisor or within easy reach, we have rapidly changing conditions and new problems of communication in all directions.

As operations become more complex, so does the need for organized administrative planning and control. The good, competent foreman is no longer in the position of supervising homogeneous activities in an area he himself can cover thoroughly and over which he can exercise complete control. If, instead of one room or one unified area of similarly skilled men operating identical machines and turning out similar products with the same materials, there are several different work areas to be managed—perhaps on different floors or levels, in different buildings, in several plants, or in distant geographical locations—then the need arises for more complicated methods of obtaining information and feeding it back. Moreover, as the number of employees increases, as their skills become more diversified, as mechanization and automation increase, and as the number of different parts of products and the geographical dispersal of the various operational elements increase, then the demands made on supervisors to fulfill their responsibilities and control operations have long since exceeded any capabilities which experience and personal competence alone can be expected to have given them.

They need help. They need information, promptly and in an organized fashion, to tell them where their operations need attention. They can no longer be everywhere, in contact with all their men all the time, and they need to know where things are happening and decisions are needed. If the right information is not made available to them promptly, they will bog down in trying to solve a problem at one location while other, more costly, difficulties are occurring elsewhere. Then the organization will operate by responding to crises, with supervisors rushing from breakdown to breakdown as fast as their experience and training will let them.

Unfortunately, again, there is no known pushbutton solution to determine exactly how much should be invested in a program of controls and staff services. It is simply a matter of economics: what expenditure will return most in efficiency and lower total costs of operation. The right way to arrive at a figure is of course through a careful analysis of all the factors in specific operations. Initially, however, the answer must principally depend on good judgment.

Good management judgment, in the last analysis, is founded primarily on a thorough understanding of the technical requirements and complexity of today's highly mechanized operations. General management has entrusted to the maintenance manager the task of seeing to it that the maintenance activity is functioning properly. It is up to him to determine what is needed and will be economically sound, plan a program to accomplish it (using all available internal advice and assistance) and then carry out that program.

USE OF STAFF SERVICES

By and large, plant engineering and maintenance management have lagged behind other manufacturing activities in the use of staff services. Manufacturing managers for several generations have made full use of the services of many staffs: accounting, industrial engineering, purchasing, personnel, and others. They have long since justified the costs. They have analyzed their operations frontward, backward, and sideways. They have found the waste-making components of their production operations and proceeded to put waste reduction programs in effects and so cut the cost of wasted materials and effort.

Manufacturing managers at all levels live by their accounting reports and have devised some form of daily control report to respond to. They have analyzed their direct labor output, set goals, re-examined their direct labor costs, and established standards under which they operate with variance reports for control, until now there is precious little money left which can be removed from direct labor costs. And these managers have been at it a long time, using systematized information from their staff services to help them do the best production job possible.

Plant engineering and maintenance managers, on the other hand, have in general not called upon other staff departments for help. The staff services have in turn been hesitant to go much beyond historical reports and accounting audits of expenditures against budgets, because plant engineering and maintenance activities are highly technical and complicated by nature and therefore mysterious to those not schooled and experienced in them. It is up to enlightened maintenance managers to seek assistance from accounting and industrial engineering and then actively to direct the development of control systems from the data made available by these staff agencies.

All plant engineering and maintenance organizations are responsible for expenditures that constitute a significant share of operating costs and, thereby, a critical share of the standard costs of the items produced by the total operation. In addition to the substantial expenditures for repair and adjustment of high-speed production machinery and the tremendous expenditures for new capital equipment and facilities, the effective productivity of plant equipment—including the elimination of excessive machine down time costs—rests in their hands.

It is a startling sign of the times that these large key expenditures are made under the direction of a maintenance manager with only a few hard-working supervisory members of his organization to serve as his staff as well as his line lieutenants. Many of today's maintenance organizations in large companies are responsible for spending more money than is spent by many entire small companies which operate with a president and a complete staff of vice presidents with staff specialists to assist them in obtaining and evaluating information to make their crucial decisions.

Few people would today think of providing a maintenance manager with a finance man and an accounting staff to help him control his operations and see that expenditures are made as effectively as possible. Few would provide him with a man to take charge of operations (responsible for an industrial engineering staff) as well as specialists in personnel, purchasing, and what have you. However, before we dismiss the idea as an utter absurdity, let us consider for a moment not only the amount of money involved but also the performance expected of the maintenance organization and the difficulty of administering it effectively. This may help us to realize that more staff assistance and more systems of control are urgently needed by maintenance management than have customarily been provided.

The principal responsibility for the void in staff assistance must rest primarily with the maintenance managers themselves. Services are made available where they can be shown to be economically advantageous. In a technical area like plant engineering and maintenance management it is up to the chief to take the lead in developing a staff program and proving its value. If he doesn't, one of these days someone else will.

The extent to which the manager should formalize control systems is determined by the size and complexity of maintenance operations. Procedures can be very simple, or they may be extensive and elaborate. The degree of their sophistication must depend on the needs and the ability of the organization to make effective use of them. The same systems will not apply to all operations or organizations. In particular, the maintenance manager must not become overenthusiastic and embark on too big a program before he has an organization ready for it. If he makes this mistake, he will do himself, his organization, his company, and the whole concept of professional maintenance management a grave injustice.

First things must come first. The basic building blocks of any well-organized system of controls must be learned; and, when each step has successfully been made a regular part of the operation, then the next may be developed. Each must be taken in sequence; no one can skip the basic steps and leap into a full-fledged program without disrupting the existing maintenance operation and risking costly failure.

The advanced stages of a thorough system of controls will make use of measured labor standards for maintenance work. But there are many things to do before even considering the use of measured time standards. We can think of progress in this direction as a road beginning with the most simple and informal of devices and proceeding on and on to more and more complicated records and procedures. We get on the train at the beginning, continue as far as is economically sound, and get off at the stop that does the most at the cost we can justify for our operation. So let us examine the various way stations along the track to measured time standards before we look at the standards themselves.

THE WORK ORDER SYSTEM

The first element of any maintenance control program is an adequate work order system. Everyone in maintenance believes he has a work order system, but it will be well worth his while to examine it critically. For this is where control starts, and if the work order system isn't functioning properly, the maintenance manager will never control his operation successfully.

Every maintenance job must be covered by a written work order. This is true whether the job is routine, planned-ahead preventive maintenance work, repair service, or emergency breakdown repair. Ordinarily the order can be prepared ahead of time by the requesting agency or the responsible maintenance foreman; in the case of emergency service, it can be prepared after the fact. The important point is that only with a written work order can the costs of the job be correctly accumulated, charged where they belong, and analyzed to determine whether the job was effectively handled—not just to see that time, manpower, machines, and money are being spent efficiently but also to determine where problems exist and to plan for improved performance in the future.

Standard nomenclature must be developed for all types of work. The terminology must be simple, understood by all who use it, and it must describe all jobs clearly and completely. If communication is poor, labor will be poorly utilized. And, if the job to be done is poorly or incompletely described, it will be poorly or incompletely done. Then it must be redone or completed at another try, and the cost of the job will amount to far more than would otherwise have been the case. In such circumstances maintenance effectiveness will quite likely never reach anywhere near 50 percent, no matter how loyal the maintenance men and how good their intentions.

A sound work order system can be reasonably simple, but it must be uniformly used and rigorously adhered to. Then maintenance jobs will be clearly understood before they are done, and they will be done well. Further, with all maintenance work covered by written orders, effective records can be kept and costs ascertained, thus providing a basis for setting standards on later jobs. With a well-installed work order system it should be possible eventually to apply standards to 90 percent or more of the total maintenance labor hours. The additional organizational and administrative cost should be at a minimum if this basic part of the system is properly established to begin with.

THE TIMEKEEPING SYSTEM

The first element of cost to record, keep track of, and charge into the work order is labor. Therefore, our next consideration is the development of an adequate timekeeping system. Obviously, some sort of system is necessary to pay employees and to fulfill legal requirements. But this simple system is not enough in itself.

The cost in labor hours and then in dollars, including associated burden, must be charged against each specific job performed. Otherwise, there is no control over performance. What a job actually did cost must be known and compared with what it should have cost. Initially, this comparison can be made by using a standard time card system. It will, however, be necessary to have more information put on the card than the time the individual shows up for work, the time he takes for lunch, and the time he leaves for the day. The time spent on different jobs must be shown, with each job properly designated—preferably by work order number. It is of course best to have the card punched on a time clock, showing the time a job is started and when it is left, so that the charge to each work order can be readily determined. The total time charged then must add up to the total time the man is to be paid for that day.

This type of time card record system can be developed into a fairly adequate timekeeping system. However, when the maintenance manager has developed timekeeping to the point where all time to be charged to jobs against the proper work order is accumulated, he will probably find job cards advantageous. Job cards are used to record time spent on jobs by work order number, and the total of these time elements, plus the standard allowances for rest and lunch, is equal to the total time shown by the individual's pay card or time card. This degree of refinement makes it possible to compare labor costs with labor standards.

MATERIAL CONTROL: THE REQUISITIONING PROCEDURE

The third element to develop in a good maintenance administration program is material control. Materials purchased specifically for a job can normally be charged directly to it by marking the work order number on the purchase requisition or purchase order. There are, however, many stockroom items which go into maintenance jobs that add up to far more significant amounts than is normally realized. These items form a part of the cost of maintenance, and they must be accounted for and charged to the job they are spent on if any reasonable degree of cost control is to be achieved.

A material requisition system can be readily adapted to any organized maintenance operation. This system uses a simple requisition form developed for keeping a record of the materials consumed and charging them to the appropriate work order. The materials needed for a job are listed on the requisition, along with the work order number. These materials are requested by the foreman responsible for the work performed, or by one of his men if he so designates, and initialed and approved by him. In a larger organization which has a planning section, the job planner may be delegated the responsibility of preparing the material requisition and obtaining the required items. The materials so requisitioned are normally then obtained from a central stock room, although in a large multi-building operation stock rooms decentralized by geographical area or type of supplies may be more efficient.

The maintenance man exchanges his requisition slips for the materials needed, and the stock room attendant uses the slips to mark his inventory records or re-order cards. The attendant then turns the requisition forms over to the accounting department or records clerk so the dollar value can be charged to the proper work order and eventually included in the total job cost. The cost of the materials can be marked on the form by the stock room clerk after he has checked the unit cost information on his perpetual inventory cards or sheets, or the notation can be made by the records clerk or accounting representative.

Unless a basic material control system is established, total job cost cannot be determined. Furthermore, job estimating and planning won't have the benefit of material unit cost data. If a control system—even one as elementary as suggested here—isn't used, the proper inventory of items needed for maintenance work will probably not be kept available. Then critical jobs will be held up while they await materials that are ordered *after* someone discovers that they are unavailable in the store room.

At this point—with a work order system, timekeeping system, and material control—the manager has assured accurate reporting of his maintenance costs. This allows him to keep track of where and how money is spent, although it does not show the degree of efficiency. Now accurate cost data can be supplied to manufacturing for redistribution to produce standard costs.

Also at this point in the development of maintenance control, the manager may wish to evaluate the advantages of a formal preventive maintenance program. The key to its success is an optimum cost balance of returned production benefits measured against the cost of the preventive service. When such a program fails, it is most commonly because in the enthusiasm for providing service costs are allowed to exceed the benefits which are returned in reduced down time and increased productivity.

THE PLANNING AND SCHEDULING SYSTEM

Until a maintenance operation develops into a very large undertaking, with large numbers of employees to schedule tasks for, the planning and scheduling system is usually operated by the foremen concerned. Then, to the greatest extent possible, the time-consuming administrative details of record keeping, time card coding, and extending should be transferred to clerks. This leaves as much time and energy as possible for the supervisor to direct the activities of his men.

An integral part of administering maintenance activities is planning the work and scheduling the appropriate employees to perform the necessary tasks, at the right time and place, on the right equipment made available at the right time, with the right tools and materials available at the workplace, and with the right craftsmen assigned in the correct sequence so that they can function efficiently without interference. Since the foreman of a shop or the supervisor of a group of maintenance personnel knows the capabilities and limitations of his men, the techniques of the service to be provided, and the characteristics of the equipment to be serviced, it logically follows that he is the one best able to do this planning and scheduling.

However, larger jobs involving several crews under the responsibility of different foremen, and particularly jobs extending over a period of time, must be coordinated by someone. The planning and scheduling must be based on information and service obtained from the maintenance foremen and from engineers responsible for certain elements of the job, but there must now obviously be a separate planning and scheduling agency.

Sometimes this agency is simply a supervisor assigned the responsibility for a particular large job and provided with the necessary clerical help, but if there is enough of this multi-job kind of activity, a planning and scheduling section must be developed. Not only does such a section pay for itself, but a company will find it very costly not to have one. If the maintenance manager has developed his administrative controls to the point where he can analyze the costs of jobs and compare those costs with what they should be, he will find that losses due to poor work performance—or to crews' being assigned to a job in the wrong sequence, for instance, and getting in each other's way—will more than equal the cost of a small section specializing in maintenance planning and scheduling.

It is from this group that the manager will be able to draw future foremen—men who have shown their ability to understand and handle maintenance responsibilities and who have received invaluable training in administering this type of work.

The planning of a maintenance job and the preparation of a schedule for it take the same basic approach, whether the planner is the supervisor himself or a staff specialist who helps him by gathering and organizing the necessary information. The requirements of the job must be ascertained from the engineers concerned, the availability of the equipment must be assured by the production supervisors, drawings or sketches must be obtained where indicated, and man-hours must be estimated by type of craft skill required for each element of the job. Commitments for the estimated man-hours of each skill must be obtained from the shop concerned and set aside for the day or days when that part of the job must be done. The shop foreman must be made aware of what materials are to be on hand at that time, or they must be ordered and made ready for him at the time of the scheduled work.

All this information can be graphically noted on a typical shop planning chart or board, with the jobs or their elements listed down the left side and the days of the month listed across the top. Then a small piece of paper showing man-hours by craft, materials, and anything else required can be inserted opposite the job element in the column under the day when the work must be performed. This arrangement quickly shows what each foreman is to provide and when and lets him determine well ahead whether he is overcommitted at any particular time, so that he will not be the cause of a job's going off schedule and becoming more costly.

Information is updated as changes occur which affect the plans for any part of a job. By reviewing these changes with the supervisors, the manager can shift the times of job performance and the man-hours scheduled for certain days. In this way the most critical jobs can be carried out first and all jobs can be carried out effectively.

Not all the hours available from each shop or craft specialty are scheduled, of course. A certain proportion must be set aside for emergency or breakdown repairs—just how many can be determined only by experience. The amount of emergency work will decrease steadily as the effectiveness of the maintenance organization increases, although there will always be a need for immediate, unplanned service in a highly mechanized industrial operation.

It is hazardous to generalize, for all operations are different. But if, on an average, much more than 20 percent of the maintenance work is done on an emergency basis, there is much room for improvement. Better planning and scheduling, more preventive maintenance, and more attention to maintenance controls will improve efficiency levels and reduce job costs. If, on the other hand, much less than 15 percent is not prescheduled or handled on an emergency basis, either the company has a very stable operation, with fewer machines and equipment that can break down and go wrong than most, or it has too large a maintenance force or even too much preventive maintenance.

The need for close communication between the man who is planning and the men who are responsible for doing the actual work is obvious. To develop this closeness most organizations have a regular, scheduled meeting each week between the planners and the shop foremen. The meeting is normally conducted by the supervisor to whom the foremen report or by his designated representative, and the major jobs planned for the coming week are briefly reviewed by the responsible planner. Typically, the meeting is held for about an hour each Thursday afternoon, and the basic schedule for the next week, minus estimated hours to cover emergency jobs, is reviewed.

MAINTENANCE STANDARDS

Now, if the manager has all the preceding elements of a good maintenance management program successfully in operation, it is time to consider some form of maintenance labor standards. These can be very simple or very complex. The degree of sophistication depends entirely on operating conditions and what can be achieved with standards toward better administration and control of maintenance. In any event, the more complicated measured time standards, extremely valuable as they are, must not be embarked upon without having all the foregoing elements of a control program functioning well.

What is meant by a maintenance standard? What does "standard" mean? It can be defined as the time an average, properly trained mechanic should take to perform a task under average conditions, working at an average rate of performance.

It is not an impossible or even a difficult-to-meet period of time within which a given task is expected to be performed. It is not a "speed-up" device. The employees will have no difficulty meeting standard times. When individual jobs take longer, it will usually be due to exceptional conditions. These delays will be compensated for by the jobs that go unusually smoothly.

However, when jobs take significantly longer than the standard time assigned, they should be looked into. This process should lead to improved conditions for future work: greater promptness in making equipment available, better job planning, better scheduling (with the right materials and tools on hand at the right time), better methods and procedures.

One main cause of relatively poor work performance is time lost between jobs. Knowing how long a job should take focuses the supervisor's attention on this lost time and leads to better assignment of the workmen's available time. Skilled craftsmen almost never perform poorly while actually working on a job. They are proud of what they do; they are craftsmen and want to be recognized as such.

It is on emergency jobs, especially major breakdowns, that a company really gets its money's worth—and more—out of its maintenance labor dollars. Of course, machine down time and lost production can eat into profits if they occur too frequently; but the mechanics will be performing far over standard. They will knock themselves out to produce, knowing without even consciously thinking of it that the maintenance manager and everyone else is fully aware of their importance. And the job results will reflect this. However, these same men may take their time about getting to the next routine job, especially if no one seems to care or to know the difference. Or, more likely, it may be that the next job is not ready or clearly defined.

Maintenance standards bring about better supervision, administration, planning, and scheduling. They point up the need for better engineering preparation, more engineering information, and helpful sketches—all of which improvements pay off. The men are not being asked to work harder or faster; they are just being helped to use their skills on more jobs assigned to them during the working day. Supervisors are encouraged to see whether more work may not be possible, and the frustrations of waiting or looking for information and materials are reduced as staff sections assist in making increased productivity possible.

THE SUPERVISOR'S ESTIMATE OF THE JOB

The most elementary form of maintenance labor standard, and the most universally used, is the estimate of the foreman responsible for the job. This is based on his past experience, his knowledge of the equipment or area concerned, and the skill and experience of the men available to him. It generally serves to get the job lined up. No planning and scheduling of any sort could be carried out without an idea of how long the tasks a given job is made up of should take, and the supervisor's estimate provides this information. Moreover, it is immediately available, and it is far better than nothing at all. The higher the caliber of the supervisor, the greater his experience and the better his judgment and the more accurate the standard.

One disadvantage is that the standard is rather too subjective. It depends not only on the experience of the individual foreman and his specific knowledge of the conditions of the task but on his biases and his allowances for the conditions he believes prevail. No two foremen would estimate a job in exactly the same way, although the better they are as supervisors of a particular type of specialty, the more accurate they will be.

We all tend to overestimate slightly, if unconsciously, to allow for unknown problems that we know are bound to arise. No one cares to have even the least dependable member of his group show up poorly before other agencies and make the maintenance force look bad in their eyes. And it does seem that if the estimate is lenient, the amount of hours charged to the job before it is closed out will come close to expectations. Parkinson's Law applies in many areas. There is, for this reason, little likelihood of continuous improvement in the performance of similar jobs, and certainly nothing to point up the need for administrative improvements in job preparation, as is the case when the performance of a good crew shows up as poor on a job with a scientifically established standard time.

USE OF HISTORICAL DATA

Another approach to job standards is the use of historical data. The man-hours actually taken to perform the same jobs in the past can be tabulated, and these accumulated data can be averaged to provide standards. Historical data give a somewhat more impartial time estimate for a job than a foreman's estimate, and they have the advantage of being based on actual experience.

Historical data serve as a good starting point in establishing time standards where none have ever existed in any form. Performance begins to improve slowly as men find they can normally meet and often improve upon the time that has been allowed for a job. There is nothing like knowing that someone is aware of what we are doing and appreciates a good job to make most of us do a little better than we would otherwise. This slow but steady improvement in job performance levels off in a year or so in most cases, however, and even the new and improved job standard based on more recent historical data still contains time that would be unnecessary if planning, scheduling, supervision, and preparation for the work were improved.

Historical data do provide one of the least expensive ways of getting started on a job standards program which uses actual data instead of subjective estimates alone, though some investment in clerical time is required to gather the information, tabulate it, and average it by types of work. One of the first points the processed data will uncover is the need for standard nomenclature in maintenance work. The data will also demonstrate the need for work orders, explicitly written for all jobs, so that later we can determine just what was done. Only then can the same work be sorted out and averaged to provide standard times on the basis of current practice.

Historical data have the disadvantages of including errors in maintenance administration and of not forcing rapid improvement in job planning, scheduling, and control. However, they are far better than nothing.

WORK SAMPLING AS A MEASUREMENT TECHNIQUE

Work sampling doesn't provide standard data, and it is not a form of maintenance standard. It is, nevertheless, worth considering as a measurement technique at this point. It is a ratio-delay study, or statistical analysis, of the percentage of time each workman or group of workmen spends on each type of activity. The different classifications can be selected to give the survey information desired, but they normally include the following activities: transportation, make ready, put away, inspection, avoidable delays, unavoidable delays, and productive work.

The study is made by tabulating the information gathered on a form which is carried by the observer; the individuals or groups are listed down the left-hand side, and the categories of activity are listed across the top. The observer makes random observations of the workmen, noting the type of activity engaged in at the time. To be effective, this must be done on a truly random basis, or the men being studied will quickly learn to "look busy" whenever the observer comes into view. The length of the study will depend on the size of the force and the plant, but to begin to achieve a reasonable degree of validity a rather large number of observations—usually well over a thousand—should be made.

Work sampling is a valuable method of comparing the activity levels of individuals and of homogeneous groups, not only to single out the productivity of one worker as opposed to that of the others but also to indicate the trend of improvement in work performance and in time utilization. If a work sampling study is made periodically—say, once a year or so—progress will be apparent and administrative assistance can be provided, as needed, to further that progress.

The technique's disadvantage is that it measures activity and not efficiency. It does not point up the need for new and better methods and procedures. It actually tells how active the workers are, not how effective. A man may climb up and down a ladder at full speed four times, but perhaps once would have been enough to do the job right. Or a mechanic may disassemble and reassemble a machine component at 100 percent effectiveness, but perhaps that is the wrong thing to do; by the time he figures out the right adjustment or the needed correction, his job effectiveness may be about 30 percent.

In some maintenance operations, it is worthwhile to combine historical data with work sampling performance ratings. The result is a form of job standards which are factored for labor activity.

MEASURED TIME STANDARDS

The ultimate in maintenance labor standards is measured time standards. A large, well-run maintenance force requires measured time standards if it is to achieve maximum effectiveness in terms of work performance and labor costs—but only after the basic elements of successful maintenance management have been achieved.

Measured time standards rely in all instances on engineered time studies of the operation concerned. They could of course be developed by having the available industrial engineering personnel make detailed time studies of all the maintenance activities. The difficulty is that the task would take more time than anyone will ever have and be more costly than anyone could ever justify. Furthermore, the additional task of training administrative as well as supervisory personnel by the maintenance manager would be practically insurmountable.

Therefore, available standard data should be used to the greatest extent possible. These data can be obtained from a number of sources, such as the U.S. Navy Department Maintenance Standards and a number of well-known concerns which specialize in this field. They can be purchased separately and installed by the maintenance organization with its own personnel, or they can be purchased as part of a service, which includes analyzing specific conditions and needs as well as training personnel in understanding and applying the standard data.

This last method is by far the most economical approach, for the initial higher cost brings quicker—and greater—eventual returns. One of the biggest hurdles that it helps to overcome is lack of self-confidence among the personnel. People find that they soon learn to use this modern technique effectively, and the specialists who assist in training the organization can do so much more effectively than the manager or his associates.

Use is made of small blocks of elemental, or incremental, data. This means that the common elements or components of mechanical activities can be extracted for time study and then made available to establish standards for a given unit of work. The advantages of this procedure are apparent: Specific sizes and lengths of pipe can be cut and threaded in the same allowed time regardless of what or where the job is. Or specific fittings can be applied, or hangers installed, and standard times developed. Standard allowances to be added in are developed for varying conditions such as location, height, weather conditions, travel distance, and number of men required for specific parts of the job.

Thus a standard time for a certain maintenance task can be developed from incremental standard data without having to study the job all over again. Only when jobs, or components of jobs, are peculiar to operations for which there are no standard data available must the manager make time studies to develop such data for his own use. And these can then become additional increments of data to be applied to future jobs containing the same activities or elements.

Standard data can be developed economically for practically any maintenance activity. In spite of the unusual characteristics of maintenance work, it is all made up of smaller components of activity for which standard data have been or can be developed. There are, of course, exceptions—complicated jobs that won't be repeated for a long time. For these it may not be feasible to spend the time and effort to develop standards; they should be covered or controlled by some other means. In some areas, such as machine setup and adjustment, it may be effective to relate the job performance to machine down time or productivity. Even this indirect coverage in a few areas is far better than no attempt at standards.

To the greatest extent possible—and, as a general rule, this means almost all the time—standards should be applied before the job is done. That is, jobs should be pre-planned with standards pre-applied, rather than checked by data after the fact, even though jobs may not be done on standards, at least not for a long time. Such a procedure makes possible better planning and scheduling. More usable information is furnished the responsible supervisor; consequently, he can better supervise and control the work. The time lost in preparation for the job, in travel, in obtaining tools and materials, and in sequencing crafts is greatly reduced, and the relative amount of work done is increased in proportion.

Perhaps most important of all, measured time standards help show the way to new and improved methods and procedures of carrying out the work. It is not enough to reach a point where work is performed at a high level of effectiveness but always in the same old way. New tools and equipment become available, new methods are developed, and new ideas are conceived to reduce the time required for the performance of maintenance tasks.

Measured time standards are a true yardstick of efficiency. They do not merely indicate the level of the men's activity or "busyness"; instead, they show the effectiveness of work performance. With this information problem areas can be investigated and improvements developed in planning, scheduling, preparation, and other techniques of administration. True, there are disadvantages: the initial cost of installation, the cost of keeping the program going and improving, and the increased complexity of administration. These drawbacks call for an ever higher level of performance from the supervisory and administrative staff as well as from the workmen.

In fact, all that usually happens so far as the men are concerned is that they work on more jobs, not harder. There is just less lost time.

*   *   *

All the members of a maintenance organization want to do a good job. The maintenance manager assumed as much when he hired them. If they wanted to loaf or just get by, they would have gone into another line of business in the first place. Where there are inefficiencies or vast areas calling for improvement, it is because help is needed—by the supervisors as well as by the craftsmen themselves. The complexity of today's mechanized operations, which will continue to increase at a logarithmic rate, makes demands that are becoming more and more difficult to meet.

These demands are being made not only on technical knowledge and mechanical and electrical techniques but also on the management and administration of a rapidly growing, highly complicated service to complex automatic lines of machinery. Therefore, the methods of maintenance management, like its systems of control, must be upgraded accordingly. Maintenance can no longer be run by the seat of the pants, by the experience of those who have been in the game for a substantial period of time.

It is up to the maintenance manager or plant engineer to develop his organization so that it can effectively provide the services needed by manufacturing. The plant engineering and maintenance function is a service to manufacturing; production is impossible without it, and it must never forget its responsibility to manufacturing.

The manager must have the specialized knowledge and the skills necessary to determine what will accomplish the most effective job. He must develop an adequate maintenance program, obtain the confidence of those to whom he is responsible, and budget the funds made available to carry out the program. His efforts in these directions will ultimately pay back far more than their cost.

THE ORGANIZATION AND RESPONSIBILITIES OF THE MATERIALS MANAGEMENT FUNCTION

By ROMEYN EVERDELL

A glance at any Sunday's *New York Times* classified advertising section shows that U.S. industry has awakened to the need for a more sophisticated materials management function. The far-sighted analysts of industrial operations have been aware for many years of the potential for improving customer service and increasing the return on inventory investment; most of the methodology has been developed, but implementation is not widespread. The trend toward emphasis and concentration on the direct and obvious opportunities for cost reduction, particularly direct labor costs, has had to run its course. The general industrial community is now turning to thorough examination of the less obvious cost reductions attainable by improving the flow and distribution of materials and by improving the return on net worth through optimum inventory investment.

Direct labor cost reporting has in the past highlighted setup costs and the time lost waiting for materials. As a result, manufacturing began to add its voice to the concern expressed by marketing for improved customer service and the pressure from finance to hold down inventories. Management recognized the interrelationships of these apparently independent factors and re-examined the organization structure of production planning and inventory control activities. These functions are now being upgraded and joined to resolve conflicting objectives, to develop better plans, and to provide controls that will assure performance which is close to the optimum obtainable.

This chapter discusses the materials management function at its present stage

ROMEYN EVERDELL is a Principal and Director of Rath & Strong, Inc., Boston, Massachusetts.

of evolution. The opportunities provided by electronic data processing, with particular emphasis on computer capabilities, have a major impact on how materials management should be organized, manned, and operated. However, the basic requirements of the function are emphasized here, leaving it to other authors elsewhere in this book to discuss data processing techniques and the total systems approach to EDP which can improve the performance of many activities and reduce administrative costs.

The Materials Management Function

If the manufacturing function, in the broadest sense, is considered as a problem in logistics, it may be viewed in two parts: (1) materials management to provide the planning for materials acquisition, storage, and flow through the conversion process to finished product inventories; (2) manufacturing management for the "doing" activities, such as fabrication, assembly, packaging. These two groups of subfunctions should report individually to the top manufacturing officer, typically a vice president in a large operation or a general manager in a small company or a division.

RESTRAINTS ON PLANS AND PROCEDURES

The materials management concept stems from the need to integrate the planning for purchasing, conversion, flow, and the inventories of finished product. The plans and procedures to be followed must allow for two restraints: sales policy and required return on investment. The factor of investment yield arises because some portion of inventory is planned to offset certain operating costs. For example:

1. Lost sales or costs of expediting and break-in on production runs resulting from unpredicted changes in demand or replenishment.
2. Indirect labor costs arising from production delays caused by lack of materials resulting from strikes, breakdowns, and so on.
3. Production costs resulting from amortization of the setup or make-ready costs over the number of items ordered.
4. Indirect costs required to review and order items to assure availability for production and distribution.
5. Poor direct labor productivity and indirect (hiring, training, or termination) costs resulting from response to fluctuations in demand.

The first two costs can be offset by the use of safety stocks in ordering and replenishing stock and banks of work in front of machines during the conversion cycle. The next two can be offset by ordering in economic lot sizes and by developing efficient and effective systems and controls. The last cost can be countered by planning more gradual changes in production level, on the basis of forecast and actual requirements, through the economical use of finished inventory.

In each case the counterbalance to minimizing those costs is the cost of carrying inventory, including the risk of obsolescence. Inventories represent an investment opportunity similar to the purchase of improved production equipment or the financing of product development and must earn a similar return. However, the problem of obtaining the proper return on inventory investment is complicated by the fact that inventory includes two other major components which are not investment opportunities: (1) work-in-process inventory, which essentially varies with volume and the production time cycle, and (2) inventory resulting from the control system's lag in detecting the need for and taking corrective measures as the result of an unexpected drop in usage (slow-moving inventory).

A further complication is the fact that investment in inventory can be made at any one of several stages in the process of accumulation: raw material, common components, subassemblies or partially complete items, or finished products at the factory, warehouse, branch sales office, or distributor's premises. Since each of these stocking points creates different costs, the decision as to where to carry inventory and in what amount at each point can be a complex one. For example, is it better to carry safety stocks of finished products in several warehouses to allow for unusually high demand or to stock at the factory and use faster but more expensive distribution methods? It may even be possible to stock material in a semifinished state, assemble to order, and air-freight the finished product; this is especially true if the assembly cycle is short and special branding, painting, or attachments are required. The various factors and alternatives make anything but simple the establishing and controlling of inventory in such a way as to minimize the total costs.

To discharge the inventory management function properly, top operating management must take part in making the controlling policy decisions. In the first place, sales management must decide what level of service is required. The materials manager may have to demonstrate the alternate costs of, say, 85, 90, or 95 percent risks of stock-out to aid in making the decision, and the cost of operating to various back-order levels should be weighed. For example, if the competitive situation allows for delivery within one week without risk of losing a sale, as opposed to having stock immediately available at all times, the inventory investment, ordering, and distribution costs can be significantly reduced. In most industries various types and classes of product have different marketing requirements which should be recognized. The materials manager must not only adhere to sales policies affecting service, but he also should participate in the decision-making process by costing alternatives to arrive at the factors which influence these important policy decisions.

In addition to the sales and service policies related to the materials management function, a financial policy on the cost of carrying inventory must be formally stated. This often-neglected procedure of converting inventory dollars to cost dollars is the other major restraint in managing the function. Without a clear understanding of this "inventory carrying charge," the determination of what inventory should be carried at what points can be made only arbitrarily, and all too frequently in the past inventories have been controlled by arbitrary standards such as the number of turns or dollar limits. An effective materials management system can quickly adjust all inventories to satisfy any specified return on investment; and, in addition, it can indicate the resultant increase or decrease in ordering and make-ready (setup) costs. Management can still increase or reduce inventories at will by varying the return required on the investment, but with assurance that the adjustment has been made at the lowest possible total cost.

THE MATERIALS MANAGER'S RESPONSIBILITY

After these two major parameters have been established—that is, the policies governing customer service and the desired return on inventory investments—the materials manager takes responsibility for designing, installing, and operating an inventory and production control system or network.

The basic purpose of the system is to develop manufacturing plans and a flow of materials that will conform to the stated policies, using inventories properly to minimize operating costs. The complexity of this system depends on the product mix, the conversion process and cycle, and the method of distribution. The simplest combination is a few products made in a single plant by a continuous process—as in a chemical plant or a newsprint mill—and distributed directly from the factory; the most complicated combination is a variety of complex assemblies produced from components purchased and manufactured through multi-operation processes, involving several plants, and distributed both directly and from warehouses or branches. Manning depends to a large extent on the degree of complexity involved.

The three basic elements of the inventory and production control system are (1) *demand*—that is, forecasts, orders, and usage; (2) *time*—that is, time to create materials lists, time to plan, the ordering cycle, purchase lead time, production cycle, setup time, waiting time, transportation time, and so on; (3) *cost*—that is, materials costs, setup costs, per-piece costs, inventory-carrying costs, and the like. The system must, as rapidly as possible, take the detailed breakdown of the product as supplied by engineering and provide an economical plan for ordering and controlling the completion and delivery of all the items to meet the sales demand. Although the complexity of the various activities required to do this varies, the materials management function in most companies breaks down into these subfunctions:

- Production planning: to develop the overall plan for response to the demand for finished product.
- Requirements planning: to explode this demand into its components and provide basic data to take ordering action.
- Stock records: to maintain stock and order balances.
- Ordering: to recognize the need for, and initiate, order action and due dates.
- Purchasing: to respond to order action on purchased items.
- Scheduling: to display demand and due date to production processes and develop detailed schedules for time sequencing.
- Dispatching and expediting: to put schedules into effect and take corrective action where shortages develop.
- Materials handling: to receive, move, and put away material.
- Shipping and distribution: to pick, pack, and ship the finished product to the customer.

The materials manager himself is generally responsible for the overall system, the basic inventory policy, and production planning. In complex situations he will need a staff for assistance in systems design, analysis, procedure writing, and the installation of input controls, records, logic, control reports, and procedural disciplines. Installation may require a large temporary group, and even a large permanent group may be needed if the system calls for maintenance, analysis, and audit by analysts capable of understanding the logic of cause-and-effect relationships and materials flow.

Thus the number of personnel assigned to the materials management function will vary from one (where the work is performed entirely by the manager) to many, depending on the type and size of the company. In complex operations it is not unusual to have a staff and supervisor for each subfunction.

The Principal Subfunctions Described

Most materials managers, even if directing the work of a large number of people, reserve the basic overall planning function for themselves. This function is necessarily a high-level one; and, if the information and control system is well designed, it is the point at which management decision and control should be placed. The subfunctions, as described below, carry out the various activities which are required to put the overall materials management plan into effect.

1. PRODUCTION PLANNING

The production planning subfunction represents the basic overall control of the materials management system, since it controls the usage or demand input. It constructs a master manufacturing plan by which the company operates, before drawing up requirements for components, purchased parts, raw materials, and so on. This plan establishes the manpower and facilities needs for the future and makes sure that near-term plans are compatible with existing capabilities.

Forecast planning. In an industry with relatively few products, the major portion of the planning function is involved in forecasting finished product demand. This requires much study of past demand patterns for each product, including the variation of actual from anticipated usage, to establish a firm base. Poor forecasts can be caused by incorrect assumptions about the present level and direction of product volume. Sales personnel generally are concerned with predicting change, but even accurate predictions can nonetheless produce the wrong quantity if applied to an incorrect base. Since the materials management function has the readiest access to the pertinent historical data, it logically retains the responsibility for furnishing updated information, on the basis of actual usage (shipments, issues, or sales), for each period. Any variations must be analyzed to predict seasonal fluctuations and to determine safety allowances which will cover unpredictable variations.

In the more complex situation of multiproduct operations, forecasts are generally made for broader product categories with only limited separation into specific finished product classifications that must take into account models, types, grades, colors, options, and so on. In this case the analysis of past usage for determining new forecasts requires combining the usage figures for many finished items into each forecast category (an obvious area for EDP assistance).

Developing the desired forecasts for future months, quarters, or, in some instances, years is generally the responsibility of the sales department. However, once these forecasts have been made, they are generally turned over to production planning in order that requirements for meeting them may be developed along with production controls related to actual as well as forecast usage.

Forecast control. Because forecasts can never be completely accurate, methods must be devised to assure quick action in the event of significant deviations. If the business carries finished inventories, then the forecast control function must evaluate usage deviations in relation to the existing inventory levels in order to determine when and how fast to react. Separating usage fluctuations from true changes in demand is a tricky business even for the best statistician; however, recognizing where stocks are sufficient (or insufficient) to defer action safely until the next period will minimize unnecessary changes in production plans due to random sales variation (called "hunting" in control theory). The planning staff should be responsible for establishing safety-stock levels for finished inventories, allowing only the necessary coverage of random sales variation and the lag in responding to longer-term trends. These safety stocks, as well as maximum finished inventory limits, should be an integral part of the forecast control system.

When the forecast is made for a business that does not stock finished products but does permit raw materials, parts, and components to be stocked, control takes the form of comparing sales orders with the forecast for the purpose of recognizing any variance that would affect the ordering and scheduling of parts made. It is the responsibility of production planning to decide what action to take when forecast quantities are under- or overabsorbed in any period. If this review indicates that delivery requests cannot be met, liaison with the sales department must be maintained to develop alternate plans that are acceptable. Coordination with the stock records and ordering sections also must be maintained. The fact that some material may have already been committed as a result of the forecast and the effect a change will have on orders and work in process must be considered when deciding whether to cancel, defer, or bring in open orders.

Made-to-order planning and the master schedule. For products made to order and not to meet forecast requirements, the planning function develops only a master schedule. In such cases, the orders are scheduled to satisfy the requested delivery dates, taking into consideration the longest-lead items and the cycle for assembly or finishing (if the process goes through several stages or levels of completion). At this point, coordination with the sales, purchasing, and ordering departments is necessary to resolve conflicts where delivery has been requested in less than the normal lead time.

The master schedule is generally the only step necessary for made-to-order operations, as opposed to make-to-inventory operations which require a forecast as well. Companies operating to inventory must freeze the forecast at some point. The master schedule to which it is then converted deals only with the finished product and generally is detailed to define options, colors, grades, and so on. It is a firm commitment to additional costs of labor and materials that becomes increasingly expensive to change. The master schedule, which usually requires top-level review and approval, is the standard for reporting performance on backlog and shipments to higher management. The production planning function, therefore, should work closely with sales, manufacturing, and general management both in the initial stages of development and in the analysis of after-the-fact performance information.

Facilities planning. Forecasts must be broken down and rearranged to reflect machine hours, man-hours, percentage of process capacity, and other general indicators which measure gross load and available capacity. Some leveling of production is usually practiced, either by loading made-to-order items to short-term normal capacity and deferring the delivery of those items that can best be delayed or by planning to build inventory in periods of low sales demand for known seasonal fluctuations and for anticipated increases. Owing to customer options, however, this may not be feasible for final assembly or finishing department operations.

The gross impact of the production plan on manufacturing and on purchasing is reflected in long-term planning. Coordination with manufacturing and financial management is critical. The materials manager must be sure that these functions will actually respond to any projection for increased or decreased activity. Inability to respond in either area must be fed back so that the plans may be adjusted accordingly, again with top management's approval and support. Too often planning has projected a need for an increase in manning and taken the indicated steps without any commitment or action on the part of operating management.

2. REQUIREMENTS PLANNING

After the overall end-product forecasts and schedules have been developed, they must be broken down into detailed requirements for raw materials, purchased and manufactured parts, and components. This function frequently reports to the production planner, and without EDP equipment it often requires a considerable staff in the case of complex product lines such as television and machine tools.

The input to the requirements planning function consists of the forecast and master schedule and any adjustments controlled by production planning. From the demand thus established, requirements planning must obtain or work up an engineering bill of material, materials list, or set of specifications. This is the point at which engineering coordination is required. In many companies detailed product definition delays the receipt of an order or sales forecast (for a new model military hardware of advanced design, custom equipment, and so on). It is necessary for requirements planning to make sure that long-lead items are designed and defined before short-lead items and that component design, procurement, and manufacture are compatible with the due date for the finished product. Furthermore, partial releases to cover long-lead items must be recorded and capable of review when the final full design is developed.

After the make-up of the product has been defined (including part-number identification for ease of record keeping and control), the "make or buy" decision must be reached. Although this decision is not usually a materials management responsibility, requirements planning cannot move ahead until it is made. Engineering, purchasing, and manufacturing engineering are generally involved at this stage. It is often possible for requirements planning to submit information on currently active components that can be substituted to save inventory and cost related to producing or purchasing essentially similar items.

Once the bills of material have been coded either "manufacture" or "purchase," the quantity forecast or ordered is exploded into all its components. There are two basic approaches for stocked items: to explode the actual requirements or to rely on established reorder points. Modern systems generally use both approaches but vary between the extremes of replenishing all items or only the least expensive "C" items (nuts, bolts, low-cost supplies) at their reorder points. Or they rely on EDP systems which control every item on the basis of exploded requirements that are continually updated to reflect sales and schedule changes.

In addition to extending demand by "units per" and consolidating the usage of finished products as well as spare parts, the planning function must consider other basic information. The figures for "used on," lead time, materials, labor, and setup costs are necessary to the operation of an effective planning system. The basic decision must be made as to how much safety stock should be carried, and simple methods of computing the allowances must be developed. Safety stocks must take into account the amounts already being carried for protection in finished product stocks and must be coordinated with overall planning. In addition, reorder points, where used extensively, must be capable of ready increase or decrease as forecasts change.

Requirements planning provides the basic data and the "used on" relationships needed by the ordering section. In fact, this close coordination of requirements planning with ordering often results in a combination of the two functions. Requirements planning also affects scheduling where complex bills-of-material explosions must offset due dates by time constants as they go back through several levels of assembly to machined or purchased items. Modern systems recognize the "date due" of the original input and set back the requirement dates for all components, depending on the individual lead times for each step of the process. Therefore, "time-phased" requirements can explode both quantity and time to recognize not only the amounts but also the schedule dates that are compatible with the promised delivery date.

Engineering change control must tie in closely with this function to be sure that bills of material or specifications are accurately maintained. The major objective of requirements planning is to provide accurate usage information for time-phased schedules and for reservations and reorder points. In addition, it must supply basic information required by ordering, scheduling, and control. Requirements planning can be most complex in terms of its role in the total materials management system as well as its relationships with other functions.

3. STOCK RECORDS

Effective inventory management requires the integrated control of all elements of the materials management function, so that control of inventory is, in the end, a responsibility of the materials manager himself.

One important element, of course, is maintaining accurate balances of items in stock at all locations. Depending on the stocking points and the equipment used—pencil and paper, posting machines, or fully operable EDP programs—the number of personnel assigned to this activity can vary greatly. The primary needs are for accuracy, timeliness, and proper sequencing of transactions. The standard receipts and issues are often complicated by requirements posting, updating of reorder points, verification of on-hand balances, and maintenance of additional on-order quantities, unreserved and reserved balances, and so forth. Proper entry (or coding, if by EDP) of transactions is dependent on good paperwork discipline and analysis and the correction of causes of error.

This stock record function is one that is seldom handled as well as it should or could be. The stock record card (or data file), it should be recognized, is actually a control record. All stock activity must be recorded; the balances thus arrived at provide the basis for financial accounting of the costs of inventory as well as the materials control function. Too many companies still maintain duplicate inventory records instead of properly controlling one set of records. And mistakes also contribute to production shortages and affect sales service. A "Marine sergeant" approach is almost essential to supervising this function. EDP can reduce the posting errors, but proper sequencing, coding, and procedures to insure complete and accurate input for all transactions are still essential.

4. ORDERING

Traditionally, a manufacturing or purchase order is triggered by comparing stock-record balances to usage or requirements as transactions affect these figures. If EDP systems have been installed, much of this activity has been, or can be, automated. When balances drop to the reorder point, the system either generates an order signal or orders an established quantity and designates the transaction for review. Frequently, it releases a printed requisition from stock records. The manning requirements for stock records and requisitioning shrink in proportion to the amount of automated routine, and the function becomes more a matter of analysis and review.

Requirements planning, stock records, and ordering must be very closely coordinated. Requirements planning establishes the basic demand information, safety-stock rules, reorder-point equations, setup and run costs, and other necessary data and policies for computing when and how much to order. Stock records maintain the physical and other balances, against which the ordering rules operate. Indeed, requirements planning, stock records, and ordering are often combined. This makes a logical grouping, particularly for small companies.

The ordering function must also coordinate its activities with purchasing, marketing, and engineering. Open-order arrangements with vendors, price breaks, off-peak delivery possibilities, and expected yearly usage may be vital factors in purchasing that require order-department inputs.

In order to limit the number of short runs on high-cost setups, direct communication with marketing is often necessary. Significant economies may be achieved by increasing order quantities when past demand or present requirements do not add up to an economical quantity. By referring to the "where used" index and by constantly reviewing the accuracy of the forecasts for end products which use the component in question, the materials manager may raise the order quantities. Conversely, he should elicit marketing and engineering inputs before releasing large-quantity parts orders for products that may become obsolete in the market or for parts that may become obsolete because of changes in design.

By and large, the ordering function must recognize that automatic order quantities are not static. Only continuous analysis and review will insure that nonroutine factors such as price breaks, the phasing out of designs, special obsolescence risks (for example, style factors), unusual physical storage problems, and erratic demand do not require modification of the indicated quantity, particularly for the expensive, high-usage items.

The ordering function usually includes writing production or work orders, controlling the necessary paperwork (prints, specifications, routing documents), entering the due date, and computing the start date by subtracting the lead time from the due date. It therefore controls the input to the scheduling function and is frequently responsible for the release of orders to the production function. In addition, all changes in dates and quantities involving an open order are controlled by ordering. Holding the orders until the start date makes any consolidation, cancellation, and change far easier to control.

5. PURCHASING

The inclusion of purchasing in the materials management function is a controversial issue. Traditionally, and especially when purchases represent a major portion of product cost, it is viewed as a separate and independent function. There is merit in this view if purchasing is buying basic commodities such as rubber for tires, wool or cotton for textiles, pulp for paper, or paper for certain converting operations. In these instances the situation requires skill in a trading capacity that is usually found only at a very high level of staffing. However, in the operations calling for a large number of diverse materials and components, purchasing is as integral a part of the logistics system as production. The response to demand in terms of quantity and due date for each item, whether made or bought, should be generated and controlled within materials management. To avoid split and conflicting responsibilities for inventories, planning, and scheduling, the materials manager must at least have the authority to plan, schedule, and control the movement of all purchased items related to the product.

The buying activities of the purchasing function include selecting vendors, establishing materials prices, drawing up contracts, developing blanket orders where justified, obtaining such services as technical assistance and transportation, and, at times, making arrangements to carry stocks in the vendors' plants. These activities require trained employees and specialized skills that are unique within the materials management function. It is possible, of course, to consider buying as an independent function and have it report elsewhere, but no matter where the function ultimately reports, it obviously must respond to directions from ordering.

Value analysis and other cost reduction projects require the participation of purchasing along with product and process engineering. Make or buy decisions, however, are administered through the requirements planning function.

6. SCHEDULING

If requirements planning is the step that breaks down the gross demand of the master manufacturing plan into detailed component-quantity requirements, scheduling is the step that breaks the gross load down into detailed schedules for processing the components.

Scheduling receives production orders from ordering with a due date which is dictated by the master schedule for the end product. It must then consider the departments and work centers, or the machines through which the parts must be processed, and schedule step-by-step processing dates for each order so as to assure completion on time. To produce such schedules, the group must know what routings and production rates have been established by manufacturing or industrial engineering. Elapsed time, by operation, is developed by adding allowances for materials movement, machine repairs, waiting times (queues), backlogs, performance, and setup or make-ready. In fact, the overall lead times which are used in establishing reorder points must consider these same factors. Scheduling apportions this lead time to each step in the process. In addition, the scheduling activity must compare scheduled loads with available capacity and feed conflicts back to production planning for resolution.

Effective scheduling can require a complex system within the materials management function. A substantial clerical force may be needed to develop date-oriented schedules and to exploit maximum production capacity in a multi-operation production process unless routings and processing times are made available by EDP. Likewise, the procedures needed to recognize changes in usage or in the master product schedules and make the proper adjustments may require substantial manpower unless an integrated data processing system has been developed.

The scheduling function may or may not include the actual dispatching of factory orders to work centers; they may have been forwarded by ordering. In this event, scheduling will release summary lists of orders and workloads for current and near-future periods.

7. DISPATCHING AND EXPEDITING

If the materials management system has been well conceived and the preceding functions properly staffed and performed, the dispatching and expediting staff should be a small one, its size being primarily dependent on the number of control stations (for example, work centers, machine groups, departments) involved. A large expediting staff is symptomatic of a lack of sound planning, loading, and scheduling. Poor design and performance mean that customer or assembly requirements and shop balance needs must be filled by locating production orders and coaxing them along by special effort. Particularly disruptive are the so-called project expediters—individuals assigned to "chase in" certain orders for a specific customer. This type of expediting usually produces conflicting demands on equipment from more than one expediter. The control of priorities at this low level is a result of the failure properly to recognize and resolve conflicts in the initial planning and scheduling stage. Not only are the results costly, but customer service always suffers.

Even with excellent materials management a need for orderly dispatching of work will always exist where several jobs wait in queues before the various processing steps. The dispatching function assures that schedules and priorities are taken into account and that jobs are ready to run when assigned—that is, tooling, paperwork, material, and so on are available when needed. This function is materials management's closest point of contact with manufacturing and, in fact, can be performed by either production supervisors or timekeepers if printed schedules are available. Dispatching may take place only in the initial release of a job. Generally, it is desirable wherever a reduction in down time can be achieved and opportunities for assignment to alternate equipment exist within a control center. On assembly operations, particularly those with subassembly feeder lines, dispatching can maintain stock banks, prepare for changeovers, and maintain materials flow to minimize lost time.

The major job of expediting in a well-designed system is to find and take the most effective action on critical jobs which cannot be allowed to run through the normal procedures without a shortage or a missed delivery. Modern EDP systems locate and indicate the critical job so that expediting merely responds by whatever methods are practical. In less effective systems expediting must often locate jobs affected by a change in demand and flag them for dispatching. Because of breakdowns, quality problems, absenteeism, and other unpredictable work stoppages, some expediting will always be necessary. However, with EDP systems that are capable of rapidly exploding changes in usage or requirements and are tracking the progress of all orders in process, expediting can concentrate on methods of response rather than on finding and flagging. Dispatching can, in short, absorb the expediting activity as realistic schedules and effective controls are achieved.

8. MATERIALS HANDLING

Materials handling is primarily a matter of receiving, moving, and putting away purchased and manufactured items; it is a simple activity in concept and application. Manning is dictated by the quantity of stocked items, the volume of sales, and the number of stocking locations. Unfortunately, materials handling is an almost neglected area of materials management whenever product identification and counts are in question. The primary input to the stock-records function is a vital link in the system. If receiving tickets, receipts, issues, or move tickets are not accurate and each transaction is not recorded, the stock-record card cannot be effective as a basic control document. Coordination with stock records must, therefore, be close, and rigid discipline is required. For this reason many companies combine the materials handling and stock-record functions.

9. SHIPPING AND DISTRIBUTION

Substantial opportunities for better service and lower costs are often uncovered by a thorough analysis of warehousing, stocking, and transportation costs for optional arrangements of stocking points and various means of transportation. Shipping and the related tasks of picking and packing may be relatively insignificant in the materials management system, or they may be quite substantial, particularly as the operation approaches a retail type of service—that is, it is characterized by large stocks of a wide variety of items and fast delivery. It is similar, in many ways, to the internal materials handling function: procedures must be disciplined firmly, shipping papers—including the inputs to the system that close out the demand cycle—must be properly handled.

Modern systems often develop shipping schedules from the scheduling function that differ, of course, from the production schedules. This additional scheduling effort is recommended when usage can vary during the final assembly process to an extent that warrants revising priorities on the basis of more recent stock-status or customer-requirement inputs. In this case shipping coordinates closely with scheduling through formal picking or shipping schedules.

Distribution frequently requires specialized skills to recognize opportunities to pool, drop ship, fill large stock demands by direct distribution from the plant, or use any of a multitude of alternate carriers and routings. If the basic materials management system maintains weight information as well as quantity and delivery data, the distribution function can be materially aided in providing carrier service to meet schedules at lowest cost. Also, coding of demand input can be used periodically to analyze distribution patterns if past sales are summarized by shipping distributions or zones. The value of this kind of coordination is only now beginning to be recognized, and companies with a substantial distribution setup and transportation cost often can control cost and improve service by attention to these relationships.

The materials management function demands a broad understanding of the methods of keeping a process or operation supplied, maintaining schedules to meet delivery policies, and developing a system for information and controls and an organization to do so. The opportunities to reduce direct and indirect costs and still operate with lower inventory investments are, in many cases, considerable. In addition, the edge that can be gained by taking time out of the total process and improving delivery estimates can be a tremendous competitive advantage.

Manufacturing management should certainly give this basic planning and control area a substantial amount of consideration and support. In the past the function has too often become the whipping post for failure to coordinate sales and production. Materials management can provide only the plans and information; sales and production must agree to the final due dates; and production must take responsibility for performance. If the materials management function is accepted as an integrative and planning one, it can provide a basis for efficient manufacturing, but to hold it responsible for missing delivery may well represent an incorrect identification of the basic cause. The manufacturing manager must be confident that materials management is developing realistic and best-possible schedules and overall plans. Then he can use the function as a developer of objectives against which the production function must be measured. Without this confidence, the alternative is a continual hint as to "who killed Cock Robin" while the customer waits impatiently for delivery.

HARD-NOSED INVENTORY MANAGEMENT

By DONALD G. HALL

Most of us, whether as members of a business organization or as stockholders of some corporation, have a direct interest in free enterprise. Even those of us who work for the government have an implied interest in least-cost operations, as is evidenced by budgetary control. Free enterprise is built on the premise of *profit*. We may simplify this and say profit means that after the expenses of heat, light, rent, materials, and adequate compensation for labor and management have been deducted from income, something should be left over for the owners or stockholders, the people who have risked their savings to provide the equipment and working capital that make the organization active. If there is no return to the investors, there will be no capital reinvested in the business. In today's fast-moving, technologically advanced, competitive marketplace, lack of reinvestment means certain death.

Let's further agree that profits are made only at the time of final sale to the customers—whether the sale be one of goods or service. All the work or value added to the raw materials purchased or mined contributes nothing to profit until the goods or service is turned into cash by a customer's purchase. No matter how efficient the manufacturing process is, how clever the research department is in designing exotic products or processes, a profit accrues only if we make our final transfer to a customer for a sum greater than our expenses.

Not every sale will be profitable, but the weighted average of all transactions must be profitable or the life of the organization will be limited. Inventory management in its broadest definition is concerned with materials planning, production scheduling, and distribution. Those involved in these functions have a unique opportunity to influence service to customers on the one hand and costs (and, therefore, profits) on the other.

These are opposing forces: service versus cost. When we increase the one,

DONALD G. HALL is Director of Inventory Control and Production Planning for Chas. Pfizer & Co., in New York City.

we decrease the other. Finding the proper balance between service and cost, selling the organization on the desirability of that balance, and operating at the chosen level contribute substantially to the success of the business enterprise.

THE IMPORTANCE OF ANALYZING FINISHED-GOODS INVENTORIES

Exhibit 1 shows a typical evaluation of the distribution of inventories in four different types of industries. The capital goods and the defense industries, as we see, carry little or no finished inventories. If a company manufactures standard items for stock, industrial, or consumer-type goods, however, its emphasis on finished goods inventory control should be proportionally greater. If our company has a large dollar investment in finished goods inventory, that should spur great control effort on the part of management; if the investment is minor, a minimal effort is called for. What is important is to attack the area with the greatest dollar concentration—drill where the oil is!

Let us find out which items contribute most heavily to a sizable finished goods inventory by making an *ABC* (Always Better Control) analysis. This technique was developed and popularized by H. Ford Dickie of General Elec-

EXHIBIT 1

INVENTORY DISTRIBUTION IN FOUR INDUSTRIES

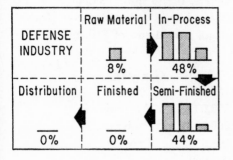
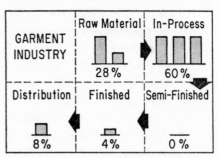
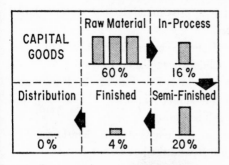
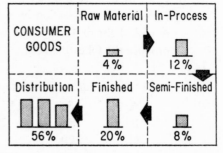

tric Company in the 1940's. The analysis is simply a ranking mechanism whereby our attention can be focused on the important contributors to the phenomenon we are interested in studying, in this case product inventory levels. Since we are interested in inventory investment and inventories are evaluated at cost—whether actual, standard, or manufacturing—the unit cost of each item will serve as the basis of our analysis.

The procedure is as follows:

1. Obtain the number of units sold or used in the latest 12-month period. It is presumed that the quantities will approximate those to be sold or used in the future; if they do not, obtain the best forecast available. The reason for using historical data is that they are usually available in summarized form and are accurate enough for this purpose.
2. Obtain the unit-cost standard for each item in Step 1. This may be standard cost, actual cost, direct cost, manufacturing cost, or whatever, depending on the individual company. It should be the same cost used to evaluate the inventory investment.
3. Multiply the annual number of units times the unit cost to obtain the annual cost of goods sold or annual through-put.
4. Arrange the items in list form in the order of descending value: the largest annual cost of goods, first; the next largest, second; and so on down to the smallest.
5. Arbitrarily divide the list into ten approximately equal sections based on the number of items per section.
6. Plot the accumulative number of items versus the accumulative cost of goods from the list, using the sections established in Step 5 to obtain ten points. Draw the curve. It will look like Exhibit 2. Percentages are shown on both scales here, but similar patterns will be observed where direct units and dollars of value are used.
7. Arbitrarily choose flexure points in the curve drawn. Mark the first segment of the curve *A*; the second, *B*; and the last *C*.
8. Find, in the list produced in Step 4, the separate sections *A*, *B*, and *C*. Subtotal each section by number of items and annual cost of goods. A typical list of 1,000 items with an annual cost of $10 million might produce the following table:

Class	Items	Cost of Goods	Inventory Management Attitude
A	80	$7,500,000	Aggressive
B	250	2,000,000	Active
C	670	500,000	Loose
Total	1,000	$10,000,000	

EXHIBIT 2

PLOTTED CURVE OF THE ABC ANALYSIS

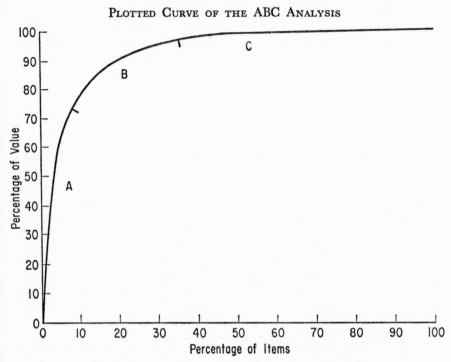

We are at once struck with the fact that 8 percent of the items are responsible for 75 percent of the annual dollar through-put or sales. An additional 25 percent of our line items contribute 20 percent of the dollar through-put. There is, in other words, 95 percent dollar concentration in 33 percent of our product line. We can now drill where the black gold is. Let's aggressively manage—by forecasting, follow-up, process improvement, lead-time control, materials handling, scheduling, and so on—the *A* products that are few in number but important in total dollars. Let's do an active job on the *B* items; but, in order to give ourselves working room in our production shops and time to concentrate our efforts on *A* and *B* items, we shall have to manage the *C* items loosely. In other words, we give each category the attention it deserves!

Making an *ABC* analysis is easy. In fact, its principles are so simple that we will want to make a similar analysis, *XYZ,* on the basis of gross profit contribution (sales minus cost of goods sold multiplied by the number of units sold) and ask the sales department or general management whether it chooses to eliminate some of the low contributors or noncontributors to profit. Each line item requires a certain amount of attention in purchasing, manufacturing, selling, accounting, and so on. Why not eliminate the outright losers and concentrate on those items that contribute the most to profit?

This process of analysis or ranking can readily be handled by clerks. Where large volumes of items are involved, computers may be employed with relatively simple programing to produce the basic listing shown in Exhibit 3. Large

EXHIBIT 3

ABC ANALYSIS OF FINISHED-GOODS INVENTORY

Item No.	Item (Card) Count	Annual Units	Unit Cost	Annual C/G	Cumulative C/G	Percentage
T 7061	1	209600	5.5187	1,156,740	1,156,740	11.56
S 6832	2	32435	35.3082	1,145,220	2,301,960	23.01
S 7036	3	208850	.6605	137,960	2,439,920	24.39
G 9655	4	206610	.6579	135,920	2,575,840	25.75
T 3320	5	439700	.2959	130,111	2,705,951	27.05
K 8946	6	418000	.3102	129,652	2,835,603	28.35
K 5322	7	27950	45.7746	127,940	2,963,543	29.63
K 2026	8	6761	18.8820	127,661	3,091,204	30.91
16267	9	15746	8.0962	127,482	3,218,686	32.18
H 1981	10	44216	2.8522	126,115	3,344,801	33.44
G 9282	11	328930	.3795	124,825	3,469,626	34.69
N 8565	364	25000	.2192	5,480	8,251,625	82.51
G 9034	365	2766	1.9794	5,475	8,257,100	82.57
G 9102	366	2500	2.1900	5,475	8,262,575	82.62
S 5678	367	38952	.1402	5,461	8,268,036	82.68
H 9339	368	59950	.0906	5,434	8,273,470	82.73
G 9109	369	18525	.2933	5,433	8,278,903	82.78
26200	370	30900	.1758	5,431	8,284,334	82.84
S 5251	371	409	13.2323	5,412	8,289,746	82.89
M 7686	372	11978	.4517	5,410	8,295,156	82.95
S 5634	991	55	.8727	48	9,999,771	99.99
S 5799	992	51	.8431	43	9,999,814	99.99
S 6121	993	71	.6056	43	9,999,857	99.99
K 2018	994	37	.8649	32	9,999,889	99.99
P 9986	995	4	7.5000	30	9,999,914	99.99
M 6621	996	25	1.2000	30	9,999,949	99.99
G 2374	997	1	20.0000	20	9,999,969	99.99
N 3501	998	135	.1333	18	9,999,987	99.99
M 2643	999	10	1.0000	10	9,999,997	99.99
S 7822	1000	1	3.0000	3	10,000,000	100.00

lists can be handled expeditiously on tab cards with simple multiplying and sorting equipment. Even with 3×5 cards, plus a pencil, a hand calculator, hand sorting, and the like, this task is not enormous. Since it is usually done annually and the payoff is so great, the results of any effort can be very rewarding.

Obviously the payoff is not in making the analysis. It is in what we do in focusing our managerial effort on the few really important items. To maximize effort on the few big payoff items, it may be necessary to relax controls on the large number of items of small dollar importance.

ECONOMIC ORDER QUANTITIES AND ORDER POINTS

There is no magic way to manage inventories; it must be done item by item, location by location. Each individual inventory decision we make about timing or quantity has its effect on profits. Too much, too early, and we get an overstock; too little, too late, and we lose sales or add to our overtime or expediting expenses.

Control of inventories is exercised only at the time of input. The inventory control manager usually has no influence over the outflow rates of any item; indeed, he does not want to deprive the sales department of material to sell since profits are *not* made at the time of manufacture or acquisition—they are made when an item is sold. The "guts" of inventory management can be summed up in the answers to the two acquisition questions:

1. *How much* input do we make?
2. *When* do we make our input?

A useful tool in inventory management is the economic order quantity formula. It is as valid as Newton's law of gravity. Whether we understand it or not, it is operative in every quantity decision we make. We learn to use it advantageously by knowing our position on the total cost curve. Q in Exhibit 4 is the economic order quantity (EOQ), the optimum quantity to order.

A dissertation on EOQ, including derivation of the Camp formula:

$$Q = \sqrt{\frac{2YS}{IC}}$$ in which Y = annual requirements in units
S = set-up cost in dollars
I = inventory carrying cost as a decimal fraction of value
C = unit cost of dollars

can be found in any standard book on inventory management. However, EOQ,

EXHIBIT 4

ECONOMIC ORDER QUANTITY

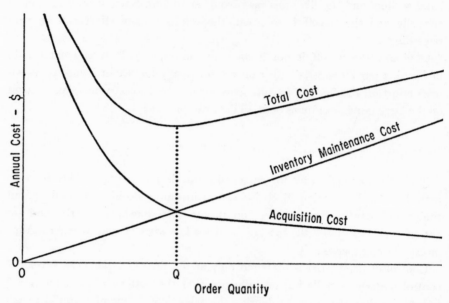

despite its usefulness, is not a universally used tool of inventory management. Yet it should be helpful in reaching purchasing, manufacturing lot size, and distribution quantity transfer decisions. The exact same formula is used in all cases; the values of the variables put into each of these calculations have quite different parameters; nevertheless, if accurate figures are given, proper answers result. The input must be valid for the time period of the resulting answer. To determine how long the economic supply will last, we simply divide Q by Y. Or, if the time period exceeds one year, we may wish to question whether proper allowance has been made for obsolescence in the cost of carrying inventory, I.

The second question—"*When* do we make our input?"—is more difficult to answer. We need to place our order for additional supplies at that point in time when our stock level will support the current rate of sale only until delivery. To state the problem simply: If we know it will take four weeks for delivery and 10 units are sold each week, we should order when the inventory level reaches 40 units.

Unfortunately, it is not that simple, because delivery does not always take four weeks; sometimes it takes two, five, three, seven, or six weeks. When the time needed for delivery is longer than our selected lead time, we run out of stock and back-order; when it is shorter, we can be overstocked with quantities we don't really need.

Some variation will probably be found in the demand pattern too. When the average usage or sale is 10 units per week, for instance, the range may well be from 2 to 25 units per week. Our inability to forecast precisely the lead time, L, or the rate of sale, E, gives rise to over- or understock. If we want to maintain continuity of supply for immediate service to our customers, as we do in most consumer goods industries, then we must add some safety stock, as illustrated in Exhibit 5.

The amount of safety stock (SS) required will vary with the length and variability of the lead time, the rate and variability of the demand, and the degree of service we wish to give our customers. Books have been written on various approaches to spotting the proper order point. The most practical solution appears to be to determine the average inventory required by three different levels of customer service and pick the one we are willing to pay for or settle for on each product. We must add up the results and see whether the company has enough money, warehouses, manpower, and so on, to service this amount of inventory. Usually this calls for some compromise between money invested and customer service. Of course, we want to give the best service on the larger-profit-margined items discovered by our XYZ analysis.

SETTLING THE CONFLICT[1]

Ideally, the conflict between service and investment is resolved on the basis of least cost, which means balancing the cost of back orders and the cost of stocking one more unit. The minimum point is reached when one unit more or one unit less in stock raises the total cost. Evaluating the total dollar cost of a back order is most impractical because customer satisfaction, lost business, expediting costs, and the like are impossible to evaluate with reasonable accuracy. Other methods must consequently be found to determine the desirable order point.

The most precise solutions require some degree of facility with statistics. And, statistically speaking, products with "normal" or Poisson distribution of demand patterns over lead time periods usually can be made to respond well to standard techniques. When the inventory manager is dealing with a large number of products in many locations, he needs a computer. Exponential smoothing is helpful where normal distribution of demand patterns exists. A and B products (about 30 percent of the total line) usually are well approximated by normal distribution patterns; *C* products usually are not. Special routines and careful scrutiny are suggested in *C* products management. Unless the manager has a computer and sufficient data to work with, empirical approaches utilizing simple formulas are recommended. At least they can be applied consistently and inexpensively by clerks and adjusted in the proper direction item by item, location by location, when results over a two- to six-month period indicate too large an inventory investment or too many back orders. To this end the empirical approach in the formula shown in Exhibit 5 is quite useful.

In Exhibit 5 the order point, *OP,* is made up of two segments:

1. The quantity, *EL*—to cover the normal or average weekly demand (*E*), multiplied by the lead time (*L*) in weeks, and
2. The safety stock, *SS*—enough additional material to cover all eventualities of increase in demand (ΔE) or increase in lead time (ΔL):

EXHIBIT 5

INVENTORY GRAPH

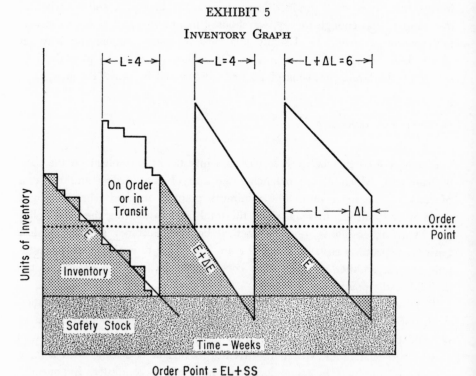

$$\text{Order Point} = EL + SS$$
$$OP = EL + \Delta EL + E\Delta L + \Delta E\Delta L$$
$$\text{Set } \Delta L = 0; \quad \text{Then } OP = EL + \Delta EL$$
$$OP = L(E + \Delta E)$$

    a. Increase in demand, normal lead time, ΔEL.

    b. Normal demand, increased lead time, $E\Delta L$.

    c. Increase in demand, increased lead time, $\Delta E\Delta L$.

If we find the record of deliveries for the past ten cycles to be 3–2–4–6–3–9–2–4–5–3 weeks, we should be willing to protect this product for a lead time up to six weeks. The one showing of nine weeks looks like a wild chance situation caused by strikes or rejections or other infrequent circumstances beyond our control. Against this we are not willing to protect ourselves; instead, we are willing to back order if and when it does happen again. Whereupon we set L at 6 and ΔL becomes zero. If we substitute ΔL for zero in our equation and multiply through, all factors containing L drop out since any quantity multiplied by zero equals zero. This leaves $OP = L(E + \Delta E)$.

The weekly demand pattern can be examined from historical records. Giving influence to seasonal factors where applicable, take the long-term average (E), with the deviation expected (ΔE) in the forward period, and multiply to get the order point. Of course, we will always order the economic order quantity Q. This procedure is classified as the "fixed quantity/variable period" system. It is inherently superior to the "variable quantity/fixed period" system because of —

1. *Timing.* Reorders are placed at the time of posting the triggering transaction.
2. *Economic orders.* The least-total-cost method of acquisition gives weight to resulting inventory versus acquisition cost.
3. *Labor.* There is an even clerical workload throughout the month.

"Variable quantity/fixed period" systems suffer by comparison with respect to these three advantages. Before such a system is adopted, its fundamentals should be seriously reviewed.

The simple "two bin" or "reserve bin" system with a combination traveling requisition and bin card complies with all the most rigid fundamentals of inventory management and does not require individual withdrawal posting. In a well-disciplined organization such a system is the most sophisticated type of operation short of a real-time computer. Isn't keeping all these records—whether by hand, tab cards, or computer—necessary only to offset lack of control? Otherwise, why not use the simple two-bin system? If we are not making a preshipment allocation days or weeks in advance of actual withdrawal from stock, we keep records only to offset our lack of supervisory control. The best system is the simplest, the one which affords the fastest reaction time. Obviously, to be sure, we need some form of records from which to make the decisions about inventory management. Computerized systems may be the answer, hand-posted records may be adequate, or even the simple two-bin system with traveling requisition and bin card may be all we need.

The test of any system is the timeliness and accuracy of the results it produces. How fast, how orderly, and how meaningful the basic data will be depend on organization discipline. The most brilliantly designed system cannot survive sloppy operation. It does not matter whether bad information inputs come from the accounting department, the receiving platform, the factory, or the store room; in any case the results are poor. A rigorous day-to-day control operation is absolutely essential with any system.

INVENTORY CODING AND COUNTING

It is imperative that each part, raw material, subassembly, and finished product be positively and exclusively identified by code. Resistors, for instance, range in size from a fraction of an inch to six feet and have values from a few cents to $500 each. It is impossible to control such diverse items unless each one is precisely identified, and a code number is the shortest, simplest way.

An all-numeric code with maximum significance results in long identification numbers, perhaps, but they usually classify items well by logical families. The life of a well-structured, all-numerical code is usually longer than that of a mnemonic, alphabetic, or block-coding system. Word descriptions are absolutely useless where there are a large number of items to identify. No two people arrange words in the same order even if they use the same ones. For data-processing purposes, moreover, an all-numeric code is less troublesome to enter into the machine than alphabetic and alphanumeric characters. Time spent in designing an adequate code pays off well on a long-term basis.

All records must, in additon, be checked occasionally for validity. Cyclical physical inventory counts are better than the "all at once" annual count. The cyclical counts are cheaper and more accurate; they offer better verification through rechecks, and yield reliable records all through the year, as opposed to once-a-year counting. Counting at the time of delivery minimizes the number of pieces to be counted, since on-hand stocks are at their lowest point and the incoming shipment must be checked in anyway. Such a system randomizes the counting load and cycle so that the most frequently ordered items (*A* and *B* products, usually) are verified most often.

We never rely only on counting from a list or product orientation. To be sure of what is in the warehouse and to verify or correct the book record, a periodic count of stock, by geographic stockroom location, is essential. It should be possible to take a small random statistical sample of all the items in a warehouse, count them, and compare the answers to the book record. If the concurrence is within, say, 2 percent on 95 percent of the items, no physical inventory is required. We set our own limits; and, if the results fall outside the desired range, we enlarge the sample and count again. If the results are still not satisfactory, take a total physical count. What we really want to ascertain is whether our records actually represent what, within reasonable limits (tight or loose), is in the warehouse. If the book records are not accurate and timely, how can we expect to make proper decisions from them?

CUMULATIVE CHARTING TECHNIQUE

Inventories, remember, are controlled *only* at the time of input. A decision that later proves to be wrong in timing or quantity cannot be rectified without some expense, be it in warehouse space, a forced discount sale, or complete obsolescence. It is most important, therefore, to exercise the utmost control when the input decision is made. The use of a cumulatively plotted graph to aid in making timing and quantity decisions is highly recommended, and it is not hard to conceive a closed-loop, computer-operated system such as that diagramed in Exhibit 6.

When we achieve a completely automated factory, all we will have to do is push the starting button and stand back. The system, once in motion, will monitor itself and make the appropriate correcting adjustments; it will feed on itself and go on to perpetuity. Or so we hear! But that's nonsense. If one piece of "dirty" data gets into the sales history, the machine will blow its diodes in trying to rebalance itself. If we are allowed to interfere with the completely automatic running of this system at only one place, the obvious choice will be before the production requirements are authorized. Once this step is passed, money will be committed for materials, energy (labor), machines, and the like. Any changed decision will result in some form of expense of cancellation, obsolescence, or oversupply. Only the best possible decision will do. Only a man with the latest information, knowledge, and background should approve the release of production authorizations.

A sharp tool for making this review, prior to authorization, is cumulatively plotted data on sales, sales estimates, inventory, actual production, and prior production commitments. Such a system of graphs for production requirements planning might be described as follows: A cumulative chart is kept for each finished product. (It may also be worthwhile to keep charts on major, multipurpose, high-volume intermediates, on subassemblies, and on a few important raw material items.) Exhibit 7 shows a typical chart containing all the required data. It is prepared and utilized as follows:

    1. The horizontal axis is divided into weeks and the vertical axis into units.

EXHIBIT 6

CLOSED LOOP INFORMATION AND MATERIALS FLOW

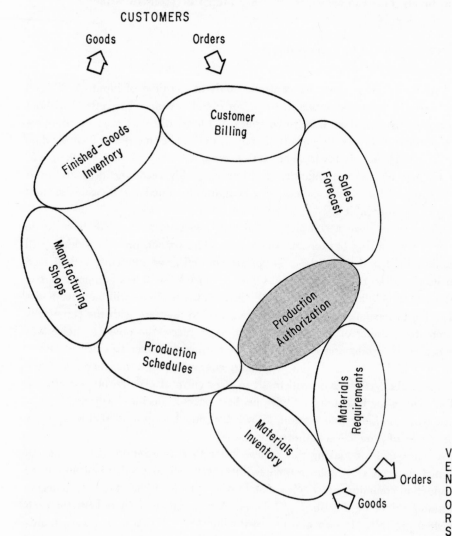

2. The double solid lines represent the opening inventory plus new production. The physical inventory quantity is entered on each chart at the beginning of the year. Each chart can be plotted on a time cycle indicative of the class of product. For instance, *A* can be items updated weekly; *B,* bi-weekly; and *C,* monthly.
3. The line of dashes represents authorized production.
4. The line of dashes separated by bullets represents actual sales, which should also be plotted as indicated on Item 2.
5. The line of bullets represents the quarterly sales forecast. It is projected as a continuation of the actual sales line each quarter, which adjusts the cumulative charts for actual performance by showing the forecast quantity as an extension of actual sales to date.
6. For intermediates, subassemblies, or raw materials the line of dashes separated by bullets represents a demand by the productive facilities. This demand is, of course, a function of the sales demand for the finished product at some future date.
7. Inventory adjustments, returns, and rejects are plotted only if they are significant.

Plotting these data on the chart provides the following important information at all times:

1. The difference between the actual sales and the actual production lines represents inventory on hand.
2. The difference between the production and the authorized production lines represents the authorized production yet to be delivered—open production orders.
3. The difference between the actual sales and the quarterly forecast lines represents the quantity by which sales deviated from forecast.
4. The difference between the production and a projection of the actual sales lines, read horizontally, represents the weeks of estimated inventory that will be on hand at any future point in time.
5. The difference between the production and the authorized production read horizontally, represents the manufacturing lead time.
6. Last year's charts should be filed under the current charts since the preceding year's pattern is a helpful tool for current planning. Seasonality, lead times, and sales rates can be readily checked.

These items of information enable production planning personnel to obtain all the pertinent information necessary for intelligent planning at a glance, without unnecessary reference to stock cards and similar documents. The need to prepare time-consuming and unwieldy production planning tables and re-

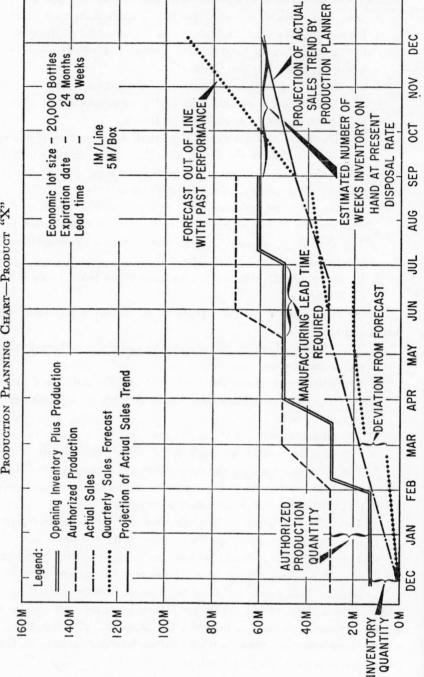

EXHIBIT 7

PRODUCTION PLANNING CHART—PRODUCT "X"

ports also is eliminated. It is the interplay of time and quantity shown spatially on the graph that makes decision making quick and accurate. To examine the same data in tables of 120 columns and relate each number to the other 119 is an impossible task which, therefore, can never be done consistently.

When the chart shows that actual sales deviate significantly from forecast, the decision-making authority delegated to the production planner enters the picture. The production planner disregards the forecast line and estimates the probable sales rate by extending the actual sales line. Production is then planned according to the projected sales trend line rather than the forecast. This projection can be entered on the charts (the single solid line on Exhibit 7) in any practical fashion. It is very important, however, to maintain satisfactory liaison with general and sales management and to consult with them whenever a significant adjustment to the forecast is made. This is necessary since recent changes and new considerations may be unknown to the planner and may have a bearing on the expected sales picture. The correct answer may be a compromise or a trend projection—quite different, not only from the projection made by the planner, but from the original forecast.

The planner's main function is to authorize the proper quantity of production at the proper time. Thus, since the inventory manager knows the lead time required for the complete manufacturing cycle, he can place timely production orders in economic lot sizes whenever the need for additional inventories is indicated by the sales trend.

Good input planning reflects the interplay of sales estimates, actual sales, inventories, planned acquisitions (production or purchasing), and actual deliveries. The absolute values of the individual numbers are unimportant; it is their interrelationship with each other and time that is significant. It is nice to have available at the time of decision historical information about such factors as seasonality of sales or production, shelf life, lead time, and lot size; these can be included as notes in one corner of the chart. It is far more important to have a simple, inexpensively kept chart which can be read in seconds and which contains the equivalent of 120 columns of data, all interrelated, plus added special information about product changes, production, sales, inventory, sales estimates, production plans, and the like, the whole displayed in time segments according to this year, last year, year to date, this month, last month, next quarter, and so on. If something is distorted or out of plan, management can focus on it and dip deeper into the reasons why; if all is in balance, the planner moves to the next chart.

The speed with which such a chart can be read allows high-caliber people instead of clerks to manage the inventory. People with knowledge, background, and understanding plan the commitment of company funds.

*   *   *

Despite all the attempts to quantify, to be scientific, and to be precise, management of inventories requires a high degree of judgment. This judgment can be improved if we think in terms of *dollars: dollars* of cost and *dollars* of investment. We must equate the consequences of our decisions with *dollars*. When an order point or quantities are set, when lead times are estimated, we should think of the results in *dollars*. When we talk about inventories, we are not dealing with lists and columns of figures but with actual dollars and cents. The greater our understanding of this one fact, the further we shall progress toward more effective inventory control.

CONTROL OF WAREHOUSING
AND SHIPPING OPERATIONS

By K. J. ALLEN

The warehouse manager in the automotive service field is confronted with two divergent factors in the development and operation of a control program: (1) the "ultimate" or "the last word" in schedule and availability demanded by the dealer and (2) operation within the framework of a profit plan, a need which it shares in common with all segments of any corporation which uses orthodox management techniques to meet its objectives. To reconcile these divergent claims on its activities, certain policies must be drawn up by warehousing management to classify and grade inventories and customer orders with related processing schedules and procedures so as to accelerate service while maintaining control of manpower, materials, and facilities. These areas of policy are defined as follows:

1. Order processing and inventory stocking practices and procedures.
2. Customer order shipping schedules and service quality.
3. Manpower and expense measurement and control.

This chapter examines each of these areas at some length. While the examples given are all of automotive service operations, it is hoped that the activities discussed are applicable to warehousing management in any industry.

Order Processing and Inventory Stocking Practices and Procedures

As a prerequisite to developing customer ordering procedures, inventories must be analyzed to determine service demands and procurement lead times to insure that the parts are stocked by priority according to the urgency of their requirement. Economics, fluctuations due to geographical factors and vehicle dispersement, and orthodox distribution practices make it impossible for *all* parts to be stocked at *all* warehouses at *all* times. Automotive vehicles servic-

---

K. J. ALLEN is Depot Manager, Parts Division, Chrysler Corporation, Center Line, Michigan.

ing has been made more complex during recent years by increasing product durability. This results in a longer span of model years being in operation, each model containing evolutionary engineering improvements and their concomitant new parts. The greater emphasis on styling, with its variations in ornamentation and trim and its multiplicity of models and sizes, has sharply affected inventory planning and stocking points. Fortunately, with the advent of the electronic computer, detailed analysis of inventories has become possible.

CLASSIFICATION OF INVENTORIES AND ESTABLISHMENT OF STOCKING POINTS

Basic procedures for inventory control start with the determination of sales frequencies. When the demand has been established, the record can be examined to determine product or model application, economics of purchase (lot size, long-time buy, setup charges, and so on), and inventory level and stocking point responsibility.

In automotive service, as in most other industries, a small percentage of the parts produces a high proportion of the demand. Approximately 5 percent produces over 90 percent of the service requirements. Conversely, 50 percent of the parts serviced produces less than 5 percent of the service requirements. By using a grading system, coupled with an examination of physical plant capacities, it is possible to assign stocking points to the respective inventory items in quantities which are adequate to meet customer demands and in the most strategic position in the warehouse to facilitate handling and processing schedules. Through coding of the part in catalogues and related publications, the dealer is made aware of which stocking point he should direct his order to in order to receive the most expeditious service.

Since service to the vehicle owner is the prime objective, it is recommended that the dealer stock the fastest-moving parts to satisfy the majority of his customers' requirements without delay. Although all orders placed with the zone depots are handled by them, the out-of-stock items being obtained by wire to the master or base area depots, the dealer, using the appropriate stocking code, can order certain items directly from the master or base area depot if his doing so will mean faster delivery.

CLASSIFYING ORDERS BY DEGREE OF URGENCY

Another factor directly affecting schedule demands is the classifying of the order according to its degree of urgency. Handling costs rise in proportion to the speed of processing required; consequently, certain incentives have been devised to encourage the dealer to place stock-replenishment orders before an emergency arises. These incentives, in effect, share the cost savings with the dealer and open the processing "pipeline" to make possible accelerated service on those orders urgently required for vehicles which are out of service. In general, three order types are recognized:

1. *Special handling order.* This type is of utmost urgency; it means a vehicle is out of service. No back ordering is permitted at the depot; the order continues through to the division inventory control department, where parts are procured directly from corporate production or from a supplier. The depot's shipping date, depending upon carrier routing, is normally the day of receipt.

2. *Emergency order.* The dealer places this order to replenish exhausted stock items for which demand is imminent; no vehicle is out of service. The depot shipping schedule is 24 hours after receipt of the order.

3. *Stock order.* The dealer purchases parts for normal stock replenishment. Transportation is prepaid, and discount allowances apply. The depot shipping schedule is two days after receipt of the order.

CUSTOMER ORDERING METHODS

Performance within the corporation is not the sole determinant of the fact that service to the ultimate consumer, the vehicle owner, will be the best attainable. Consequently, the ordering habits of the dealer should be examined.

The most critical area of service is the "car down," for which the special handling (wire or telephone) order was designed. Many such orders are actually received in the mail or are accorded special handling upon examination because of an urgent situation spotted by corporate employees who enter the orders into processing. To measure the degree to which order policies are followed, samplings of order receipts are obtained from each of the depots. As an added evaluation of the degree to which emergency fill-in orders contain urgent items, this category should also be included in the sampling or dealer practices.

When reporting indicates a significant deviation from expedient ordering habits, more detailed data about the area and the individual dealer can be furnished to the sales department for administrative purposes.

PERFORMANCE OF COMMON CARRIERS

Although they are not directly under corporate control, the common carriers' performance should be measured because of their effect upon the final quality of service received by the customer.

One method through which common carrier performance can be measured involves registered mail and the enclosure of a registered postcard with each order shipped during one week of each quarter. A tabulation of replies by the respective depot traffic departments indicates those carriers that have schedule deviations. Each carrier is made aware of his performance by the traffic manager. Summary reporting to the division traffic department provides the data required to control carriers operating at the national level.

Shipping Schedules and Service Quality

Although external factors definitely affect service performance, the principal areas controlling order processing lie within the corporation. To keep field and division management apprised of the status of this performance, control reports must be issued and procedures must be established and followed through.

SHIPPING SCHEDULE

Whether service performance is being maintained in accordance with established processing schedules is evident at the shipping dock. Although the time of shipment is of paramount importance, other factors are related to the ultimate completion of the customer's order and the satisfaction of his requirements. The initial order schedule is readily measurable, but the factors of stock availability and effective routing also apply to the ultimate result.

Order schedule. With the policies pertaining to classification of the order and processing schedule as a guide, the quality of performance can be measured. The measuring base is the "order day"—that is, the number of orders multiplied by the schedule days allotted. The deviation percentage is computed by comparing the number of days each order is behind schedule to this base. For example, the policy for stock order schedule is three working days. Therefore, each stock order shipped represents a base of three order days. If the order is shipped on the fourth day, the schedule is one day, or 33⅓ percent, delinquent.

Obviously, division management is interested in the service accorded each individual customer, but since examination of the individual orders, except on a test basis, is impossible, the percentage of order days delinquency is an effective measure of the schedule performance of each depot and a gauge of customer satisfaction.

The same formula applies to emergency, with the base adjusted to "1." The sensitivity of the comparison is apparent, as each order day behind schedule represents 100 percent deviation, and with this small basing point, a minor quantity of delinquent orders results in a significant percentage of deviation.

Stock availability; back orders. Effective control of back orders is vital to maintenance of service standards. Shipment of the initial order is not a true measurement of customer satisfaction, since a back-ordered item is necessary for the completion of the order. Daily wires and a weekly, manually tabulated summary of shipping schedule reports indicate the degree of availability (order fill). With the help of computer reporting, assignment of responsibility by part number to the respective inventory control department and individual procurement man is feasible. (Exhibit 1 is an example of daily and weekly order shipment reporting.)

Carrier routing schedules. In the majority of procedures, when there are no complexities in distribution and transportation, it is logical to process orders by the FIFO (first in, first out) method, allotting to each order category its priority on the basis of its degree of urgency. When distribution is wide geographically, there are a choice of carriers and a myriad of possible routings and pick-up schedules. It is consequently wise to examine the last delivery schedule attained and process the order to ship in accordance with carrier pick-up schedules rather than with priority. In many instances, special handling orders may be delayed in processing and still achieve the same result as if the order was processed and awaited pick-up by the carrier on the shipping dock.

QUALITY OF SERVICE

The condition of the material and the accuracy of the item count and the part numbers shipped also have a significant effect upon ultimate timing and completion of the customer's order. The loading practices of corporate and common carrier personnel, the accuracy of the stock pickers, and the use of containers and dunnage must be carefully controlled.

Loading practices. Improper loading, storing, or carrier handling damages the stock received at the parts depots, thereby affecting the availability of material for service. Control of such operations can be helped and strengthened by accurate reports issued by the receiving activity (Exhibit 2). The reports are made more effective when they are supplemented by Polaroid pictures of the damage being described. These reports do not supplant the normal damaged material and claims reports used for financial control but, rather, add to their usefulness in settling claims.

EXHIBIT 1

CUSTOMER SERVICE REPORT

Location_____

_____Ending _____

			LINE ITEM VOLUME							
ORDER TYPE	Beginning on Hand	Rec'd	COMPLETED							Ending on Hand
			Ref'd.		Shipped		Back Ord.		Void	
			N.S.	B.O.	Orders	Lines	Whse.	Pre,De,		
(A)	(B)	(C)	(D)	(E)	(F)	(G)	(H)	(I)	(J)	(K)
DOMESTIC-WHOLESALER										
1 Stock										
2 Carlot										
3 Emergency										
4 Back Orders										
5 Total Domestic-Wholesaler										
DOMESTIC-DEALER										
6 Stock-Over $ 1,000										
7 Stock-Under $ 1,000										
8 Emergency										
9 Back Orders										
10 Total Domestic-Dealer										
OTHER & SIMCA										
11 Other-Inter Division										
12 Simca										
EXPORT										
13 Original Order - Del.										
14 Original Order - Det.										
15 Back Orders										
16 Total Export										
17 Total Plant										

PERCENT OF ORDER LINES FILLED						
	DOMESTIC			Simca	Export	Total
	Stk. & Carlot	Emergency	B. O. Rel.			
Reference Lines	1, 2,6 & 7	3 & 8	4 & 9	12	16	17
Percent						
Percent of Lines filled equals Column G ÷ Sum of Columns G-H & I						

DELINQUENT ORDER REPORT								
Order Type	Days Over Schedule						Shipped on Schedule	Total Orders Shipped
	Over 5	5	4	3	2	1		
Domestic - Stock								
Domestic - Carlot								
Domestic - Emergency								
Simca								

Depot Manager's Signature_____

EXHIBIT 2

INTER COMPANY CORRESPONDENCE

PARTS DIVISION

		FILE CODE	DATE Jan. 23, 1965
TO - NAME K. J. Allen	DEPT. Depot Manager	DIVISION Parts	PLANT/OFFICE Detroit Depot
FROM - NAME R. A. Brand	DEPT. Supv. Package Engineering	DIVISION Parts	PLANT/OFFICE Detroit Depot

SUBJECT: SHIPPING, MATERIAL HANDLING, PACKAGING METHODS DEVIATION REPORT

TO: PACKAGE ENGINEERING, DETROIT PARTS DEPOT

FROM:

ALLEN PARK ☐	CLEVELAND ☐	INDIANAPOLIS ☐	MARYSVILLE ☐	PORTLAND ☐
ATLANTA ☐	DALLAS ☐	JACKSONVILLE ☐	MEMPHIS ☐	RICHMOND ☐
BOSTON ☐	DENVER ☐	KANSAS CITY ☐	MINNEAPOLIS ☐	SAN LEANDRO ☒
CEDAR GROVE ☐	DETROIT ☐	LOS ANGELES ☐	NEWARK ☐	ST. LOUIS ☐
CHICAGO ☐	☐	☐	☐	☐

Center Line (DPD)

(REC'D FROM)   (POINT OF ORIGIN OR LOCATION)   REPORT NO.

(DEPOT: VENDOR NAME, OR CODE) 3102   DATE ___/___/___

GENERAL INFORMATION

CAR OR TRAILER NO. **SPRR**   PHOTO ATTACHED YES ☐ NO ☐   MAT'L HNDLG. LOST TIME ____ /HRS.

DATE SHIPPED **12** /**30** / **64**   DATE UNLOADED ___/___/___   SHIPPER NO. _____

PART NO.	PART NAME	RACK OR QTY./CONTAINER	QTY. SHIPPED	QTY. OF PIECES DAMAGED
2404 540	Bumper	48		25

ARRIVAL CONDITION & REMARKS DETAILED – ALSO RECOMMENDATIONS   (USE SUPPLEMENTAL SHEET IF NECESSARY)

We have noted the pallets of bumpers received, which have cardboard strapped
to the sides and ends arrived in good condition. - 25 pcs. received damaged -
chrome nicked and scratched.
The pallet load of bumpers, was floor loaded in one end of car. During transit
the spacer boards between the layers of bumpers, slipped out, which allowed the
load to break down.

SIGNED: N. D. Johnston   DATE 1 / 15 / 65

REPLY: _____

SIGNED: _____   DATE ___/___/___

1 – INDUSTRIAL ENG.

Order-picking quality control. Since order preparation is automated, since there is such a high volume of picking tickets and documents to process through the warehouse, and since several hundred employees are engaged in picking orders, it is difficult to preassign orders to any specific picker. However, we can still identify which picker is responsible for an order by using a manually operated Royal McBee notching device. It notches a standard IBM card with the picker's number at the sign-out desk. The device will notch up to 50 tickets at a time, and no specially printed card is required. This method provides verification of the picker while the order is in the plant and when the ticket is returned by the dealer with his claim.

Customer claims. No matter how many preventive and control measures a company sets up, the customer will not always receive the quality of service to which he is entitled. Many of these lapses in quality lead the dealer to request credit, a substitution of the correct part, or a return of the defective material. To minimize correspondence and standardize processing methods, a multicopy form is useful. The form is filled out by the dealer and submitted for approval to return material or receive credit. Upon verification, the claim is processed for credit or returned to the dealer for inclusion with the material he is returning.

One copy of this customer claim report may be used to record the type of error made and to assign the responsibility for the error. A monthly summary of discrepancies indicates the number and types of errors and clearly points to areas where additional control efforts must be exerted. The level of quality for each depot is determined by taking the total lines shipped as a base and figuring the ratio of errors to this base. (See Exhibits 3, 4, 5, and 6.)

Manpower and Expense Measurement and Control

The majority of manufacturing and processing plants have had manpower and expense measurement controls for many years. The demand for tying in these controls with time studies, pricing, cost estimating, and profit and loss performance by product line has given rise to a coordinated reporting system whereby the floor manager has readily available data with which to deploy his personnel. Chrysler Motors also has an integrated group of staff members from industrial engineering, production control, and budget analysis which measures the floor manager's variances from established norms and examines his operating methods. Until recent years this measurement has not been common practice in the service operations of manufacturing activities. Service was considered to be storage and product support activity, and it was staffed at

EXHIBIT 3

REQUEST FOR CREDIT OR MATERIAL RETURN AUTHORIZATION

* CLAIM CLASSIFICATION	
R — ORDERED IN ERROR	
E — SHIPPED IN ERROR	
T — WRONG PART REC'D	
U — NEW DEFECTIVE	
R — SEE REMARKS	
N	
C — SHORTAGE	
R — OVERAGE	
E — TRANSPORTATION CHG.	
D — INVOICING	
I — SEE REMARKS	
T	

PARTS DIVISION — **CHRYSLER** MOTORS CORPORATION

REQUEST FOR CREDIT OR MATERIAL RETURN AUTHORIZATION

(THIS FORM MUST BE TYPEWRITTEN)

DEPOT CODE — **328298**

CLAIM NUMBER

CHRYSLER MOTORS CORP.

CHRYSLER CORP.

* DATE ISSUED

* SHIPPING LOCATION   * CODE

* SUBMITTED BY   CODE

FIRM NAME

STREET ADDRESS

CITY   (ZONE)   (STATE)

* CREDIT TO   CODE

FIRM NAME

STREET ADDRESS

CITY   (ZONE)   (STATE)

ITEM	* PART NUMBER	QC	* PART NAME	* INVOICE NO.	INV. DATE	*QTY	UNIT PRICE	TOTAL GROSS	TMC	MCC	PCC	DISC. CODE	DISP. CODE	NET EXTENSION NON TAXABLE	TAX INCLUDED
1															
2															
3															
4															
5															

*	REASONS FOR SUBMITTING		
1		TOTAL GROSS CREDIT	
2		LESS DISCOUNT	
3		SUB TOTAL	
4		LESS 2 PERCENT CASH DISCOUNT	
5		SUB TOTAL	
*REMARKS:		— LESS	
		+ PLUS	
		+ PLUS	
		— LESS	
		TOTAL ALLOWABLE CREDIT	

X REF.   PRICE   VERIFY

SIGNATURE   DATE

RECEIVING		INSPECTION DISPOSITION	QTY	CODE	ACCTG. AUTHORIZATION DATE
DATE MAT'L REC'D	1				PARTS DEPOT DISPOSITION
NO. OF PKGS.	2				☐ OK TO RETURN MAT'L. (SEE BELOW)
WGT.	3				☐ OK FOR CREDIT (SEE BELOW)
B/L NO.	4				☐ UNACCEPTABLE (SEE BELOW)
CARR-IER	5				DEPOT MANAGER DATE
PPD. AMT.					
COLL. AMT.		DATE BY		APPROVED	

☐ ALLOW TRANSPORTATION   ☐ DO NOT ALLOW TRANSPORTATION

FRT. IN   FRT. OUT   ☐ OTHER

PREPARE IN ACCORDANCE WITH INSTRUCTIONS ON COPY NO. 5

1   PARTS ORDER - NUMERICAL FILE COPY

EXHIBIT 4

REQUEST FOR CREDIT OR MATERIAL RETURN AUTHORIZATION

* CLAIM CLASSIFICATION

R E T U R N	ORDERED IN ERROR
	SHIPPED IN ERROR
	WRONG PART REC'D
	NEW DEFECTIVE
	SEE REMARKS
C R E D I T	SHORTAGE
	OVERAGE
	TRANSPORTATION CHG.
	INVOICING
	SEE REMARKS

PARTS DIVISION ★ **CHRYSLER** MOTORS CORPORATION

REQUEST FOR CREDIT
OR
MATERIAL RETURN AUTHORIZATION
(THIS FORM MUST BE TYPEWRITTEN)

DEPOT CODE   **328298**
CLAIM NUMBER
CHRYSLER MOTORS CORP.
CHRYSLER CORP.
* DATE ISSUED
* SHIPPING LOCATION   * CODE

* SUBMITTED BY   CODE   *** CREDIT TO**   CODE
FIRM NAME   FIRM NAME

STREET ADDRESS   STREET ADDRESS

CITY   (ZONE)   (STATE)   CITY   (ZONE)   (STATE)

ITEM	* PART NUMBER	Q C	* PART NAME	* INVOICE NO.	INV. DATE	* Q T Y			QUALITY REPORT		
1								QLTY. CODE	REASON FOR CLAIM	ITEM	
2								XX	WAREHOUSE ERRORS	XX	
3								31	QUANTITY SHORT		
4								32	QUANTITY OVER		
5								33	WRONG PART SHIPPED		
								34	WAREHOUSE DAMAGE		
*			REASONS FOR SUBMITTING					35	TRAFFIC ERROR		
1								36	SHIPPING ERROR		
2								37	OTHER WAREHOUSE		
3								40	TABULATING & ACCT'G		
4								41	EXCISE TAX FUND		
5								50	PARTS ORDER		
								60	ALL OTHER PLANT		
*REMARKS:								61	UNIT PACK		
								71	POLICY		
								71A	SPECIAL PROGRAM RETURNS		
								72	CUSTOMER ERROR		
								73	NEW DEFECTIVE		
								74	OTHER		
		SIGNATURE		DATE				75	SPARK PLUG		
	INVESTIGATION REMARKS AND DISPOSITION				QTY	QR. CODE		80	BRANCH ERROR		

INVESTIGATION REMARKS AND DISPOSITION   QTY   QR. CODE

PARTS DEPOT DISPOSITION
☐ OK TO RETURN MAT'L.   (SEE BELOW)
☐ OK FOR CREDIT   (SEE BELOW)
☐ UNACCEPTABLE   (SEE BELOW)

1	
2	
3	
4	
5	

DEPOT MANAGER   DATE

| APPROVED | |
| REJECTED | BY_____ DEPT____ |

☐ ALLOW TRANSPORTATION   ☐ DO NOT ALLOW TRANSPORTATION
FRT. IN   FRT. OUT   ☐ OTHER

4   PARTS ORDER ALPHABETICAL FILE COPY   PREPARE IN ACCORDANCE WITH INSTRUCTIONS ON COPY NO, 5

EXHIBIT 5

REQUEST FOR CREDIT OR MATERIAL RETURN AUTHORIZATION

★ CLAIM CLASSIFICATION

R E T U R N	ORDERED IN ERROR
	SHIPPED IN ERROR
	WRONG PART REC'D
	NEW DEFECTIVE
	SEE REMARKS
C R E D I T	SHORTAGE
	OVERAGE
	TRANSPORTATION CHG.
	INVOICING
	SEE REMARKS

PARTS DIVISION ★ **CHRYSLER** MOTORS CORPORATION

REQUEST FOR CREDIT
OR
MATERIAL RETURN AUTHORIZATION
(THIS FORM MUST BE TYPEWRITTEN)

DEPOT CODE	**328298**
CLAIM NUMBER	
CHRYSLER MOTORS CORP.	
CHRYSLER CORP.	
★ DATE ISSUED	
★ SHIPPING LOCATION	★ CODE

★ SUBMITTED BY	CODE	★ CREDIT TO	CODE
FIRM NAME		FIRM NAME	
STREET ADDRESS		STREET ADDRESS	
CITY (ZONE) (STATE)		CITY	

ITEM	★ PART NUMBER	Q C	★ PART NAME	★ INVOICE NO.	INV. DATE	★ QTY		
1								
2								
3								
4								
5								

SECTION B--INSTRUCTIONS FOR RETURNING MATERIAL

1 — MATERIAL MUST BE SHIPPED FREIGHT PREPAID, VIA THE MOST ECONOMICAL MEANS WITHIN 30 CALENDAR DAYS FROM DATE OF AUTHORIZATION.

2 — ALL RETURNS MUST BE MADE AS INSTRUCTED. ANY ADDITIONAL CHARGES FOR RE-ROUTING WILL BE DEDUCTED FROM FINAL CREDIT.

3 — ENCLOSE CLAIM COPIES NO. 1-3 IN AN ENVELOPE AND ATTACH TO THE MATERIAL BEING RETURNED.

4 — COPY NO. 2 WILL BE RETURNED TO YOU AS ACKNOWLEDGEMENT THAT MATERIAL HAD BEEN RECEIVED AND CREDIT ISSUED.

★ REASONS FOR SUBMITTING

★	
1	
2	
3	
4	
5	

★REMARKS:

SECTIONS C--PARTS DEPOT SHIPPER NUMBER PREFIX CODES

10—DETROIT
11—CHICAGO
12—INDIANAPOLIS
15—MARYSVILLE
21—CEDAR GROVE
23—ATLANTA
24—KANSAS CITY
25—SAN LEANDRO
27—ST. LOUIS
28—NEWARK

SIGNATURE　　　　DATE

SECTION A--INSTRUCTIONS FOR FILING CLAIM

1 — DO NOT RETURN MATERIAL UNTIL AUTHORIZATION IS RECEIVED ON COPIES 1-3.

2 — USE THIS FORM TO REQUEST CREDIT OR AUTHORITY TO RETURN MATERIAL FOR REASONS LISTED UNDER CLAIM CLASSIFICATION. THIS COVERS ONLY NEW, UNUSED SERVICE MATERIAL RECEIVED FROM PARTS DEPOT LISTED IN SECTION C THIS PAGE.

3 — DO NOT USE THIS FORM TO REQUEST ADJUSTMENT FOR MATERIAL ORIGINALLY INSTALLED ON NEW VEHICLES OR ALLEGEDLY DEFECTIVE MATERIAL DISCOVERED AFTER INSTALLATION OR PUT INTO SERVICE. THIS TYPE OF ADJUSTMENT MAY BE HANDLED ON WARRANTY SERVICE CLAIM NO. CC-5607.

4 — THIS FORM MUST BE TYPEWRITTEN. FILL IN ALL SECTIONS ABOVE HEAVY LINE DENOTED BY ASTERISK (★). SET TYPEWRITER FOR SINGLE SPACING.

5 — CLAIM CLASSIFICATION — INDICATE TYPE OF CLAIM BY "X" IN APPROPRIATE BOX. SUBMIT A SEPARATE CLAIM FOR RETURN AND CREDIT CATEGORIES.

6 — DATE ISSUED, SHIPPING LOCATION AND CODE — DATE CLAIM TYPED, SHIPPING LOCATION AND CODE, PER SECTION C. USE SEPARATE CLAIM FOR EACH LOCATION.

7 — PART NO., DESCRIPTION AND INVOICE NO. — ENTER EXACTLY AS INVOICED.

8 — QUANTITY — ENTER QUANTITY APPLICABLE TO THE SUBJECT CLAIM.

9 — REASONS FOR SUBMITTING — LIST REASON IN SPACE CORRESPONDING TO ABOVE PART NOS. IF MAT'L DISCREPANCY, INDICATE PART NO. AND DESCRIPTION OF MAT'L REC'D. IF DEFECTIVE, ENTER NATURE AND LOCALE OF DEFECT, E.G., SAND HOLE AT NO. 2 CYL., ETC.

10 — REQUESTS FOR TRANSPORTATION CHG. ADJUSTMENTS MUST BE SUPPORTED BY RECEIPTED FREIGHT BILL.

11 — DAMAGED MATERIAL CLAIMS FROM OTHER THAN "UNDER SEAL" AND "PARCEL POST" SHIPMENTS SHOULD BE INITIATED WITH THE DELIVERING CARRIER. ANY SUCH CLAIMS REJECTED BY THE CARRIER MAY BE SUBMITTED ON THIS FORM BUT MUST BE ACCOMPANIED BY THE CARRIER'S DENIAL OF RESPONSIBILITY STATEMENT.

12 — DETACH AND RETAIN THIS NO. 5 COPY — MAIL COPIES 1 THROUGH 4 TO THE APPROPRIATE PARTS DEPOT.

5　CUSTOMER FOLLOWUP COPY

EXHIBIT 6

CHRYSLER CORPORATION SERVICE PARTS AND ACCESSORIES DIVISION
MONTHLY QUALITY REPORT

Location _____
Month of _____

ANALYSIS OF CHARGEABLE ERRORS			
Quality Code	REASON FOR CLAIM	Line Items	% of Total
	Warehouse Errors		
31	Quantity Short		
32	Quantity Over		
33	Wrong Part Shipped		
34	Warehouse Damage		
35	Traffic Error		
36	Shipping Error		
37	Other Warehouse		
40	Tabulating and Accounting		
50	Parts Order		
60	All Other Plants		
	Total Plant Chargeable Errors		
61	Unit Pack Errors		
71	Policy		
72	Customer Error		
73	New Defective		
74	Other		
80	Branch Error		
	Total Errors		

RATIO OF ERRORS TO LINE ITEMS SHIPPED		
	Month	Year
Total Line Items Shipped		
Total Chargeable Errors		
Ratio: Chargeable Error / Line Items Shipped		

RATIO OF DELINQUENT CLAIMS PROCESSED TO TOTAL CLAIMS PROCESSED				
	Approved		Returned	
	Month	Year	Month	Year
Total Processed				
Total Delinquent				
Ratio: Delinquent / Processed				

AGE OF UNPROCESSED CLAIMS ON HAND							
FOR APPROVAL							
Age (Days)	1	2	3	4	5	Over 5	Total
Quantity							
FOR CREDIT — MATERIAL RETURNED							
Age (Days)	1	2	3	4	5	Over 5	Total
Quantity							

Plant Manager

a planned operating level, generally on a fixed-manpower basis. For this reason the biggest problem in installing a variable control system in service operations is to develop a man-hour concept to replace the man-per-job concept which numerous managers and foreman have developed under the fixed-manpower system.

Because of the many mechanical, automated, and organizational concepts of order preparation, only the physical warehousing functions have been considered in this chapter. Regardless of the office methods used, the warehouse receives a shipping document, with or without related picking or processing documents, from which the processing workload can be determined. If a great deal of clerical labor is required to issue workload reports, it may be practical to install mechanical or automated equipment in the offices in order to implement the control system.

MANPOWER MEASUREMENT AND CONTROL

Warehousing activities are, at best, difficult to measure in the areas of manpower deployment and utilization. Except in those warehouses where product type and unit volume remain relatively uniform, orthodox time study and engineered standards are demanding, complex, and costly to maintain. In a large warehouse where the physical layout is obscured by racks and bins and the workload product mix fluctuates, the "historical" standard, supplemented by work sampling and spot time studying, produces the greatest return per dollar of expense. The installation and operation of a manpower control program require—

- Defining the function to be measured.
- Defining the workload representative of the function.
- Establishing data-collection points for both workload and man-hours.
- Designing and timing reports.
- Administering the results.

Defining the function to be measured. The size and complexity of the warehouse operation should determine the degree of detail to include in the reports. If functions and operations cannot be clearly defined and reported, the distortion resulting from "guesstimating" man-hour and workload allocation makes the resulting reports useless for operating purposes. In general, automotive service warehousing consists of the receiving, stockkeeping, picking, packing, and shipping functions. Depending upon the size of the organization, the breakdown of the subfunctions could be related to handling a specific type of order or material or a specific clerical function not physically applicable to the material.

EXHIBIT 7

PLANT LABOR BUDGET REPORT

CONFIDENTIAL

| | | LOCATION | | | | | | | | | |
| | | | | | ENDING | | | | | | |

L I N E	FUNCTIONS	ACTUAL			BUDGET		VARIANCE			ACTUAL OUTPUT PER HOUR
		OUTPUT	HOURS WORKED		WORKLOAD ALLOWANCE	HOURS ALLOWED	HOURS	%	PERS.	
			O.T.	TOTAL						
	A	B	C	D	E	F	G	H	J	K
	MISCELLANEOUS NON-VARIABLE									
1	Truck Drivers, Fire Brigade									
2	Non-Prod. Mat'l.-Pick/Pack/Store									
3	Skid & Pallet Assembly Repair									
4	Reclamation-Rework, Unit Pack									
5	Bale Waste Paper & Carton Salvage									
6	Security Check									
7	Rearrangement									
8	Lost Time - Union Activity									
9	Lost Time - Other									
10	Special Truck Service									
11	Build Crates & Boxes									
12	Total Misc. Non-Variable									
	TOTAL STOCKHANDLING SALES									
13	Salary - Fixed									
14	Salary - Variable									
15	Hourly - Fixed									
16	Hourly - Variable									
17	Total Stockhandling									
18	Equivalent Persons									
	DEALER TERMINATIONS AND RECLASS MATERIAL									
19	Reclass Mat'l. - Receiving									
20	Reclass Mat'l. - Picking									
21	Reclass Mat'l. - Stockkeeping									
22	Dealer Term. - Receiving									
23	Dealer Term. - Handling & Checking									
24	Dealer Term. - Stockkeeping									
25	Total Dealer Term. & Reclass Mat'l.									
26	Equivalent Persons									
	PARTS PLANT TRANSFERS									
27	Picking									
28	Picking - Internal									
29	Picking - Export									
30	Packing (& Mat'l. Allocation - CL)									
31	Pick/Pack - Sheet Metal									
32	Pick/Pack - Other									
33	Shipping (& Mat'l. Hdlg.-CL) (SM-MV)									
34	Shipping - Other (MV Only)									
35	Clerical									
36	Total Parts Plant Transfers									
37	Equivalent Persons									
	INSPECTION									
38	Normal Inspection									
39	Claims Inspection									
40	Scrap & Misc. Handling									
41	Dealer Termination									
42	Clerical - Salary									
43	Total Inspection									
44	Equivalent Persons									
	RECEIVING - DISTRIBUTION									
45	Receiving - Distribution									
46	Vacation - SCP									
47	Total Receiving - Distribution									
48	Equivalent Persons									

Although a breakdown by department function may be readily attainable, there are many functions which cross department lines or are fractional responsibilities of several foremen. In these instances the function should be clearly defined and the responsibility for cost control assigned to one person.

Defining the workload. Effective use of workload reporting is dependent upon—

1. Workload data which are representative of the function performed.
2. Reports which are auditable and reconcilable to an operating or financial statement.
3. Timing which is coincidental with manpower expenditure.

Three major workload measures used in automotive warehousing are:

1. Weight, as noted on bills of lading received and issued.
2. Line items. One line of data pertaining to a specific part number appears on a shipping, receiving, or internally processed document.
3. Order (document covering shipment of service stock to customer in compliance with his purchase order).

If there is a significant product mix, the line items may be graded by type, order, or material; by their weight; and by the type and method applicable to the weight of the stock received or shipped. (Exhibit 7 is representative of the categorization of workload and the type of measurement.)

Establishing data-collection points. The sources for the majority of data required are usually already in existence and need only slight modification to detail the additional functions brought about by the new reporting system. For example, a receiving register is maintained which records the vendor, B/L, carrier, and freight bill numbers. The addition of columns for recording total weights or types of weight is all that is required for the reporting system.

Similar reporting is usual in the shipping or traffic departments. The control of documents issued from the offices to the plant provides the means of obtaining line item and order counts.

Workload is tied in with manpower by establishing a chart of accounts which is to be utilized by the foreman when preparing the daily time sheet.

Designing the reports. At the inception of a new system there is a tendency to convert from reporting too little information to including too much detail. When the supervisor is made aware that his operation is being measured, he will undoubtedly demand recognition for many minor items which do not appear as specific workload in the proposed reporting. For psychological reasons it may be preferable to segregate these items during the initial installation; but after a reasonable period, when it can be shown that they represent no significant workload, they should be included in one of the major categories to be compensated for in the "mix."

EXHIBIT 8

ANALYSIS OF EXPENSE AND BUDGET PERFORMANCE

LOCATION _____   MONTH _____   PAGE _____   OF _____

Acct No.		MONTH				YEAR TO DATE			
		Actual	Budget	Variance	%	Actual	Budget	Variance	%
1	xxx	BASE MANPOWER							
2	xxx	Premium Manpower							
3	xxx	Salaries and Wages							
4	Var	Base Salaries and Wages							
5	151	Overtime Slry (St.Time & Prem)							
6	241	Overtime Hrly (Prem only)							
7	Var	Inventory Labor							
8	Var	Project Labor							
9		Total Salaries and Wages							
10									
11	Var	Empl.Benefits excl.Hrly O.T.							
12	242	Night Shift Premium							
13	xxx	Total Personnel Costs							
14									
15	xxx	MAINTENANCE MATERIALS							
16	Var	Normal Maintenance (324–342)							
17	Var	Special Major Maint (350–384)							
18	xxx	Total Maintenance Mat'ls							
19									
20		PROJECT AND PERISH. EQUIP.							
21	Var	Furn.& Fixt (434) Mach.,Equip (454)							
22	423	Project Material							
23	424	Perishable Equipment							
24		Total Proj. and Perish. Equip.							
25									
26		SUPPLIES							
27	621A	P&S Supplies – Domestic							
28	621B	" " – Export							
29	621C	" " – Government							
30	631	Fuel							
31	683	Stationery – Tab Forms							
32	Var	Other Supplies							
33									
34									
35									
36		Total Supplies							
37									
38	xxx	FIXED EXPENSE							
39	Var	Taxes							
40	Var	Depreciation							

Depending upon the complexity of the reporting, the desired time-reporting accounts should be made readily identifiable by category: for instance, 100 may be receiving, 200 stockkeeping, 300 picking, and so on. The subaccounts will then use the digits to denote the specific order or product type: 301 will be picking stock orders, 302 will be picking emergency orders, and so forth. The time-account breakdown will be summarized in conjunction with payroll preparation or time-card reconciliation.

EXPENSE MEASUREMENT AND CONTROL

The manner of measuring expenses other than labor should not differ significantly from what is normal in manufacturing plants; however, the emphasis upon transportation methods, the use of shipping supplies, and communications media cause these areas to become more vital to the cost picture in service operations. Because of the presence of a choice at the floor level in using many of the services or supplies, there is a greater demand for a more minute expense examination of transportation, shipping supplies, and communications.

All expenses, including labor, must be summarized to insure that emphasis upon labor control is not accomplished through neglect of all other items of expense. (Exhibit 8 is a typical summary of expense.)

ADMINISTRATION OF THE REPORTING FUNCTION

Current labor contracts with their related fringe benefits tend to make stabilization of the workforce desirable from an overall cost viewpoint. Workload status reporting and the related availability of data with which to forecast trends are vital to stabilizing the workforce and scheduling the annual programs.

In automotive service operations, in addition to traditional annual physical inventory, there are:

1. A stock reclassification program, adding and removing parts from field depots because of volume changes.
2. A scrap program, removing from stock parts which are no longer salable.
3. A new-model stocking and shipping program.

The data made available by the reporting methods described may help to schedule the timing of many programs to coincide with workload decreases, thereby reducing new hirings and layoffs, except in periods of economic fluctuations beyond the immediate control of depot management.

*   *   *

Successful implementation of a service standards program rests on—

1. Recognition of the effect which dealer ordering and stocking practices have on the warehouse.
2. Administration of a sound shipping schedule with related surveillance of all outside handling which affects the ultimate service to the customer.
3. Maintenance of a sound cost control program of sufficient depth to provide plant management with adequate data with which to adjust daily operations and forecast future requirements.

PHYSICAL DISTRIBUTION MANAGEMENT

By BAYARD F. ROWAN

The primary goal of today's intelligent businessman continues to be profit—profit wherever he can find it, for himself as a major stockholder or for the company to which he has committed his talents. Anyone taking time to read this article is reaching for a goal. That goal is profit. Everything revolves around profit. Every management action must be considered in the light of profit.

In physical distribution this profit goal is reached through two specific means: (1) improving customer service and (2) improving return on investment by the proper application of company assets. These vehicles, or directives, can also very properly be called distribution's objectives.

At the core of good management is planning. It is a rudiment of our trade. Planning, organizing, controlling, and evaluating are the tools of all our management activity. We deal here with planning for profit. It is not always necessary that this profit be immediately available; therefore, our plan can and must have future applications. Some U.S. industries in which profits are at a relative standstill despite the accelerating expansion of volume are developing a new answer to the cost–price squeeze: the physical distribution concept.

THE EVOLUTION OF DISTRIBUTION AS A MANAGEMENT CONCEPT

Profit is the mathematical difference between "make and sell" or "give and get." In the early development of American industry the most significant problem was the lack of "make" ability—the scarcity of goods and services—which resulted in the studious application of organizational principles and techniques to the problems of production and tended to place the engineer, toolmaker,

BAYARD F. ROWAN is Senior Consultant, A. T. Kearney & Company, Chicago, Illinois.

and innovator in the forefront of the business organization. Characteristic of this period were the many chief executives whose business careers started in the tool room or die shop. The concentration on "make" ability forced production or manufacturing management to come to the fore as the first major stage of industrial development in the 20th century.

When production had been developed to a point sufficient to meet demand, it became necessary to cultivate and expand sales. Marketing began to come into its own as an industrial management concept in the late 1940's, at which time there was much unused manufacturing capacity.

Only about ten years ago, distribution—the third major management concept—began to assume a responsible position alongside marketing. Management activity in manufacturing and marketing could not continue to sustain the large percentage of return on investment which had been obtainable in earlier years. In order to keep profit at an acceptable level, management had to examine its concepts of physical organization to discover large new pools of untapped profitability. Most of us have always logically broken down corporate life into manufacturing and marketing—the make and the sale. That large pool of untapped profitability has been found in the lacuna *between* the make and the sale and has been defined as physical distribution.

Marketing is a sales-generating force. Distribution is a sales-satisfying force. The ultimate goal of any well-managed company is to produce and market a product that will reach the consumer at a *cost,* at a *time,* and in the *condition* he desires. Plainly, distribution involves place and time factors. Physical distribution can be defined in many ways. One is "taking your product to market profitably." Even though there have been improved marketing techniques and increased efficiencies in clerical activity, profit margins in many companies have continued to decline in recent years. But, although much effort has been devoted to improving management skills and reducing costs in the areas of marketing and manufacturing, relatively little attention has been directed to moving the finished product from the end of the production line to the customer's door. This area of physical distribution, industry's third largest cost, is where tremendous opportunities for profit improvement have been found.

Recent U.S. Government and industrial statistics indicate that more than 18 cents of every manufacturer's sales dollar goes toward paying for physical distribution. This cost is exceeded only by direct materials costs and direct labor costs. It is a larger business expense than general administration, capital acquisition, or selling and promotion. In 1963 it increased to 21.8 cents of every sales dollar.

Dr. Edward W. Smykay, Professor of Marketing and Transportation Management at Michigan State University, points out in his book, *Physical Distribution Management,* that most large companies devote much attention to the advertising budget at board meetings and that most have a vice president in charge of advertising. Very few companies give as much attention to distribution. Dr. Smykay underlines his point with a comparison. The nationwide bill for advertising is about $12 billion annually. The annual bill for distribution from the end of the production line to the consumer is more than $50 billion. It is apparent that more top-level attention to distribution can be expected in the future. Physical distribution management (PDM) demands detailed, expert study of each element in the cost of distribution. It also calls for follow-up attention and close supervision from higher management.

Again, physical distribution is the key link between manufacturing and the creating of demand. It has profound effect on the success of both these activities and, consequently, on the basic profitability of the enterprise.

FUNCTIONS WITHIN THE PDM SYSTEM

Physical distribution is really a system of varied functional activities. These diverse but interrelated functional activities are often called "cogs." The responsibilies or cogs most frequently included in the distribution system are:

1. Packaging or cartoning for protection.
2. Warehousing of finished goods at distribution centers, providing regional availability.
3. Field warehousing, providing metropolitan availability of finished goods.
4. Site location.
5. Materials handling.
6. Inventory control.
7. Production planning.
8. Market forecasting.
9. Order processing.
10. Traffic and transportation, including inbound, intracompany, and outbound.

There are other functions involved in the PDM system which are, in most instances, related in some respect to the ten above. In many cases too the following functions are byproducts of those listed above and represent the concentration of management ability in areas which can contribute measurably to the corporate profit:

11. Packing and shipping.
12. Customer service in the areas of transit time; availability and product condition at time of receipt.
13. Liaison between manufacturing and marketing (primarily a communication responsibility).
14. Receiving.
15. Accounting for distribution.
16. Management of company real estate.
17. Commercial travel reservations.
18. Management of company-owned or leased automobiles and aircraft.
19. Facilities planning, layout, and space utilization.
20. Equipment planning and maintenance.
21. Electronic data processing.
22. Operations research.
23. Private carriage operations.

These responsibilities are probably not all-inclusive. At the same time, no known corporate physical distribution group will at any time be able to embrace the entire scope of activity represented here. Individual companies have always handled all these functions, but responsibility has been spread among too many department heads, resulting in a low probability of success. For example, manufacturing will usually control inventories, receiving, and inbound transportation; the financial or administrative department will often control real estate and company aircraft; marketing usually retains customer service and packaging.

ORGANIZING PHYSICAL DISTRIBUTION

Within the last several years there has developed, along with the management concept of physical distribution, an organizational trend to unify many of the functions noted above in a single corporate department recognized as *physical distribution*. Through such a department, top management can place emphasis and urgency on those very costly areas which now contain a large potential for possible improvement. A physical distribution organization insures that there is a group dedicated to constant cost improvement and improved customer service, for profit improvement and customer satisfaction are the dual objectives of this newly defined management concept and organization.

A typical physical distribution organization chart includes the following departments:

• Regional warehousing ("direct line" operating department).

- Field warehousing ("direct line" operating department).
- Materials handling (staff function).
- Transportation (staff function).
- Package engineering (staff function).
- Services and controls (staff function).

The detailed responsibilities of these departments are as follows:

1. *Regional and field warehousing.* Receiving, storage, packaging, and shipping of finished goods; operating procedures, order-filling operations, picking lines, coordination of product packing, warehousing, transportation; determining trade-off points between transportation, packing, and inventory carrying costs; stock picking, order assembly, marking.

2. *Materials handling.* Handling into, through, and out of warehouses, terminals, and distribution centers. Planning the facility: size and shape of structure, location on site, column spacing, clearance heights, floor loads, dock sizes, utility requirements, layout of space, materials flow patterns, storage and stacking methods, aisle widths, equipment requirements.

3. *Transportation.* Establishment of routings to utilize the best service available with respect to both time and cost. Auditing of freight bills to assure error prevention; filing of claims for loss and damage. Control and maintenance of company automobiles and aircraft. Providing reservation service to the entire company for commercial aircraft, company aircraft, and other travel accommodations. Selection of carriers: private carriage or leased trucking systems and their related contract negotiations. Negotiation of new transportation arrangements and rates.

4. *Package engineering.* Protective packaging, cushioning materials, mechanization of packaging and filling lines, unit load design, palletization, containerization.

5. *Services and controls.* Site location, communications equipment, EDP locater systems, sales forecasting, order points and quantities, product planning, labor supply, building costs, general real estate control, work simplification, standards and methods, order-processing systems, office procedures, forms design and control, operations research.

PHYSICAL DISTRIBUTION COSTS

The cost of physical distribution is an obvious object of attack for two basic reasons. The first is that it is pure expense, a dead weight on industry. Unlike the production processes themselves, physical distribution adds nothing to the product except time and place value. The second reason is that this cost is consuming an ever greater percentage of the sales dollar.

We have briefly considered our goal—profit in physical distribution. Now let's look at how we can reach that goal. Before costs can be analyzed, they must be identified. The component costs of physical distribution fall under several headings:

1. *Transportation expenses,* which amount to approximately 23 percent of total cost. Even though transportation is the third largest cost of doing business in America, it is only one element of overall physical distribution. Therefore, the one-time concept of the transportation manager's job is passing from the scene as industry and carriers strive to streamline ways of bringing raw materials to the plant and distributing finished products to the customer. Today's concept places new demands and increasing responsibility on the shoulders of managers who once were charged only with knowing intimately all the complexities of rates and routes. The transportation manager of a few years ago was expected to save money only by choosing one method of shipping over another. Often overlooked, however, was the fact that such a simple choice may have boosted the overall cost of distribution. Unrecognized additional warehouse charges, uncertain or costly labor market conditions, additional handling and paperwork, for example, may have canceled out the money saved. The fault lay not with the traffic manager who carried out his duties in keeping with his job definition, but with top management in its failure to recognize the total complexity of physical distribution.

2. *Distribution center costs,* which include land and building occupancy, interest on inventory investment, insurance, payroll, utilities, supplies, equipment, packaging and shipping, personal property taxes.

3. *Control and communications costs,* which include communications, shipment billing, order preparation, and related data processing equipment.

4. *Distribution costs from plant to warehouse,* which include freight charges and inventory transit expense.

Once identified, these costs can be controlled; but good administrative judgment must be used when embarking on cost studies. Frequently, data are collected that are of no value when compared with the cost of collection. Management must analyze and solidify its ideas, try them out, and then evaluate the results. There is nothing that "can't be done." We just don't know how yet.

In analyzing costs, value analysis techniques are directly applicable to two areas of physical distribution: (1) the study of existing methods, equipment, and procedures and (2) the design of new methods, equipment, and procedures. In both areas the major objective of value analysis is similar or better service at a lower price.

Savings in physical distribution will come primarily from cost analysis in any of the following seven areas:

1. *Simplification of the system.* For example, it is an established fact that 25 strategically located field warehouses can provide next-day delivery to more than 90 percent of the total U.S. market. Five strategically located distribution centers can provide delivery by the second day to more than 80 percent of the market.

2. *Reduced inventories.* In general, field inventories serve only to provide local availability on short notice and to act as a buffer against interruptions in supply by the factory. It is frequently possible to reduce inventories and attain increased utilization of what remains through warehouse consolidation or elimination. Byproduct effects of reduced inventories include reduced obsolescence and damage and the availability of fresher stocks. This is especially important for a product with limited shelf life.

3. *Improved packaging.* Packaging of such items as door knobs and mop handles can be done at the plant or in the field. Labeling and identification can also be revamped so that one inventory will do the job of two or more.

4. *More efficient methods and procedures.* Not only is it important to eliminate cost through simplification of the distribution system, thus producing a system which has an inherently lower operating cost, but it is also important to assure attainment of maximum efficiency from whatever system is being used. Attention must be given to the selection and use of the most efficient materials handling procedures and equipment, warehouse layout and utilization, warehousing and shipping methods, order-processing procedures, and usage of alternate modes of transportation and types of transportation equipment. Frequently, there are enough opportunities for improvement in present methods to offset the cost of complete redesign of the overall distribution system.

5. *Integrated transportation,* such as private carriage, piggyback, fishyback, truck-rail-truck, and truck-air-truck, combines the cost savings available through reduced handling and use of the least expensive form of long-haul transportation.

6. *Technical innovations,* such as containerization, air freight, high-speed computers and communications equipment, more automatic materials handling equipment, and advances in packaging materials. This category should also include technical assistance to wholesalers, particularly in those areas of materials handling in which a company is especially skilled.

7. *Revised channels of distribution.* It is entirely possible that the basic reason for high distribution costs may be found in the channels of distribution being used; certain channels are inherently higher in cost than others. Depending upon the company's volume, its sales objectives and policies, and the nature of its markets, it may be possible appreciably to lower distribution costs by revising the channels of distribution, if this can be done without impairing marketing effectiveness. The marketing aspects of the problem are closely interrelated with the physical aspects. The purpose of physical distribution is to move goods with optimum care at maximum speed and minimum cost, making the product available to the customer when, where, and how he wants it. Owing to its market proximity, the distribution organization is alert to marketing changes and needs and can react to these stimuli through its immediate liaison with the marketing and manufacturing groups.

OPERATIONS RESEARCH

"Operations research" describes a technique which is very helpful in solving physical distribution problems. Generally, operations research is considered to be the employment of mathematical techniques for the better understanding of complex operational relationships and for problem solving. It is in effect a feasibility analysis, statistically testing and sampling proposed alternatives to determine the best possible choice. Others feel, however, that "OR" is merely a sophisticated term applied to the basic responsibilities and functions of managers. Our job is to improve profit. To do this we need to know our costs and our methods. Once these are known we can, theoretically, then rearrange all our methods and procedures in an effort to arrive at a system which entails lower costs.

Actually, this process should be conducted without regard for practicality. If a lower-cost method does present itself, it can then be compared with predetermined policies or fixed methods in order to see if it is practical as well as economical. The use of the operations research technique does not always require computers or complex mechanical formulas. The lack of advanced equipment and techniques in an individual company cannot excuse management from carrying out its fundamental responsibility—improving profit.

PROFIT IMPROVEMENT IN PDM

Profit improvement, rather than cost reduction, is an atmosphere—one that must be developed throughout physical distribution administration. New people must grow in it, and senior employees must be permeated by it. What we want is cost concern rather than cost control. The following six elements are basic to the successful operation of a physical distribution department:

1. Plan objectives.
2. Arrange an intelligently and technically balanced organization.
3. Define our method of operation through the publication of policies and procedures.
4. Develop our people. Our tools are our people; management is getting results through people. When a manager manages in this way, his own personal development takes care of itself. It is necessary that we create for our people a profit-improvement atmosphere—an attitude of creativity, optimism, and progress—and foster pride in accomplishment.
5. Develop comprehensive performance standards to provide a yardstick for measurement.
6. Finally, appraise results effectively.

REPORTS TO MANAGEMENT

By LAWRENCE M. MATTHEWS

Reports are one of the means—and probably the most important means—by which management of an enterprise is exercised. It is a truism that the larger the enterprise the greater the need for good reports. The sheer size and complexity of a large enterprise demand reports as the basic tool for its management.

In the case of small businesses, even very small ones, the most common failing is lack of knowledge about what is really happening. Repeated surveys have shown that the most frequent cause of business failures is insufficient capital. But capital needs are determined by turnover of receivables, labor usage and costs, material usage and costs, inventory levels, and a host of other factors. Without reports, no management can keep an eye cocked at all the factors of production and operation.

The so-called paperwork explosion has done much to focus attention on the subject of reports. This is good, because anything that brings increasing awareness of such an important means of management can only have good results. However, there is also the danger of throwing out the nut with the shell. Certainly no professional systems and procedures analyst and no manager would dare to reduce the necessary intelligence data being provided to the operators of an enterprise.

Finally, the continually developing techniques of electronic data processing have had far-reaching effects on reports to management. It is now often practical and economical to provide data and regular reports that heretofore were completely unfeasible. This same ability, however, also has its dangers. The four-inch-thick monthly sales analysis that no one has either the time or the inclination to study is a poor report. With modern EDP techniques it is possible to generate exception data that meet the needs of exception reporting, which

LAWRENCE M. MATTHEWS is Vice President, Stevenson, Jordan & Harrison, Management Consultants, Inc., New York.

in turn becomes increasingly important the higher the level of the manager who is exercising control.

Purpose of Reports

Reports to management have only one purpose—*control*. The Merriam-Webster Unabridged New International Dictionary defines "control" as follows: "To exercise restraining or directing influence over; to dominate; regulate; hence to hold from action, to curb."

Good managers exercise a directing, guiding influence over subordinates by establishing expected standards of performance. Good managers also exercise a restraining or curbing influence over subordinates when actual performance does not meet the standards of excellence that have been established. Thus a report must have as its purpose one or both of these two control actions. The logic is this: Reports are needed for control; control requires standards and reports of performance to standards.

Any discussion of reports inevitably leads to a discussion of management, of how the reports are used. This chapter has as its basic purpose the review of the reports themselves, their characteristics, frequency, types, and maintenance.

Many reports to management are "one time" affairs. Typical examples are reports on possible acquisitions, new product development, and special market studies. The most common reports to management, however, are the continuing, periodic reports on the various functions within the enterprise by which management exercises its controlling responsibilities. It is these continuing, periodic reports that concern us in this chapter.

Characteristics of a Good Report

The number, the contents, the users, and the frequency of the reports issued within an enterprise depend on the conditions which are peculiar to each given situation. Any good report must have certain characteristics. No one report can have all these characteristics, but the more it has, and the closer it approaches all of them, the better it is.

1. *Necessary and meaningful.* It belabors the obvious to say that any report

should be needed and that its contents should be meaningful. The implications of these characteristics, however, are not always so obvious.

Whether a report is necessary or not depends on the given situation. As a general rule, the more inept the management of a function within an enterprise, the greater the need by executive management for closer control and more detailed reports. Thus the division that is losing money is more closely watched and controlled. For example, the process of rejuvenating a failing business always demands more frequent and more detailed reports on operations. Conversely, the highly profitable division can be watched and controlled with simpler, less frequent reports. In other words, conditions determine the necessity of a report, and it is a wise management that knows how few and how detailed the reports that it receives must be.

In like manner, the characteristic of meaningfulness depends upon the organization's internal conditions. Often a great deal of trial and error, in addition to careful planning, is required before the proper report is finally developed. The peculiarities of a given situation, even the personal quirks of the manager, must be taken into account to make a report meaningful. A pertinent report on a given function in one company may not be meaningful for the same function in another company in the same industry. Also, for a report to be meaningful, it must be adapted to its audience. For example, some executives react to graphic presentations, whereas tables of data fail to obtain their attention and action. The report's format, detail, and frequency must be designed for the given situation and audience.

2. *Clear and well defined.* A good report must be clear and must use well-defined, commonly understood terms. To attain this characteristic, the first requirement is to achieve a happy balance between too much and too little. A common fault is to include too much in a report, and as a result, it is complicated, overdetailed, and very much in danger of receiving too little attention from its audience. It just isn't clear enough.

The next requirement for clarity is the use of well-defined terms. It is a mistake to overestimate one's audience. The production or marketing technician all too often presupposes that his audience has his own expert knowledge of terms. It all too frequently does not. Presumably, any doubts will be voiced and questions as to meaning will be asked. However, it is a commonly encountered and very human tendency on the part of managers to assume a meaning and interpretation which may not be correct. A report is an attempt at "communication," and to communicate we all know that we must use well-understood terms.

A third requirement for clarity is a good format or layout. Here, even a little bit of care and thought can improve the attractiveness of the report, the ease with which it can be read, and, thus, the attention paid to it by managers and its eventual effectiveness.

Most reports contain figures; indeed, many are composed mainly of figures. In such cases, thought about how the human eye is used can make the material much easier to read and thus much clearer. The proper use of spacing, guidelines, isolation of summary figures, upper and lower case letters, and a host of other elements can be most effective.

Finally, an attempt should be made to build into the format one or more distinctive and unusual characteristics, however small. These need not take such elaborate forms as colored paper or shaded borders; they can be as simple as an artful placement of the title, double lines, or upper case letters. These distinctive touches repeated in successive reports result in automatic recognition on the part of the recipients that speeds up identification and adds to their ease of understanding.

3. *Properly originated.* As a general rule, the originator of a report should be the person or persons whose function is being reported upon. Thus a report on delivery performance is best made by the production manager responsible for delivery performance.

This characteristic of good reporting has an excellent psychological advantage. The very act of making up the report focuses the originator's attention on the function being reported and serves as a continuing reminder of actual performance to date. Unfortunately, the responsible group frequently does not have the staff, talent, or data to assemble the report. For example, the production department's performance against budgeted standard costs must be reported by accounting rather than production. When and where possible, however, each function should be the source of the necessary reports on its own performance.

4. *Accurate.* The data provided by a report should be as accurate as it is economically feasible to make them. The originator should make every attempt to insure that the figures included are correct and that judgments, evaluations, or estimates are identified as such.

It is a common human tendency to accept as true whatever is reported, particularly when the report is formal and periodic. However, a corollary tendency is to have continuing doubts and mental reservations about a given report if it has been wrong in the past. Continuing accuracy in a report prevents such doubts from arising. Maintaining management confidence is worth a lot of extra effort.

If an inaccuracy occurs, the report's originator should be, if possible, the one to issue the correction. If the inaccuracy is a major one, a revised report should be issued immediately. If needed, an explanatory phone call or visit to the recipients should precede the revised report. If the error is a minor one, the correction may be made in the next issue of the report. The prompt correction of occasional errors can increase management's confidence in a report. Management is made aware of the reporting executive's efforts to achieve accuracy. Confidence is damaged when inaccuracies are not immediately revealed and corrected.

5. *Prompt.* Any good report should be issued as soon as possible after the event being reported or as close as possible to the end of the reporting period. As with accuracy, the need for maximum promptness must be balanced against the costs involved, but within the limits of economic feasibility the good report is a timely report.

The need for promptness is obvious to everyone in management. Directive or corrective action is much more effective if it is taken after the event, and serious loss or danger is more likely to be avoided. Every report has its own predictive inferences for the knowledgeable reader. The sooner the report is received, the closer management's control can be.

6. *Simple.* Simplicity is very closely allied to clarity. Almost inevitably, the simpler the report, the clearer it is to the reader and the more likely it is to receive attention from a busy manager. On the other hand, the executive who seeks stark simplicity in the reports he receives had better have very simple problems. Many situations covered by periodic reports are complex and intricate and require presentations that can never be simple if they are to be usable.

The objective must always be to prune the unneeded detail, to seek combinations that present a single meaningful figure where two existed before. It takes ingenuity to reconcile the often opposing characteristics of meaningfulness, clarity, and simplicity, but the reward is a good report.

7. *Providing comparable past figures.* A current report is often best utilized by comparing it with recent past reports. In other words, because a report is most frequently a picture of a performance to some standard, it is necessary to compare current performance with the recent past before intelligent action can be taken by management. Because of this, the good report includes comparable past figures, where needed and where possible. Thus management is saved the labor of having previous reports searched out, laying successive reports side by side, and going through all the steps otherwise required.

8. *Incorporating self-checks.* In many situations it is possible to design a report to contain built-in checks of its accuracy and completeness. It is so

constructed that it can be "added up." It cannot attest to the accuracy of the data reported; however, it can provide the originator with a check of his accuracy and a reminder of the need for continued precision. Also, because the reader can make his own checks if he so wishes, some additional measure of confidence may be added.

It is interesting to note that the two most widely used business reports, the balance sheet and the profit and loss statement, incorporate such self-checks.

Three Examples of Reports

The variety of management situations is so tremendous that no single report (not even a small group of reports) can be called representative. It is true that every human enterprise or organization uses or should use a balance sheet and profit and loss statement in some form. These two reports, however, have their own highly formal make-up and rules and may be considered special and exceptional. Hence, for the purposes of this discussion, no single example can be offered as completely typical of all reports to management. Instead, three examples are given of reports that have proved very practical and that combine many of the characteristics considered desirable. For each example a short outline of the background and need for the report, as well as of its use, is provided.

A DELIVERY REPORT

Background and need. An electronics component manufacturer had a pressing need to improve delivery performance on both sample and production orders. It was important to produce and ship sample orders as soon as possible to insure use of the company's components on the design "breadboards" and thus gain entry to the customer's specifications. In the case of production orders, shipping promises were the basis of production schedules which could be expensively disrupted by late deliveries. On both types of orders delivery performance by production was poor. At the same time, sales department promises to customers were all too often unrealistic. Production and sales blamed each other for the company's poor service performance and customer dissatisfaction.

Solution and report. Since the company made a wide variety of electronic

EXHIBIT 1

INDUSTRIAL OIL CAPACITORS—PRODUCTION ORDERS

(Standard Lead Time—Four Weeks)

		Week Ending —/—/—	Week Ending —/—/—	Week Ending —/—/—	Week Ending —/—/—	Week Ending —/—/—	Week Ending —/—/—
Backlog—Start of Week	Orders	419	426	456	451		
	Pieces	132,505	125,166	121,397	119,104		
Total Received	Orders	82	84	100	81		
	Pieces	5,081	8,278	11,166	4,742		
Total Canceled	Orders	—	1	1	1		
	Pieces	—	692	725	280		
Total Shipped	Orders	75	53	104	100		
	Pieces	12,420	11,355	12,734	13,827		
Shipped Late	Orders	12	21	67	57		
	Pieces	5,044	6,112	6,908	8,917		
Backlog—End of Week	Orders	426	456	451	431		
	Pieces	125,166	121,397	119,104	109,749		
Late in Backlog	Orders	109	103	88	83		
	Pieces	24,253	22,215	16,311	14,468		

components, the problem was approached on a product-by-product basis. In each case the first step was to establish "standard lead times" that provided production with sufficient time to do all the manufacturing and testing. Knowing what manufacturing time was needed, sales was asked to approve the lead times as competitive. Since the proposed lead times were markedly better than current performance, the approval of sales was obtained in all cases. Sales personnel were to use them in making shipping promises to customers.

With standard lead times that were accepted by both production and sales, the company had an objective basis upon which to measure delivery performance. The next step was to improve the present poor delivery performance. However, even before this work was started, a weekly management report (Exhibit 1) was designed and installed to provide a "before" picture of existing performance. The following features of this report are important:

1. It fills a vital management need—control over delivery performance that was poor and had to be improved.

2. It is clear to both originator and recipient. Standard lead times are established for both sample and production orders for each product. Therefore, the term "late" is well defined.

3. The orginators are the production people responsible for meeting the lead times. The very act of making up the weekly report requires weekly review of their progress.

4. The report is issued on Tuesday of the week following the one being reported.

5. The report is simple, showing only backlog, new orders, shipments, and "late" orders. It could have been made even simpler, but as it stands it represents the consensus of judgments on what was wanted.

6. Comparable past figures are provided. Exhibit 1 shows four weeks of performance. In the fifth week the master includes and reproduces the fifth week's data. The same sequence is followed in the sixth week. In the seventh week a blank master is used, and the last three weeks from the previous report are included with the data for the seventh week. Thus any given week's report can have on it a minimum of four weeks' performance and a maximum of six weeks' performance.

7. The report "adds up"; that is, beginning backlog plus new orders less shipments equals ending backlog. This requires care and self-checking on the part of the originators, which, in itself, is a beneficial feature of the report.

Use of the report. The reports of delivery performance for sample orders and for production orders for each product are sent weekly to the plant super-

EXHIBIT 2

SALES AND PROFIT/VOLUME ANALYSIS MONTH OF MAY 19—

BY WARE TYPE:

WARE TYPE	GROSS SOLD	NET $ SALES LESS FREIGHT	THIS MONTH % OF TOTAL	VARIABLE COST	OVERHEAD & PROFIT CONTRIBUTION	P/V	YEAR TO DATE NET $ SALES	% OF TOTAL	P/V
FOOD	66,370	$ 254,500	20.8%	177,895	76,605	30.1%	$ 1,494,149	22.2%	30.0%
COSMETICS	52,790	271,600	22.2%	134,714	136,886	50.4%	1,379,732	20.5%	49.9%
LIQUOR	45,650	386,500	31.7%	237,697	148,803	38.5%	2,429,674	36.1%	39.5%
UTILITY	38,780	230,100	18.9%	135,759	94,341	41.0%	1,177,820	17.5%	41.5%
WINE	11,470	73,600	6.4%	51,373	22,227	30.2%	249,025	3.7%	32.2%
TOTAL	215,060	$ 1,216,300	100.0%	737,438	478,862	39.4%	$ 6,730,400	100.0%	39.6%

BY COLOR:

	GROSS SOLD	NET $ SALES LESS FREIGHT	THIS MONTH % OF TOTAL	VARIABLE COST	OVERHEAD & PROFIT CONTRIBUTION	P/V	YEAR TO DATE NET $ SALES	% OF TOTAL	P/V
FLINT	81,880	$ 511,174	42.0%	290,347	220,827	43.2%	$ 2,813,306	41.8%	43.4%
EMERALD GREEN	76,810	456,917	37.6%	293,450	163,467	35.8%	2,550,822	37.9%	35.5%
AMBER	56,370	248,209	20.4%	153,641	94,568	38.1%	1,366,272	20.3%	39.4%
TOTAL	215,060	$ 1,216,300	100.0%	737,438	478,862	39.4%	$ 6,730,400	100.0%	39.6%

intendents, to the factory managers under whose control the given product is made, and to the manufacturing vice president.

The first two levels of production management use the reports weekly to initiate corrective action where needed. The manufacturing vice president follows a system under which any given report is studied once every four weeks. Everyone knows that he receives and studies the reports. The results have been excellent (sales management soon demanded shorter lead times). Most gratifying is the fact that other company plants have imitated the report and installed it for use with their own products.

A SALES AND PROFIT REPORT

Background and need. Almost every manufacturing enterprise makes more than one product or more than one type or model of its product. Most service organizations have more than one operating or profit center. Thus, in all but the most simple situations, management needs to know operating results by product or by profit center. The monthly profit and loss statement provides only the overall picture.

All too often profitable products or centers "carry" losing items or activities. Management does not know the extent of the losses being incurred by given parts of the business. It does not know where or how to take action, and, as a result, the business may make a profit of 3 instead of 5 percent. And, since every company has only a limited amount of money to spend for selling and for cost improvement efforts, it is vitally important that these limited resources be expended effectively. Sales concentration must be on the more profitable lines, and cost improvement efforts must be directed toward the losing or low-margin items.

In the glass container industry any given plant as well as any given company makes a variety of wares—that is, food bottles, cosmetic bottles, liquor bottles, and so on. Frequently this variety is also made in several colors. Thus management must know with a reasonable degree of certainty the profitability of each of its ware lines and each of its colors.

Solution and report. Among the most useful of modern costing techniques is "direct costing." By this means cost standards are established for those items of cost, such as material, labor, and fuel, that vary directly with production or activity. These costs are incurred only if the company makes the product or actually operates the center, not if it purchases the product from outside. When these standard direct costs are deducted from sales income for

EXHIBIT 3

COST AND VARIANCE STATEMENT

Sept. 30, 19--

PERIOD						YEAR TO DATE	
PER CENT ACTIVITY	UNITS PRODUCED	UNITS BUDGETED	UNIT OF MEASUREMENT Standard Press Hours			UNITS BUDGETED / PRODUCED	PER CENT ACTIVITY
85.0	680	800				5,600 / 7,234	129.2
VARIANCE IN DOLLARS	ACTUAL COST	BUDGET ALLOWANCE	EXTRA BUDGETARY ALLOWANCE	ACCOUNT NO.	DESCRIPTION	ACTUAL COST	VARIANCE IN DOLLARS
(125)	3,964	3,839		01	Direct Labor – on Standard	41,469	(562)
(179)	329	150		02	Direct Labor – non Standard	1,606	25
70	81	151		03	Clean Tanks	1,516	(1,216)
(292)	453	161		04	Clean up – Change Clothes	1,229	(359)
(60)	105	45		05	Idle Time	412	(53)
(100)	100			06	Rework	320	(320)
	480	480		12	Supervision	3,360	
				13	Technical		
				14	Clerical		
				15	Material Handling		
(170)	337	167		16	Maintenance – Mach. & Equip.	1,688	(382)
45		45		17	Maintenance – Land & Bldgs.	915	93
(59)	164	105		21	Overtime Premium	3,771	(2,650)
(200)	300	100		22	Holiday Pay	900	(138)
(163)	290	127		23	Vacation Pay	1,384	62
(1,233)	6,603	5,370			Total Labor	58,570	(3,068)
(1,021)	1,871	850		31	Machine Parts & Small Tools	11,599	(2,529)
(50)	118	68		32	Machine Repair Service	651	72
	200	200		33	Machine Rental	1,400	
(15)	185	170		34	Building Materials & Supplies	1,597	123
(100)	200	100		35	Water & Waste Treating Supplies	1,322	(292)
(153)	362	209		36	Miscellaneous Supplies		
				37	Stationery & Printing		
(20)	70	50		38	Medical Supplies & Service	578	(46)
				39	Canteen Supplies & Service		
(193)	493	300		41	Electric Power & Light	3,516	(220)
(132)	382	250		42	Fuel	2,744	82
				43	Water & Sewerage		
				44	Telephone & Telegraph		
				45	Postage		
				46	Plant Protection		
				48	Subscriptions		
				49	Freight & Express – In		
				51	Travel Expense		
				59	Freight & Express – Out		
				61	Social Security Expense		
				62	Insurance – Blue Cross, etc.		
				63	Pensions		
				69	Automobile Expense		
22	1,195	1,217		71	Depreciation – Mach. & Equip.	8,519	217
	250	250		72	Depreciation – Land & Buildings	1,750	
200		200		73	Insurance – Bldgs. & Equip.	1,400	(129)
				74	Taxes – Bldgs. & Equip.		
				75	Sales Taxes		
(1,462)	5,326	3,864			TOTAL EXPENSE	35,076	(2,722)
(2,695)	11,929	9,234			TOTAL LABOR & EXPENSE	93,646	(5,790)

FORMING DEPT.   DEPT. FORMING

the product or operating center, the residual dollars are the contribution to overhead and profit. Dividing these residual dollars by the sales income yields a percentage that can be called the overhead and profit to volume relationship, which is known as the product's or center's P/V ratio.

If we assume relatively the same capital and equipment requirements, the products or models with the higher P/V ratios are the more attractive to make and sell. Thus, if a given glass container manufacturer knows the P/V ratio of each of his lines and of each of his colors, he will know how to spend his sales and cost improvement dollars most effectively. In general, he will concentrate his selling effort on the lines with the higher P/V ratios and his cost improvement effort on the lines with the lowest P/V ratios.

Exhibit 2 is a sales and profit/volume report that has met the needs of a number of glass container manufacturers. The report shows, not only the P/V ratio by type of ware and color, but the gross sold and the percentage of total for each type of ware and color. The report is issued monthly and serves as the basis for important management decisions.

Use of the report. No bottle manufacturer is able to change his "mix" of sales overnight or make immediate drastic reductions to large segments of his costs. Such actions take careful planning. Also, while every bottle manufacturer knows that certain of his lines are more profitable than others, he is usually startled to see that one line contributes 67 percent more to overhead and profit than another.

With the kind of data provided by this report, he is able to direct sales effort where it will be most productive and cost reduction improvements where they are most needed. It may take some years to accomplish, but the direction is well marked by such a report.

COST AND VARIANCE REPORT

Background and need. Unwatched expenses are always a fertile field for reductions that immediately improve profits or free monies for other, more productive uses such as equipment improvement or product development. If management is to control expenses, it must have—

1. A standard against which to measure actual expenses; and
2. A report that shows standard versus actual performance.

Solution and report. Exhibit 3 is a cost and variance report that shows management what should have been spent and what actually was spent. It is part of a standard cost and flexible budget installation and is issued monthly for each cost of operating center within the company. Its objective is "responsibility accounting," and it reports performance to standard for a segment of the enterprise that is supervised by a given member of management, in this case a departmental foreman.

Cost and variance statements are widely used in many industries—textiles, chemicals, metalworking, paper, and others. The report format is designed for the given industry and company. However, it always shows the dollars allowed for each given item of expense, the dollars actually spent, and the difference or variance between the two. In addition, it shows not only these data for the month but actual cost and variance for the year to date.

Uses of the report. By means of monthly cost and variance reports management is able to know, and thus to control, the money actually spent for each item of cost within individual departments. Since the standard amounts are also shown, the existence of out-of-line spending is highlighted for corrective action.

Frequency and Distribution

Even after a good report is developed, questions remain as to how often and to whom it should be distributed. The frequency with which a given report should be issued depends upon the conditions of the given situation. The objective is to issue the report only as often as is necessary. Generally, the more critical, or the more poorly managed, the function, the greater the frequency required. To coin a phrase—"reporting frequency varies inversely with eptness." Another factor affecting the frequency of reporting is the nature of the audience. One or more of the recipients may require the control data once a week or even daily, but other managers may need only monthly or quarterly summary reports. The uses to which the recipients put the report thus determine the frequency with which they should receive it. As a rule of thumb, the closer the responsibility, the greater the frequency of the reporting.

Who is to receive a given report depends, again, upon the individual situation. Obviously the general rule should be that the report is issued only to those managers who really need it. The key word here, of course, is "really." A very common occurrence is that recipients who had a temporary or one-time need for a particular report continue to receive it after their need no longer exists. The real test is the action each addressee can and does take as the result of receiving the report.

Maintenance of Reports

Every report, then, is developed and issued to meet a management need. It may be an attempt on the part of the issuer to get certain action. More commonly, it is the result of a need for closer control on the part of the recipient. However, any given management requirement is subject to change. It may even disappear completely. Therefore, it is very important that reports to management be properly maintained.

The issuer always plays an important role in reporting maintenance. This is particularly true where a given report is still needed but has not been as effective as it should be. Frequently, however, maintenance of reporting effectiveness is the responsibility of the systems and procedures staff, if there is one. But in many companies this function is handled by industrial engineering, the controller's staff, administrative assistants, or by no one. If responsibility has never been assigned specifically, there is usually great potential for improvement.

The steps of maintenance vary with the report and the conditions within the enterprise. However, certain general guides can be offered to achieving continued reporting effectiveness.

1. A report whose use and effectiveness have not been reviewed within the last two years should be suspect. This time limit is arbitrary, but it is a good starting point in the pursuit of improvement.

2. Some one group, and preferably some one person within each organization, should be responsible for periodically reviewing existing reports. This is particularly important in the smaller business where the review function is most frequently ignored. The review can be quite simple, but it should be done.

   Very frequently this review leads to new questions of management policy and action that can be profitably discussed. Another advantage of the specific assignment of this responsibility is that it brings another mind to bear on each report. Presumably, the issuer and the recipients are continually alert to revise and improve the ineffective or drop the unneeded report. However, it usually doesn't work that way, and it is often not until an outside opinion is obtained that the necessary changes are made.

3. The acid test for any report is the action it causes. Therefore, an important guide in the review and maintenance of a given report is to determine what management action it has given rise to. If it is obviously needed but has caused little or no action, then an attempt must be made to make it more effective. If the need is not obvious and if no

action has been taken as a result of the report, an attempt should be made to abandon it.

4. The actual maintenance review, however simple, should include the following:
   a. Managers receiving the report should be asked for their evaluation of its accuracy, promptness, and clarity.
   b. On the basis of a review of the report's use by its various recipients, decisions should be made as to possible changes in its frequency, or at least in the frequency with which it is sent to various recipients.
   c. The number of people receiving the report should be reviewed to see if the mailing list can be reduced.
   d. The various files of the report throughout the organization should be reviewed to develop proposals on the length of time it should be kept.

Common Management Reports

The number of reports to management varies with the size and complexity of the enterprise. No listing of continuing periodic reports would be complete for all businesses. However, certain basic reports are generally encountered, many of which most businesses utilize in one form or another. No one business may use them all, and all businesses have special reports tailored to their individual needs. Therefore, the list below includes only the more common reports to management.

FINANCIAL AND ACCOUNTING

Profit and Loss Statement
Balance Sheet
Cash Flow
Analysis of Surplus
Profit/Volume Ratio by Product
Over-Age Accounts Receivable
Report of Discounts Taken or Over-Age Accounts Payable

PRODUCTION

Shipping Report
Delivery Performance Report

Production Backlog and Capacity Forecast
Cost and Variance—Labor and Supplies
Cost and Variance—Materials
Labor Efficiency Report
Overtime Report
Performance to Capital Budget and Projects

SALES

Sales Performance by Product, Outlet, and Territory
Sales Budget and Forecast

QUALITY CONTROL

Report of Rejection of Material Received
Report of Manufactured Quality

PURCHASING

Purchase Performance Report
Vendor Rating Report

ENGINEERING

Engineering Project Progress Report

PERSONNEL

Manpower Report
Manpower Forecast

THE TOTAL SYSTEMS CONCEPT AND ITS EFFECTS ON MANUFACTURING OPERATIONS

By GEORGE J. MICHEL, JR.

Over the past few years a great deal of attention has been given to systems, which certainly are not new. They have always existed in one form or another, but in today's complex industrial society we must clearly design new ones, refine them, and put them into practice in order to maintain control and perpetuate our highly sophisticated organization structures. This is not a simple task and it has, therefore, commanded much attention.

The demands placed on individuals and organizations for control in today's competitive race are too great to be solved by one or two individuals or by simple decisions from any one quarter. It takes many people, with broad perspective at all levels, to maintain control. Where, then, do systems really begin?

When a manager is given responsibility, and he does not delegate part of it, his performance will be only as good as what he himself can achieve. But, if he delegates any or all of his responsibility, his performance is measured only by his ability to control. In order to delegate, a man must set up an organization and establish controls by developing systems. We build an organization and then devise a system, in other words; we do not devise a system and then build an organization.

A manager's system of controlling people can be compared to the basic elements of control in the human sensory system. The five sense organs collect information about the immediate surroundings and transmit these data to the brain. The brain processes this input and arrives at some conclusion about what action the body must take. By means of a communication network in-

GEORGE J. MICHEL, JR. is Vice President of Hancock Telecontrol Corporation in Old Greenwich, Connecticut.

structions are transmitted to muscles that will give the directed response and thus close the loop.

Applying these principles to system design, we can say that the basic elements of control are:

- The collection and transmission of data or information.
- The preparation, organization, and display of timely information for decision making.
- A communications network and organizational mechanism for converting the decision or plan into action.

These elements have been listed in sequential order, but the order is not meant to convey a priority of importance for any one element. For that reason we can picture these elements in the form of a triangle to show that the omission or weakening of any one side will cause the collapse of the structure and loss of control.

THE TOTAL SYSTEM

It is easy to forget that those who have delegated responsibility are developing systems; those to whom responsibility has been delegated are designing systems to control *their* operations; and so on, all the way down the line, to the extent that at practically every level of the business people charged with responsibility are devising systems. Many of these systems work at cross purposes, which emphasizes the need for an overall plan. Futhermore, these small systems lose their force because of an inability to use the new tools economically.

It is now time to step back and consider the total system, which we can define simply as the integration of all systems into one overall system whose objective is to provide better control of manpower, facilities, and material. For the sake of simplicity and this book's area of interest we shall confine our study to manufacturing's function in the total system. Specifically, the objectives or goals of this total system are:

1. Tighter control and improved utilization and conservation of physical resources.
2. Greater utilization of managerial talents by allowing routine decisions to be made routinely.
3. More information for long- and short-range planning.
4. Communication of pertinent data to the proper persons in time to allow action to be taken. This objective is one of the most important and takes into account the dimension of time.

THE PLACE OF PRODUCTION CONTROL AND
SERVICE INPUTS IN THE TOTAL SYSTEM

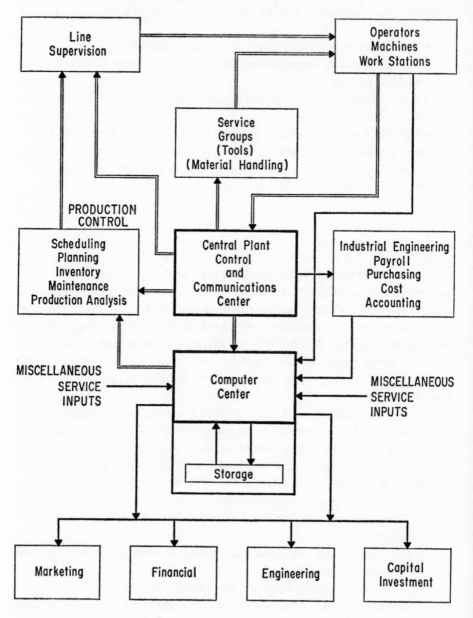

If acceptable control is to be obtained, the elapsed time between reports must be shorter than the time period for which a man is normally held responsible. The supervisor, for example, if he is held responsible for daily performance, must have reports of hourly or minute-by-minute status.

Reducing expenses is not included in the list above. Too many times companies set up the reduction of expenses as an objective only to discover later on that it has not been achieved or that the system has failed to function because too much meat was taken off the bone. "Expense" or "overhead" by itself is not an unpleasant word. Poor utilization or inadequate returns from these expenses do concern management, however. Our purpose, then, is to get more horsepower from our expense dollar so that we may move ever upward.

THE TOOLS OF CONTROL SYSTEMS

Formerly, most of the tools available for manufacturing control systems focused around timekeepers, expediters, floor schedulers, clerks, analyzers, and the like, but today a manager has at his disposal new equipment that can be applied to control. For instance, electronic data processing personnel and equipment, including data handlers, central processors, and storage devices such as cores, tapes, magnetic drums, cards, and so on, have opened new avenues for the system designer. The objective of providing timely, meaningful information can now be a reality.

Sensing devices, transmission equipment, recorders, and display hardware for status information make possible an accurate and timely collection of data and their display in a form that can generate intelligent decisions. For communication we harness such hardware as public address systems, radio, and telephone to support the elements of control.

Having taken into account the available tools, the objectives of the system, and the basic elements of control, we begin to look at the composition of a total system. Referring to the accompanying exhibit, we can break the system into two functional parts: control and service.

The control (plotted double lines) *is concerned primarily with the management of operations.* Following the "information flow" arrows, we can see that the control system is made up of many smaller control loops whose objective is to achieve maximum performance of equipment and personnel against some plan. Information is transmitted from the work stations to the control center. In response to these data the control center may dispatch a service group and at the same time notify the production control function and line supervision. Or the data may be passed on directly to the computer center where they are processed and fed to production control for action, through line supervision, on the work station's problem.

The service system is designed primarily for checking performance and managing capital. There is less need for closed-loop control because, generally, the dimension of time is broad enough. However, in order for the service system to function it must have accurate and timely data input and a means for assimilating vast quantities of data. These processed data must be presented in a form that will enable the managers of the various departments, such as manufacturing, to arrive at a plan for their groups which takes into account the factors which bear on other departments and functions. It is obvious from studying the flow diagram that the total system crosses almost every departmental boundary.

IMPACT ON ORGANIZATION

There are many immediate problems in applying a total system to a group organization—as well as some longer-range philosophical problems. One of the first questions we must ask is: Who should control the system? Some will say that it must be in the hands of an operating man; others support the claim that responsibility must rest with the controller's office. Regardless of the industry, there is a distinct point of view generated by each of the two functions.

To an operating man, control is the analytical process which leads to decisions about future courses of action and about routine decisions which control the function within some pre-established plan. To the controller, control is the surveillance of—generally—after-the-fact summations which are compared with some normal historical performance. These two points of view are quite different; and, needless to say, neither is totally correct. There must be a balance between them.

The second problem in applying a total system is the fundamental flaw of group organizations: Groups tend to exist for themselves. Any social group naturally is concerned primarily with its own well-being and preservation. This can be carried to the point where an organization becomes so tightly inbred with its own activity and mismanagement that it becomes ignorant of the total picture and lives only for itself.

The third problem is the line-versus-staff conflict and the strain it places on middle management. Line managers usually cannot define their problems in a manner that can be readily understood, not because they are incapable of doing so, but merely because they cannot (or at least do not) take the time. Staff, on the other hand, is a created function, with time to analyze and recommend, but it often fails to understand the problems of instituting a plan while maintaining the existing pace of operations without severe interruptions.

Middle managers are strained when considering a total system because they are often forced to commit to writing objectives, policies, plans, and procedures. This is a task most middle-level managers do not like; often they do not have the proper training for it. Also, they are inclined to be resentful if staff personnel attempt to expose their operation in the light of what other functions are doing. For these reasons they can resist the total system approach strenuously.

Ignorance of new procedures and techniques is also a problem besetting any organization which tries to construct a total system. Conflict of interest is still another. These problems are not exclusive to total systems, of course, nor is there some magical formula to eliminate them. They suggest, however, that greater creativity and skill are required in our organizational concepts if they are to be overcome.

DEVELOPING A TOTAL SYSTEMS APPROACH

Having designed in our minds a framework for a total system and having recognized the impact it can have upon an organization, we come to an interesting paradox. Earlier we said that if we are to succeed with any system we must build an organization and then devise a system, but a total system is difficult to establish in existing organizations. How, then, do we install a total system without restructuring the whole organization? Have we indeed taken on a project with no future? If we realize that many of the problems in the establishment of total systems are the same as those that impede progress elsewhere and that obviously some organizational changes may be required, we can proceed to adopt a total system for the organization.

The first step is to design a logical management system, which means reviewing the organization structure and redefining responsibility where necessary. Levels of authority and accountability must be established with the recognition that time is a vital element in the description of responsibility. The functional approach to organization must be reviewed to determine and overcome the obstacles to instituting a control system. Where necessary, we create new functions—not departments—and employ the concept of task groups.

The second step is to analyze management information needs. Anyone who has worked on information or control systems knows this is a monumental task that can be frustrating. Most people approach the problem from the point of view of reports to be generated, and so they often do not recognize or appreciate the fact that what is important or vital today or in weeks to come will seem insignificant in a few months, when a different type of data will be needed. On this day, summaries of reports will be adequate in certain areas; on that, details will be required. In some cases data will be collected only to be stored or to receive cursory treatment. The reason is not that the data are not meaningful, but that there are other problems that demand management's attention. Because of this we can identify a fundamental objective in our approach: flexibility. If we don't recognize at the outset that our system will change at a rate consistent with business changes, then our task is hopeless.

To discover what information management needs, we must look at the longer-range objectives of the business. A few typical questions we must answer are:

- What products will we be selling in the future?
- What kind of service or support must the customers have?
- What type of sales organization will we have?
- Will all products be manufactured?
- What degree of standardization will there be?
- What facilities will we have?
- What kinds of talents and skills will the employees of the organization have?

After the conditions under which the business will probably operate in the future have been studied and its future information requirements have been specified, the long-range objectives which the information-processing system must satisfy can be defined. These objectives may be specific (like the requirement that each foreman be provided daily with a detailed manpower and machine-loading schedule for the next three days) or general (stating, for example, that all stock orders be shipped and billed within six hours of receipt). But, whether specific or general, they must be understood by management.

If the objectives of the information system are to be achieved, systems design must provide a step-by-step plan. This may require discarding many traditions and ignoring many taboos if the maximum benefit is to be derived from an integrated systems concept. The step-by-step approach cannot be overemphasized. Developing and instituting a total system, like taking a journey, must start with the first step. Too often companies have devoted time to development with the thought of coming up with the ultimate system, but usually so much time is consumed in trying to design the ultimate system in detail on paper that when it is ready to be implemented, changes are required. It is, in other words, obsolete before it is implemented.

Without an implementation plan a system can never be instituted as originally designed. Therefore, a vital step in the approach to total systems is to design for each function a control system that will fit into an overall plan which utilizes the basic elements of control. Each control system in the overall plan must have current and timely inputs and a means for bringing data to a meaningful presentation. This means that accurate and rapid collection and transmission of data must be assured. The data have to be sorted and summarized and exceptions reported. Each control system also must include a mechanism for converting any decision into action.

When a logical management information system, in which individual control systems are designed to fit into an overall plan, has been established, we then must choose the tools available for putting the system into effect. There is no one tool or master machine that can fill the demands of the system; rather, there are many varied types, some very simple and others very complex. *The choice of tools must assure the proper balance of those designed to check performance with those designed to obtain performance.* Too often we see attempts at total systems which do a good job of collecting, sorting, analyzing, and reporting but merely check performance. To make a total system approach effective, it bears repeating, there must be some mechanism to obtain better performance. We don't buy a micrometer to check a carpenter's work. If we want a higher degree of precision, we buy tools that can work to the required accuracy and train people to use them.

* * *

Developing and installing a total system require a great deal of careful planning, a large amount of human effort, much new equipment, a lot of time, and a considerable sum of money to make companywide changes of the magnitude proposed. And there are problems to be faced in making this transition. But what happens if companies do not even make an attempt to gain productively through better information handling? On an industry basis they must accept a loss in the marketplace to competitors who can meet the customers' demands. On the national scale they face the even greater threat of foreign competition. All too often, by the time it is recognized that greater efficiency through better control and information is required, it is too late to catch up.

Undoubtedly, those companies with imagination and courage are going to find the application of new information and control systems the key to manufacturing leadership. We have already seen that progressive companies continue to make new advances and develop new techniques; this suggests that efficiency begets efficiency.

MANAGEMENT ASPECTS OF NUMERICAL CONTROL

By LEON B. MUSSER

The efficient manufacturing manager, to perform his functions properly, must not only concern himself with day-to-day questions of facilities, personnel, and maintaining production schedules, he must also look to the future and be constantly aware of new developments. What new machines perform more efficiently? Do new processes and techniques enable his company to become more competitive through cost reductions? These are only two of the questions which he must be prepared to answer at all times.

Had he been looking over the horizon only a few years ago, the manufacturing manager would have discovered answers to his questions in a new development: numerical control, which has eliminated many tedious manual operations in directing a machine tool and replaced them with control by numbers. Without going into the fine details of the process, it may be said that these numbers describe a part to be manufactured; normally, they are dimensional data. They are presented to an electronic control unit in coded form on one of several control media: punched paper or plastic tape, magnetic tape, punched cards, or magnetic drums. The numbers are transformed by the control unit into electronic impulses to move the slides of machine tools.

EARLY DEVELOPMENTS IN NUMERICAL CONTROL

An elementary form of numerical control was first developed in the early 19th century by Joseph Marie Jacquard, whose loom used a form of punched cards to weave patterns into cloth. The process underwent little further development until about 1950, when John Parsons of Traverse City, Michigan, a manufacturer of helicopter rotor blades, was faced with having to assure accuracy and interchangeability of parts. His solution was to use numbers,

---

LEON B. MUSSER is the Atlantic Regional Manager of the Bendix Corporation, Industrial Controls Division, Detroit, Michigan.

rather than models, templates, or cams, to define the shape of the parts of the blades. Since the numbers were not subject to deviation, he could be assured of improved quality and part-to-part repeatability. From his early ideas an entire new industry was developed—numerical control of machine tools.

As this radical new technique gained acceptance, many byproducts of its application were discovered. As early as 1954 the Bendix Corporation placed the first numerically controlled production machine in operation in its South Bend plant. This special milling machine, with its new electronic control, was used to alleviate several problems in the manufacture of complex, three-dimensional cams. These devices for metering fuel in jet engines had to be absolutely accurate and, of course, identical so that they did not have to be fitted selectively to a specific engine. Bendix foresaw the solution to its problems in numerical control. Of even greater importance was a major reduction in the lead time required to produce a newly designed cam.

Techniques existing before numerical control required designing *for each cam* (or other part) a series of templates representing cross-sections of the cam along its longitudinal axis at intervals of .050 of an inch. Next, the template of each cross-section was enlarged to ten times actual size. Employees in the model shop then assembled the templates and filled in the space between them to produce a 10X model of the original cam. From this template a master was produced to be used for testing purposes and for making identical cams on existing duplicating equipment. But 14 weeks had elapsed from the time the design was finished until the first master cam was available. If the cam surface did not provide the correct fuel flow characteristics, how much more time would be lost in revising the model before a producible cam would be available?

It became much simpler to define the cams by mathematical parameters. The cam functions were fed into a computer, and a programed tape was produced to operate the new control system. Even in 1954 only two weeks were required to proceed from drawing to finished part. Lead time was reduced from 14 to two weeks, and engineering changes became simpler to accomplish, merely by cutting into the control tape and splicing in a change in the numerical definition of the cam surface. This, of course, is only one example of one advantage of numerical control—reduction in lead time.

ADVANTAGES OF NUMERICAL CONTROL SYSTEMS

Another major area of savings through numerical control is costs. Accountants often can't place an exact dollars-and-cents value on a reduction of 12 weeks in lead time. Other areas can be measured; one is tooling. In the case of the previous example several highly skilled, highly paid model makers worked for 14 weeks to make the 10X model. When the change was made to numerical control, a few mathematicians combined their efforts and, with the aid of a computer, took only two weeks to generate a control tape which represented, by punched holes, all the data on the model plus information to control the feed rate, coolant flow, and other functions which could not be handled by the model. All this was accomplished at a saving in tooling costs of approximately 80 percent.

The selling price of any product is heavily influenced by the cost of its production. Here is another area of savings created by numerical control. A wave guide cavity plate, with a variety of geometrical and nongeometrical cavities for an antenna assembly of a very sophisticated missile design, was produced by numerical control methods on a single spindle milling machine at a cost of $200. When it was manufactured by conventional methods, its cost had been $600.

The wave guide for a Doppler radar antenna manufactured by the Bendix Corporation is machined from a rectangular, hollow piece of extruded aluminum. The part formerly had been produced on a jig borer because of its high tolerance. This conventional method required 60 hours to produce tooling, six hours to set up on the machine, and eight hours to machine the wave guide. When the identical part was produced on a numerically controlled milling machine, lead time was reduced to four and one-half hours, setup to one hour, and machining time to four and one-half minutes. Numerical control for this wave guide resulted in clear savings of 90 percent in lead time, 85 percent in setup time, and 98 percent in machining time. The setup and machining time savings can be directly translated into dollar savings in the cost of the product.

In studying numerical control the manager should realize that he is looking not only at a new method but also at a new breed of machine tools. When machines are actuated by contact between a stylus and a cam, template, or model, their motions are often restricted. Slide feed rates are by necessity limited at high speeds by the inability of the tracing stylus to follow sudden changes in the contour of a model. Human operators have to slow down well before reaching the end point of a straight-line motion or of one which signifies a change in direction.

The advent of numerical control caused many successful machine tool manufacturers to take second looks at their designs. They found it necessary to build machines more rigidly in order to take advantage of the high dynamic responses inherent in the new drive systems. Not only were the basic machine members improved with integral stiffening, but many of the operating components were upgraded. Where a small diameter lead screw formerly sufficed, it became necessary to resort to larger-diameter precision screws with recirculating ball nuts to drive the machine slides. Stiffer bearings accommodated the higher loads imposed by high-frequency signals. All these machine modifications, which originated from a need for higher machine dynamics, resulted in standard machine tools with far greater accuracy than those previously manufactured by the same builders. Thus numerical control indirectly has provided the metalworking industry with machines of higher quality.

More rigid machine tool standards are just one facet of the increased accuracy attainable with numerical control. By definition, this new method denotes control by numbers, which are absolute and not influenced by tolerances of any sort. Therefore, the dimensional information recorded on the control medium is translated directly to slide motion. Part accuracy becomes a function of machine and electronic accuracy only. No longer does the machinist concern himself with the tolerance of the model, the loss of precision through the tracer mechanism, and further losses in the tracer system; with numerical control, he is concerned only with the accuracy of the data which serve as input to his control.

Once his requirements for increased accuracy have been satisfied, the manufacturing manager must face the problem of part-to-part similarity, or repeatability. Again, we can look to the control data as our source. The numbers are absolute and lack tolerance, but they apply identically from part to part. No operator intervenes even where rates are considered. Instead, the same numbers define the dimensional locations and other machining parameters on the first part and on the hundredth, thousandth, and, if need be, on the ten thousandth part. If the cutting tools are maintained within the desired tolerance limits, part-to-part variations will be held to an absolute minimum. As a result of these advantages of increased accuracy and repeatability, the manufacturing manager will realize a decided reduction in his scrap rate and his rework requirements.

Many indirect savings can result from the use of numerical control, although a specific value in dollars and cents cannot always be established. However, considerable dollar savings are possible in overhead and indirect labor. One further advantage is a reduction in inspection requirements, which reduces the number of inspection personnel and the time spent on inspection. When numerical control methods are used in manufacturing, it is common practice to inspect the first part manufactured in its entirety with a tape. When the accuracy of the part has been proved to be within allowable tolerances, the tape is certified by the inspection department and the production run uses copies of this certified tape. Spot checks of parts made during the production run can be made on only a few sections of the part, such as hole diameters and web thicknesses, to determine whether the cutting tools are still within tolerances. It is no longer necessary to make a complete inspection of every part off the production line.

Another peripheral advantage of numerical control is increased ability of the production staff to schedule operations in the shop. As an adjunct to numerical control programing, the production time for a part or an operation can be determined quite readily. In the case of a part manufactured on a simple point-to-point machine where the tape is prepared manually, the traverse rates and machine operation times can be estimated within reasonable limits. Where a complex part is to be manufactured on a machine operated by a numerical contouring control system, the tape would normally be prepared by a computer. The computer program calculates and prints out at the conclusion of the tape preparation the exact time required for machining the part. Since these times have been determined on the basis of machine capabilities, they represent standards, and deviations from them indicate that an operator is intervening in the machining process. The fact that the times for the operations are known makes it possible for the production scheduling staff to utilize available machine tools more efficiently by planning for new jobs on the machine as soon as one job is finished. Furthermore, a tighter rein may be kept on the operator because of the mathematical accuracy in planning a production operation on a specific machine.

Further advantages accrue through the reduction of hard tooling requirements. Where the manager was formerly faced with storing special fixtures and large models, cams, or templates, he now has a roll of tape to look after. In his former production methods, large areas of floor space were required for storing the tooling for the tracer system. Now he can often get by with a file cabinet for storage.

Many savings have been realized through the proper use of numerical control. However, no one can flatly state that it is the cure-all for every production problem. Many misconceptions arise regarding its use, particularly because it is often referred to as "automation." Many production managers, seeing this word, picture in their minds the Detroit type of manufacturing where parts roll off the production lines in tens of thousands a day. This is not the realm of numerical control, although it could conceivably in special cases fit into mass production operations. Numerical control is designed for shorter-run applications whose cost of tooling is relatively high for the number of parts manufactured. If tooling cost can be reduced substantially, as it normally can by using numerical control, then the individual part cost can be reduced. As longer production runs are possible, the tooling costs are amortized over a larger number of pieces. Therefore, savings in tooling do not represent as great a part of the individual piece cost.

Numerical control has also been the salvation of manufacturing managers when a part is of extreme complexity. This is particulary true of contouring operations in which it is very difficult to define the part for tracer control. Parts which formerly were impossible to produce can now be manufactured by numerical control. The mathematical description of the part which is fed into the computer can be translated readily by the existing computer routines into a series of coordinate dimensions which define the part's surface. While it was necessary in the past to make assemblies or to change the design of parts, many are now made as integral pieces in accordance with good engineering design practices.

Another area in which numerical control has proved valuable is product development. In many existing operations a part is designed and prototypes are manually prepared in a model shop. After a few prototypes have been made, they are tested. On the first try the part may be found lacking in some design characteristics so that it becomes necessary to redesign it. The model must then be revised or a new model produced manually. This procedure is repeated as often as required, until a satisfactory working part is obtained. With numerical control it is possible in many cases to simplify the design operation by defining the part by mathematical parameters, and the first prototype model can be made from the tape which has been programed in accordance with the original design engineering calculations. If the part does not meet requirements, it is necessary not to remake or rework a model but only to regenerate a section of tape which describes the area to be changed. If a change is made, its configuration is inserted in the tape from which the prototype part is made. When the part is finally accepted as meeting specifications, the tape can be regenerated into several copies and production of a part can begin much earlier than would be possible under former methods.

Numerical control can also prove valuable in maintaining a spare-parts inventory. Every manager is well aware of the amount of space required to stock sufficient spare parts to fulfill future customer requirements. At the completion of a production run, a large number of spares are run off and stocked. If this stock reaches a critically low point, the hard tooling is removed from storage and set up on the machine. Because of the time and cost of this lengthy setup procedure, a large number of spare parts will again be manufactured to replenish stocks. This method of operation is costly from the standpoint of using floor space to stock the large quantities of spares and also from the standpoint of tying up capital in a spare-parts inventory. How much more efficient, and how much less costly, it would be if smaller quantities could be run for spare-parts inventory at lower costs. Numerical control again provides the answer. The setup problem is reduced merely by inserting a tape into a control unit. Since loading the control with a tape is a simple operation, small quantities of spare parts can be run off economically, as contrasted to the expensive hard tooling methods. And of course, if a smaller spare-parts inventory is maintained, a smaller amount of an organization's capital will be tied up. More will be available for investment and expansion of the organization.

QUESTIONS THE MANUFACTURING MANAGER SHOULD ASK

The manufacturing manager, before making any decision regarding numerical control, will want to review within his organization all the points covered earlier in this chapter. He will want to investigate the present production costs, tooling costs, productivity ratios, scrap rates, inspection time, and other economic factors of his present methods. He will want to compare these factors with those which are attainable through numerical control in order to make a sound decision on the purchase of new manufacturing facilities. Once he has made up his mind to use numerical control, he still must investigate many considerations.

The first area deserving inspection is the type of tool and system to choose for his first step into numerical control. Should a simple machine with a point-to-point system be purchased, or should he jump right in with both feet and obtain a complex, continuous-path machining system? He will find no simple answer. The manager should first investigate his needs and the areas where his production schedules are affected by shortcomings in his existing machining operations. One factor to consider is that a drilling machine or a jig borer, with a point-to-point control system, requires less preparation for its use. With a simple point-to-point system it is necessary only to define mathematically the points at which machine operations, such as drilling and boring, are to occur. These points represent nothing more than dimensional information from a drawing or tabulation. No complex computer routines are required to make a tape for this type of equipment. However, simple computer programs may assist in programing where the hole pattern is repetitious. Conversely, if the manager should decide to begin with a contouring system, then he must give more consideration to his programing methods and the availability of computers.

In either case the manager should approach the introduction of numerical control from three aspects. The first is his programing or data-preparation operation. Again, consideration will have to be given to the type of control (point-to-point or continuous path) and the type of machine. If he is to prepare his tapes without the aid of computers, where will he obtain the programers? What is the volume of work? Many manufacturers have found it expedient to utilize members of their tool engineering staff to set up and organize the manual programing operation. The tool engineers are familiar with the machining operations and with tool design. It is only one step more from designing hard tooling to designing tape tooling. This type of employee can, with very little additional training, prove to be excellent in part programing.

The more complex machining systems in which computers are used for tape preparation present a different problem. A multiplicity of skills is required. First, these systems demand mathematicians who are familiar with manufacturing operations to prepare computer programs which transpose a mathematical definition of the part into coded signals on a control medium. Programers, who may be mathematicians with lower-level skill, are also required to prepare the computer inputs on the basis of the mathematical analysis. And finally, part programers must utilize the new computer language to define the part to be manufactured. Of course, these requirements have been partially met by various industry groups which have pooled their strengths and developed various computer programs.

If existing programs are used, their applicability to available computers should be investigated. Programs are available for large, complex computers and for smaller, less sophisticated data processing equipment. However, numerical control programs are not available for all the computers on the market. If a computer for which a program has been written is not available, the manager might consider leasing time at a local data processing center.

In any event he will have to train subordinates in the use of computer languages. He should investigate the various programing languages and their capabilities to determine how difficult it is to train employees in their use. While some computer programs may seem economical because they do not require extensive equipment, their language may be very difficult and inefficient. In other cases the language may be quite simple and straightforward but require a large, expensive computer installation for its utilization. The manufacturing manager must investigate and consider all these factors.

A second area of management concern is the manufacturing operation itself. The manufacturing manager may want to reorganize his entire operation in order to use his numerically controlled machines most effectively. Because of increased production rates and lower production costs it may be desirable to funnel work from other manufacturing operations through the numerically controlled equipment. This will upset the existing production scheduling procedures and will require re-education of the production personnel.

A group may be set up to determine which parts should be manufactured under numerical control and which on conventional equipment. This group must be highly specialized and capable of judging the best production methods for specific items at an early stage in design. If the probable cost savings indicate a turn toward numerical control, then the production specialist should work with engineering designers to have the parts specified in such a manner as to simplify programing. The selection of the parts to be produced on numerically controlled machines is an important responsibility and will determine the success or failure of a numerical control operation.

As numerical control gains a foothold within an organization, the engineering department should realign its thinking toward designing more and more with this new manufacturing technique in mind. This may require revision of existing dimensioning procedures. Where production designers were formerly interested in providing a machine operator or a tool engineer with a set of dimensions to facilitate operation of the machine tool, consideration for numerically controlled production should attempt to ease the programer's burden. This can be accomplished in accordance with a Cartesian coordinate system in which all dimensions are referred to the origin of the coordinate system, which may be on or off the part. Since these dimensions are in absolute form, they may be used readily for manual preparation of tapes or preparation of data for computer input. An alternative method is to indicate the location of specific points on the part drawing and then to tabulate the dimensional information. For more complex parts, in which highly sophisticated computer routines are used, it is more practical to leave the part without dimensions as they are currently understood. Instead, part surfaces and part profiles should be defined by mathematical definitions which are then used as input for the more specialized computer programs.

WHAT ABOUT MAINTENANCE?

The final consideration to be made after deciding to employ numerical control is maintenance of the equipment. The initial task is evaluating the equipment to be purchased to assess its maintainability. Most of the newer numerical control systems utilize solid-state circuitry in their logic. The components are considerably more reliable than those in the earlier vacuum-tube types of logic. However, the electronic components are not completely failureproof, so the evaluators must insure that the systems under consideration are easily maintained, both in scheduled and in unscheduled servicing. The system should assure that the components are readily accessible to maintenance personnel. The best arrangement is to use small, compact, printed circuit cards, each containing a limited amount of circuitry. Thus, if a failure occurs within the system, it is relatively simple to locate the module with the defective component and to replace it. Maintenance is assisted greatly if the control system has checkpoints at which electronic signals are measured. The more checkpoints, the simpler it becomes for the maintenance technician to locate the source of trouble. Some manufacturers of numerical control systems provide integral test signals. This feature further eases the job of the technician, for he can track down the source of difficulty through the use of buttons and switches already installed in the control. Little if any peripheral test equipment is required.

The manufacturing manager must plan for periodic preventive maintenance of the equipment. It is not enough to operate a numerical control system until it fails and then attempt to locate the source of failure. If this method is followed, the production employees may find themselves irreparably damaging parts on which a large number of machining hours have been spent, or perhaps even damaging the machine itself. A more sensible procedure is to schedule periodic inspections of the numerical control system. A simple visual check should be made each day before beginning machining operations. The more failure-prone circuits should be tested weekly to determine their operational capabilities. A more intensive and time-consuming test of the control system should be conducted monthly. At least once a year, and perhaps more frequently depending upon the operating environment, the entire system should be checked and all marginal components replaced. In most cases the numerical control manufacturer provides a recommended maintenance schedule for his equipment so the systems will operate with a minimum of unscheduled down time.

System maintainability and a well-coordinated preventive maintenance schedule are only two parts of the program. The final part, and the one without which the other two become unworkable, is selection of maintenance employees. Even the simplest drilling machine system requires a knowledgeable electronic technician for its proper maintenance. The plant electrician, with his screwdriver and a pair of pliers, can hardly be expected to understand this new generation of highly complex systems. Instead, highly skilled electronic technicians must be selected to assure maximum operating time of the numerical control systems. A ready source of good technicians is the armed services. Much of the most recent radar and missile electronic circuitry is similar to that used in numerical control systems. A man with a good background in maintenance of military electronics should have little difficulty adapting himself to machine tool controls.

Again, a good source of information regarding electronic maintenance requirements is the numerical control manufacturers. Most of them offer training courses in maintenance and have established prerequisites for attendance. Where a large amount of numerically controlled equipment is expected to be installed, it may be more economical for an organization to initiate its own training program guided by information provided by the manufacturer. This will permit promotion from within, thus developing the capabilities of employees to suit the organization's requirements. But no matter what method is chosen for obtaining maintenance employees, it is still of the utmost importance that highly qualified, efficient electronic technicians be available to assure the maximum payback of the numerical control systems through high use factors on the equipment.

*   *   *

If an organization has made a thorough study of its manufacturing facilities, it will normally find that it needs numerical control. All members of general management are interested in reductions in cost and lead time, improved quality, higher orders or accuracy, reduced inspection and storage requirements, and the other advantages reviewed earlier. The particular area of general interest will be concerned with the final cost of the product and how it relates to the competitive position in the marketplace.

Other managers will find it necessary to revise their thinking about internal procedures. New engineering and design techniques may develop from the use of numerical control; new maintenance methods will be established; the data processing department will gain new importance. No matter how many other employees are involved in various aspects of the numerical control process, it is still the manufacturing manager who must weigh the advantages, select the correct equipment, coordinate the programing and maintenance operations, and schedule production. The major responsibility for the successful implementation of numerical control rests on his shoulders.

PART THREE

Related Functions and Services

PROFILES OF INDUSTRIAL ENGINEERING

By JOSEPH E. KOCHMAR

Industrial engineers represent different things to different people in different companies. Regardless of their diversity of activity, however, they strive toward similar objectives, employ a common methodology, and perform a like range of related functions.

Industrial engineers assume a number of specialized roles and are known by a variety of names, depending upon the nuance of emphasis used by their employers. For example, the "labor control" engineer is primarily engaged in time study, job evaluation, and wage incentives; the "cost control" engineer extends his scope to include machine efficiency, materials utilization, and overhead expense; the "cost planning" engineer specifies product costs and prepares cost budgets; the "production" engineer concentrates on mechanical problems, maintenance requirements, and equipment improvements; the "methods" engineer pursues work simplification, process flow, and plant layout; the "economics" engineer evaluates the profitability of new products, processes, and facilities.

All these engineering specialties—whether practiced in breadth or in depth—are united by their purpose and methodology. Industrial engineering may be defined as the discipline which applies the scientific method toward the end of realizing the best possible return on manufacturing investment through attaining the highest productivity and at the least cost. It utilizes a body of technical knowledge derived primarily from physics, chemistry, mathematics, economics, and psychology. As an applied science, it follows the inductive approach of observation, analysis, and synthesis for determining manufacturing requirements. As an industrial art, it requires proficiency in defining

JOSEPH E. KOCHMAR is Director of Industrial Engineering, Continental Can Company, Inc., New York.

production problems, in ascertaining their specific causes, and in proposing alternatives for their solution.

The effective industrial engineer is primarily interested in creating and maintaining profits. He integrates his activities with the income and cost objectives of manufacturing management. The line manager of manufacturing looks to him as a medium for gaining an advantage over competitors.

The well-rounded industrial engineer understands the delicate balance of quality, service, and cost in the manufacturing operation. He recognizes that costs must be controlled and reduced, but he also appreciates the demands of quality and service. Above all, he realizes the priority of profit. He is result-oriented rather than technique-oriented; this means that he is more concerned with contributing to expected results than with applying sophisticated techniques. He is, to put it grandly, dedicated to optimizing the opportunities and minimizing the risks of the manufacturing enterprise.

VISTAS OF MANUFACTURING

The imaginative industrial engineer envisions a revolutionary change in the character of manufacturing operations. He anticipates the rate of technological change applicable to his particular industry as well as to his individual company. He recognizes, for instance, that the forces of competition, domestic as well as international, will intensify their squeeze on prices, costs, and profits. Marketing demands will continue to cause new products to be generated more frequently and introduced into the market more quickly. The average product life will decrease, and product turnover will increase. As a corollary, the economic lifetime of manufacturing processes, production facilities, and plant layout will diminish.

Production demands will accelerate the automation of the line process for manufacturing volume products. Furthermore, the many special-purpose machines for job-lot products will be replaced by single multipurpose machines. In both instances, equipment will be constructed of modules and will operate to closer tolerances. Equipment tended by operators will give way to equipment programed by tapes.

The manufacturing organization is evolving into three basic categories of personnel: process monitors, maintenance mechanics, and technical managers, whose common purpose is to keep the facilities operating continuously. Consequently, the fullest possible equipment utilization and machine efficiency will be accentuated, and idle capacity and down time must be eliminated as much as is consistent with safe operations. Maintenance and repair expenses will thus become relatively more significant than direct labor costs as factors in overall product cost.

The technology of automatic data processing will minimize many of the areas of what is now considered to be clerical work, while giving rise to new concepts of clerical duties. Source data for manufacturing will be correlated to serve the needs of sales and finance; the planning and control of manufacturing operations will be unified in the framework of a total management information system. These changes are covered more fully elsewhere in this volume. All we need do here is to remark how, in this fast-changing climate, the industrial engineer is indeed presented with a challenge to identify and meet the future needs for his professional services.

Measurement, productivity, incentive, and organization engineering deal primarily with short-range opportunities for improvement. Methods, venture, and project engineering, on the other hand, deal essentially with long-term potentialities. All these functions are technical pursuits of industrial engineering, and all are growth areas for its services; consequently we shall discuss each of them at some length. Some companies employ industrial engineers in such duties as cost estimating, financial budgeting, office systems, quality control, and production planning. These functions, however, are not normally included in the scope of industrial engineering, and, since most of them are covered elsewhere, we shall not be concerned with them.

MEASURING ENGINEERING

Many companies apply engineered standards only to measure labor costs. However, others use engineered criteria to specify requirements for production volume, manufacturing costs, factory income, and plant investment. This broader use of operating measurements will become even more prevalent in progressive companies, for the new era of manufacturing will emphasize the measurement of the total enterprise rather than of individual segments. For example, in physical resources the fundamental yardstick will be production capacity. Supplementary criteria will be equipment utilization, space utilization, and inventory turnover.

Maintenance and repairs are becoming more significant items of expense control, as we have seen. Material yield will remain a substantial cost in many industries. Direct labor, however, will dwindle into an ever smaller element of cost control.

The techniques of measurement—motion analysis, time study, work sampling, controlled experimentation, linear programing, or system simulation—are all aspects of the same scientific method involving factual observations, comprehensive analyses, and valid conclusions. The conventional approach of measuring performance by comparing standards with actual results will in the future be overshadowed by a new dimension in manufacturing measurement—the measurement of progress toward the attainment of *total plant profit potential*. This overall criterion is based on predetermination of maximum income from full production levels and least-cost methods in combination with minimum capital for facilities and inventories.

PRODUCTIVITY ENGINEERING

Productivity engineering comprises the design and installation of systems for planning, organizing, and controlling manufacturing profit improvement through the full utilization of available resources at minimum cost. The essential ingredients are specific objectives, definitive programs, and systematic follow-up.

Objectives for productivity improvement should be formulated by the factory manager, with the counsel of the industrial engineer, and communicated down the line. They should be formalized in terms of the degree of improvement required for a specified time period, all in relation to "total plant profit potential." Specific objectives should be established for plant capacity, equipment utilization, space utilization, inventory turnover, and significant items of cost control. Definitive productivity improvement programs specify the actions planned, assign individual responsibilities, establish time schedules, and estimate anticipated results. These programs should be required by the line manager from every supervisor and be coordinated by his staff industrial engineer.

Effective control requires follow-up of progress in relation to programs; that is, reviewing current status, probable bottlenecks, and changes in plans. Overall results should be appraised at least monthly.

There is no universal prescription or magic formula for productivity improvement. However lamentable this fact may be, it is also understandable since each plant has a character of its own with its individual potentials, individual problems, individual managers, and individual engineers. Nonetheless, some common practices have generated substantial rates of profit increase. Potentials and problems are analyzed in depth. Specific objectives for productivity improvement are understood and accepted by all supervisors. Explicit programs for increasing productivity are developed by the supervisors in each area of responsibility. Progress is evaluated by the industrial engineer and communicated by the plant manager to all supervisors. This integrated approach of *engineered management,* when applied in a climate of enthusiasm and persistence, generates outstanding results.

INCENTIVE ENGINEERING

Wage incentive plans are continuing to fall out of favor in major corporations because highly mechanized plants automatically shift the production pace from the hands of the worker to the wheels of the machine. Managerial incentive plans are evolving as a superior method of promoting the most effective application of technical and supervisory skills. They stimulate the attainment of "total plant profit potential" from lower manufacturing costs as well as from higher production volume. They motivate higher earnings by eliciting greater attention to corporate profit and investment goals. They also encourage personal growth for individual supervisors by broadening their perspective of concept and of activity.

Industrial engineers should expand their responsibilities to include developing systems of management incentives that are fully integrated with plant profit, cost, and investment objectives. Incentives for manufacturing management should be designed to permit eventual correlation with incentives for other management personnel.

ORGANIZATION ENGINEERING

Determination of job content for hourly workers and definition of responsibilities for supervisory employees will continue to be industrial engineering functions in the field of organization. However, analysis of job specifications will become more technical and more demanding because of the increasing complexity of manufacturing operations. Since this is true, the nontechnical duties of job and salary evaluation can best be transferred from industrial engineering to the industrial relations or the personnel department.

The industrial engineer is expected to establish qualitative and quantitative criteria to guide manufacturing management in evaluating satisfactory performance of process monitors, maintenance mechanics, and technical managers, as we have seen. Merit ratings of individuals and performance appraisals of groups will increase in practice, which will create an even more significant demand from manufacturing for the industrial engineering staff functions.

METHODS ENGINEERING

Increased productivity and improved production methods are recognized throughout industry as essential to the progress and growth of a manufacturing enterprise. While productivity improvement deals with the present and is achieved by meeting objectives with current practices, materials, and equipment, methods engineering challenges the present and deals with creativity in manufacturing.

Opportunities to lower costs through better methods continue to expand as a result of numerous technological advancements. Line managers should consider the reduction of manufacturing cost of such critical importance that they enlist the abilities of every employee in this effort. In particular, the primary responsibility for methods improvements should be vested in all levels of management from the chairman of the board to the first-line supervisor. Assistance to management in exploiting the fullest use of new methods to improve profit should be unleashed by industrial engineering through its analytical techniques, creative abilities, and imaginative skills.

Consistent with the concept of "total plant profit potential," the industrial engineer maintains a log of all methods ideas in his plant and company. These potentials should be translated into objectives and programs to be realized by individual supervisors, group departments, and overall plants. The industrial engineer initiates, develops, and evaluates specific proposals for managerial decisions. He coordinates the detailed plans for installing methods projects in collaboration with appropriate line and staff members. Most of all, he participates in the installation of each methods project and follows it up to its successful completion.

The most significant responsibility of the industrial engineer in methods improvement is the constant stimulation and motivation of all supervisors to an attitude of transcending conventional patterns. He must be inquisitive and enthusiastic. Methods improvement is neither a one-man job nor a one-shot proposition. It must be a way of life for every supervisor in the company. In fact, it must be the predominant activity of every industrial engineer in every manufacturing operation.

VENTURE ENGINEERING

The industrial engineer, to be successful, must coordinate his activities with the product development, equipment engineering, and manufacturing departments. He translates product, process, and equipment objectives into terms meaningful to manufacturing and determines their probable effects on income, cost, and investment. He also estimates the financial and technical resources necessary to complete the projects. In his venture analysis it is essential for the industrial engineer to take into consideration the full range of alternatives from "greatest opportunity and highest risk" to "smallest opportunity and lowest risk."

The industrial engineer assigns the function of venture engineering to an engineer or his staff who can devote his talents exclusively to projects that pertain to the future growth of the enterprise. This subordinate should be familiar with the capabilities as well as the limitations of present products, processes, and equipment, and he must keep abreast of all technological and competitive developments affecting his industry. Above all, he should be an engineer of vision, imagination, and creativity, for venture engineering demands just these qualities.

PROJECT ENGINEERING

If the rate of technological change requires faster decisions, as it does, it certainly also demands faster action. New products are being commercialized as rapidly as possible, and new equipment must be operated at the earliest practicable date.

Project engineering, also called project management, is concerned with the design and application of systems for planning and controlling major changes in manufacturing resources. A complete system which is intended to integrate technical and financial requirements must include the following elements:

1. Project proposal summarizing overall objectives and means of accomplishment.
2. Project substantiation detailing need, work, and material requirements, as well as time and cost schedules.
3. Project progress reporting of the degree of success and the status of time and cost plans.
4. Project realization appraising achievement of results and performance against time and cost schedules.

The function of project engineering should be handled by an engineer who possesses specialized abilities in planning, organizing, and control. He should be familiar with modern planning and control tools such as Critical Path Method (CPM), Program Evaluation and Review Technique (PERT), and other offsprings of the Gantt charting technique whose purpose is to aid the project manager in getting his job done with the least repetition, in the correct sequence of events, with the least amount of material, and in the quickest time consistent with efficiency.

THE PLACE OF INDUSTRIAL ENGINEERING
IN THE OVERALL ORGANIZATION STRUCTURE

The future place of the industrial engineering function in the organization structure depends upon the character and size of the company, its needs for such services, and its organizational philosophy. The following examples represent actual company practices which cover the complete range of diversity.

In a small company with several food processing plants, the chief industrial engineer reports to a corporate manager of manufacturing and directs a staff of specialists who provide consulting services to the various plant facilities.

In a medium-size multiplant company which manufactures clothing fasteners, the manager of industrial engineering reports to a general manager of production. Corporate staff engineers as well as resident plant industrial engineers report to the manager of industrial engineering.

In a large multidivision and multiplant company which manufactures a diversified line of packaging products, industrial engineering is organized within the manufacturing department at the corporate, divisional, and plant levels. At headquarters the director of industrial engineering reports to a general manager of operations engineering who is responsible for coordinating the disciplines of manufacturing, plant, and industrial engineering. The director has centralized responsibility for developing policies and procedures and for designing managerial systems and engineering techniques for companywide application. Furthermore, he appraises for corporate management the potentials, objectives, programs, results, and trends relative to the best use of the total manufacturing resources within the company. At the divisional level a manager of industrial engineering reports on a line to the manager of manufacturing and functionally to the corporate director of industrial engineering. The division manager is responsible for implementing company policies, procedures, systems, and techniques and provides consulting services to his respective plants. At the factory level a plant industrial engineer reports directly to the plant manager and functionally to the division manager of industrial engineering. In this decentralized concept the plant industrial engineer is regarded as a member of the plant manager's team and also as a consultant to all plant supervisors.

Regardless of the size or complexity of the company, industrial engineering can be tailored to an organization structure of centralization, decentralization, or any combination thereof. The form of organization structure is, actually, secondary in importance to the qualifications of the staff.

THE MARK OF A PROFESSIONAL

Whether industrial engineering will continue to broaden its range depends primarily upon the professionalism of the practitioners and their ability to adapt their future efforts toward the changing needs of manufacturing management.

The professional industrial engineer has the characteristics of an innovator, a technician, a manager, and a salesman. He draws on the reservoir of scientific principles, adapts his knowledge to technical and managerial determinations, and attains results by the authority of his abilities and his persuasiveness.

As a man of integrity, he is factual in his observations, analyses, and conclusions. He establishes operating measurements on the basis of objective requirements, not subjective opinions. He reports actual conditions and expresses his convictions, regardless of whether they are popular.

The professional industrial engineer is dependable. He defines problems in their proper perspective, and he reports relevant facts with accuracy and draws pertinent conclusions with validity. He achieves his objectives in total and accomplishes results on schedule.

The professional also generates enthusiasm. He reflects an intense desire to excel in all his endeavors. He is dedicated to his profession and to his company. He regards serious problems not as insurmountable handicaps but as challenging opportunities.

The industrial engineer may be educated either as a specialist in mechanical, chemical, or management engineering or as a generalist in the physical, mathematical, or social sciences. He continues to keep abreast of the technology of industrial engineering and related fields. He possesses a wealth of experience as a practitioner in a broad range of industrial engineering activities. The professional industrial engineer is also an exemplar of managerial ability to his subordinates, colleagues, and superiors. He formulates objectives, develops programs, defines projects, and specifies responsibility. He selects and develops future "pros." He evaluates the results of his own organization for progressive improvement.

The professional industrial engineer is recognized as a leader when he effectively communicates his knowledge up and down and along the line; when he successfully persuades his superiors, motivates his colleagues, and inspires his subordinates; when he applies his creative talents to originate technologies for his profession and his company.

In short, integrity, dependability, enthusiasm, ability, and leadership are the hallmarks of an ideal professional industrial engineer. Any individual industrial engineer will measure his self-development against these ideal traits.

As a prerequisite to its future success, the profession of industrial engineering must apply the scientific method to its own practices and practitioners. First, industrial engineering must identify both the short- and long-range needs of the company. In this connection, it should appraise the available manufacturing profit potential from full production levels and least-cost methods in conjunction with minimum resources for facilities and inventories. It should also envision the growth opportunities of the enterprise through product innovations and revolutionary facilities. Second, industrial engineering must fulfill these specific needs through a staff of technically competent and energetic engineers. This professional approach represents the difference between mediocrity and excellence of industrial engineering in American industry.

AN ORGANIZED APPROACH TO LOWER MANUFACTURING COSTS

By RICHARD A. SEAGRAVE

Today, more than ever before in history, to be successful in the appliance industry—as in many others—requires the right combination of high quality, large volume, and low-cost manufacturing. Although the sales volume of appliances has increased substantially in the past five years, the pressures of extreme competition in the marketplace have lowered retail prices each year. For example: The price of an automatic washer today is roughly 85 percent of what it was between 1947 and 1949.[1] Its quality, features, reliability, and capacity have been vastly improved. This decline in selling price has taken place in spite of increased labor and raw-material costs. During the same period of time, the selling-price index of automobiles has increased to 137 percent of that prevailing from 1947 to 1949. Yet the manufacture of automatic washers and the manufacture of automobiles require similar materials, skills, and technologies.

Those manufacturers that have survived and still make profits have been able to lower prices by continually reducing their costs; to continue to do so in the future is the challenge facing every appliance maker, for those companies which meet this challenge successfully will be the future leaders in their industry. Of course, a great deal of attention must also be given to reducing marketing and distribution costs, but the highest cost factor in the delivered price of an appliance is still what it always has been: manufacturing, which includes material, labor, and overhead.

Since the primary objective of *any* manufacturing organization must be to increase profits by reducing costs and improving quality, an outline of the principles employed by Whirlpool's manufacturing engineering department to

RICHARD A. SEAGRAVE is Director of Manufacturing Engineering, Whirlpool Corporation, St. Joseph Division, St. Joseph, Michigan.

[1] Source: Bureau of Labor Statistics.

accomplish these objectives may be of interest. For purposes of illustration, it might be well to use as an example a program which has been carried out over the past five years. It involved the expenditure of approximately $10 million on facilities and tooling. More than 100 major pieces of equipment were procured and placed in production, including an automated transfer line for gear case housings; a transfer line for machining, grinding, and spline rolling agitator shafts; a hobbing line for pinions; a chucker; a hobber; and a special-purpose drilling and tapping machine for two transmission gears. We obtained carbide tooled screw machines and such other items as automatic welders, brazers, and induction heat treating equipment.

The results achieved through this total program, using the principles to be discussed here, have been proof to us that we have a firm foundation of management concepts on which to build in the future. Some of the measurable benefits are a significant decrease in labor costs, a higher production volume capability, and improved product reliability. This product reliability—that is, the ability of the product to function in the customer's home without breakdowns—is obviously an important contributor to the overall quality image of the company and its product in the consumer's mind.

To accomplish these results with a minimum investment of time and money while continuing to produce at peak schedules required the proper mix of concepts, practices, and understanding on the part of many different groups. Our approach can be summarized under the following headings:

1. Common goals and objectives.
2. Organization—function and responsibilities.
    a. Processing (tools and operations) :
        (1) New-model program.
        (2) Make-buy evaluation.
        (3) Parts to print.
        (4) Production performance specifications.
        (5) Training.
        (6) Turnover.
    b. Maintenance:
        (1) Work order system.
        (2) Planned maintenance.
        (3) Maintenance performance indicators.
    c. Plant engineering:
        (1) Facility engineering.
        (2) Material handling and utilities engineering.
    d. Industrial engineering:
        (1) Labor standards.

(2) Financial analysis.
  e. Process capability:
    (1) Statistical analysis.
    (2) Equipment and process capability.
  f. Administration and control:
    (1) New-model and project program control.
    (2) Post-audit.
    (3) Cost reduction.
3. Financial control:
  a. Profit-awareness.
  b. Budgets ("checkbook" concept).
  c. Trend indicators:
    (1) Expense dollar areas.
    (2) Tooling dollar areas.
    (3) Capital dollar areas.
  d. Perishable tools and factory supplies.

Common Goals and Objectives

Too much cannot be said about instilling a motivation for cooperation and teamwork throughout the entire company, for such a spirit must exist if the best results are to be obtained in any program, regardless of its magnitude. All the departments of a company participate in one way or another in all its projects and have a stake in the outcome of each.

Any company can buy equipment and materials; the people who use them make the difference. Managers should constantly motivate employees to work together toward common objectives and goals. Each individual must feel his responsibility for the end results, and credit for accomplishment certainly must be given to all who participate in a program. At the same time, the responsibility for specific results can be spelled out by supervisors so that the proper periodic judgments of individual performance can be made.

Whirlpool's system for accomplishing common goals and objectives is built on the concept that continuous improvement in individual performance is necessary—and will be possible if the proper attitudes and management climate exist. Each year overall key objectives are developed for every division. Each objective is broken down into specific goals for each manager during a job-understanding discussion between him and his supervisor. These goals are recorded and reviewed periodically by the participants during the year. At the end of the year, a complete report of performance compared with objectives or goals is made out and discussed. The use of available facts—not opinions—induces productive understanding. Operations which are progressing smoothly are noted and balanced against items in need of improvement during the following year. This system has been most helpful in promoting the achievement of common goals and in developing coordination and cooperation between individuals and departments.

Organization

At Whirlpool's St. Joseph Division the manufacturing engineering section has prime responsibility for executing new production ventures and phasing in new models. Tied in closely with the program from start to finish, however, are the manufacturing, quality control, material control, controller, industrial relations, and resident engineering departments.

EXHIBIT 1

ORGANIZATION OF THE PRIMARY FUNCTIONS OF MANUFACTURING
ENGINEERING

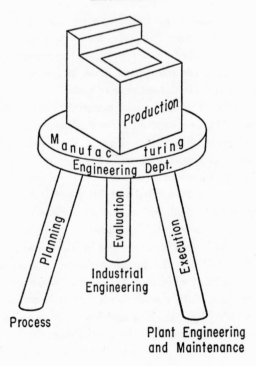

The organization of the manufacturing engineering section is based on the idea that three primary functions must be effective if the desired results are to be accomplished: planning, evaluation, and execution. Figuratively, the three functions can be shown as three columns which support production, each of them equally responsible for supporting the load.

The responsibility for performing each function is given to one of the following groups, all of which act in coordination to meet the established objectives:

- *Planning:* Process, tool, and methods engineering (prime responsibility).
- *Evaluation:* Industrial engineering.
- *Execution:* Plant engineering and maintenance.

This concept can be diagramed as shown in Exhibit 1.

The manufacturing engineering section is a flexible unit which is altered as the needs of the division and the talents of its personnel dictate. The organizational structure which has been utilized for the past several years is shown in Exhibit 2.

In order to gain further insight into the workings of the organization, we shall discuss each area separately, outlining some of the principal functions, policies, and responsibilities.

PROCESSING (TOOLS AND OPERATIONS DEPARTMENT)

Since the process group is the function which is considered to be responsible for initiating changes, let's discuss it first. What is processing and how is it done? Exhibit 3 represents a chart of our current organization pattern.

New-model program. In our system, processing is the function which translates product engineering designs into reality at the lowest possible cost and within quality specifications. The process engineer and the product engineer work hand in hand to bring new models into production. This can be shown by the step diagram of the new model pre-production planning system which is reproduced as Exhibit 4. By studying this outline, it can be seen that the process engineer is a key participant in making changes from the idea stage on through production. He is responsible for arriving at the original cost estimate and then for keeping within limits he has established. His job performance is measured by his ability to meet cost and quality goals.

The process engineers are responsible for the execution of each step in the new-model program. They must communicate closely with the other departments concerned and resolve problems as they arise.

Make-buy evaluation. One of the first processing activities is to resolve the make-buy question. It is our goal to make parts in our plants if making is more profitable over the long run. In most cases past experience, availability

EXHIBIT 2

MANUFACTURING ENGINEERING ORGANIZATION

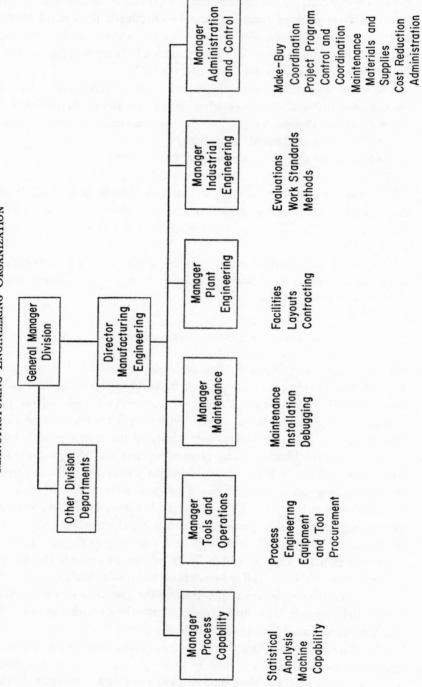

EXHIBIT 3

ORGANIZATION OF THE TOOLS AND OPERATIONS DEPARTMENT

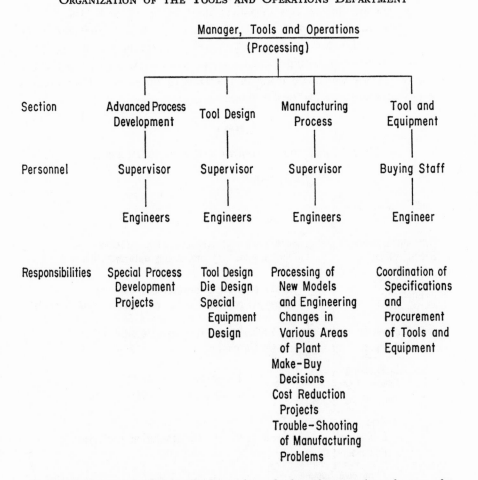

of equipment, and facilities will determine whether the part is to be a make or a buy item. The manufacture of many parts which formerly were purchased has been integrated into our plants, and this has been a major factor in improving our costs. Each purchased part was evaluated, and a venture analysis was completed on it which took account of cost, quality, and other factors and included a return-on-investment and breakeven calculation. In general, the decision has been made to make a part if it will improve our overall profitability as measured by return on investment. Occasionally, however, a part which has heretofore been made is changed to a buy item because of cost or lack of capacity.

Parts to print. In order to reduce production problems and insure the high quality of the finished product, a firm policy has been established regarding parts to print. This policy states that parts and prints must agree where fit and function are factors. Any deviations must be approved by the resident engineer before quality control will approve a process for production. The policy requires the process engineer to develop means of making the parts according to the engineering specs before production starts. It also requires that any changes which are made in tolerance be approved by the product engineer who is responsible for the design.

EXHIBIT 4

NEW MODEL PRE-PRODUCTION PLANNING PROGRAM

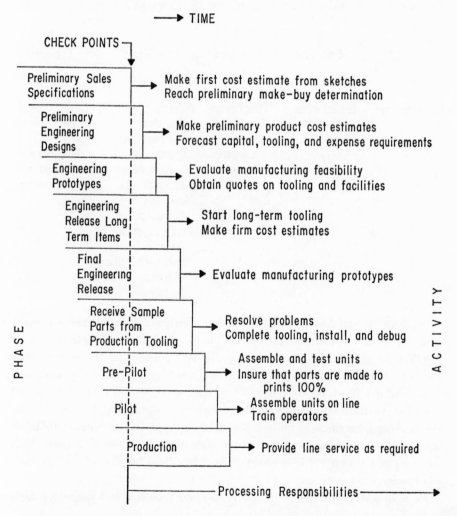

→ TIME

CHECK POINTS

| Preliminary Sales Specifications | → Make first cost estimate from sketches
Reach preliminary make–buy determination |

Preliminary Engineering Designs → Make preliminary product cost estimates
Forecast capital, tooling, and expense requirements

Engineering Prototypes → Evaluate manufacturing feasibility
Obtain quotes on tooling and facilities

Engineering Release Long Term Items → Start long-term tooling
Make firm cost estimates

Final Engineering Release → Evaluate manufacturing prototypes

Receive Sample Parts from Production Tooling → Resolve problems
Complete tooling, install, and debug

Pre-Pilot → Assemble and test units
Insure that parts are made to prints 100%

Pilot → Assemble units on line
Train operators

Production → Provide line service as required

PHASE   ACTIVITY

————— Processing Responsibilities —————→

The process engineer is responsible for making a part to meet the engineering print. He reviews the print design before release, and his acceptance of the design when it is released constitutes an agreement to make the part to print. If he is in doubt about a particular tolerance or dimension after the print has been issued, he must treat it as an exception. This system provides a definite measurement of the process engineer's performance in carrying out his responsibility for quality processes and design.

Production performance specifications. The process engineer is responsible for establishing production performance specifications. In addition to spelling out cycle times for the equipment and quality specs, he must see that each piece of equipment is run under simulated production conditions on the vendor's floor before it is approved for shipment. The production acceptance run of two hours is the specified minimum, and in some cases a run may last four hours or more. Production estimates are established by the process engineer in conjunction with the industrial engineering department and include normal tool changes. Goals are set on each piece of equipment, after installation in our plant, in terms of pieces per gross equipment-hour, including all down time and the like. For example, on the gear case transfer line, the goals were as follows:

Cycle time	250 pieces per hour
Net pieces, including tool change time	220 per hour
Net pieces per gross equipment-hour (10 percent down time)	200
Net pieces per gross equipment-hour (15 percent down time)	180 (goal)

The process engineer has not met his objective until the goal of 180 pieces per hour is met and sustained in production.

Training. Another important ingredient of successful production performance is training, including management development. Toward this desirable end, Whirlpool production foremen, operators, maintenance foremen, and craftsmen were sent to observe and operate the more complex machines during their tryouts in the vendors' shops. Such a training program is well worth the money, for it makes it possible for employees to become familiar with equipment before delivery. Since much of the equipment Whirlpool purchased for its cost improvement program achieved savings in labor costs, early training of employees was most important to the overall success of the program. Exposure to new equipment diminished the employees' natural fear of the unknown, and reduced criticism of new equipment after its installation. In fact, several suggestions for improvements were made by the trainees and completed before shipment.

EXHIBIT 5

Maintenance Organization and Responsibilities

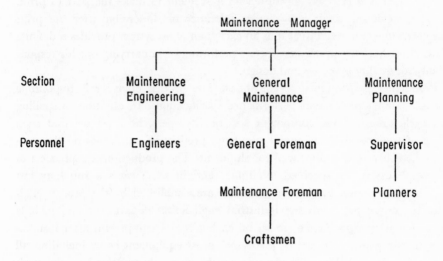

Maintenance Manager		

Section	Maintenance Engineering	General Maintenance	Maintenance Planning
Personnel	Engineers	General Foreman	Supervisor
		Maintenance Foreman	Planners
		Craftsmen	

| Responsibilities | Preventive Maintenance Program Analysis of Major Breakdowns for Prevention Oiling Program Equipment Maintenance Procedures Computer Control of Various Systems such as Conveyor Oiling and Inspection, Machine Oiling and Inspection, and Utility Maintenance of Steam, Air, Water, Gas, and Electricity | Janitorial Services Material Ordering Labor Relations Craft Supervision Safety Problem Solving Service | Work Order: Scheduling Estimating Programing Ordering of Materials Identification of Backlogs Follow-up on Major Projects Supervision of Outside Contractors Gathering of Cost Information Maintenance Material Control Records and Reports Salvage Department Overtime Schedule |

The turnover concept. A formal "turnover" date was established for each piece of equipment after its production start-up. At the specified time the process engineer turned over the responsibility for equipment performance to the manufacturing foreman, who agreed that it was acceptable for sustained production and would meet cost and quality objectives. A formal turnover date does much to reduce the long period of debugging, and it pinpoints the responsibility for solving problems as belonging to the process engineer who designed and purchased the equipment. After turnover, the process engineer is still available to trouble-shoot specific problems when requested, but he is free to go on to new projects once he has met his objectives.

MAINTENANCE

A top-notch maintenance department is worth its weight in gold to a manufacturing plant. It is the aim of all of us; however, knowing how to get it is a challenge of the highest order. To try to improve our understanding of this function, let us discuss some of the more important aspects of building an effective maintenance operation and review some of the measurements which will let us know how well it is performing and whether we are making progress or not.

The basic maintenance organization and responsibilities can be outlined as in Exhibit 5. The specific functions of the groups are noted on the chart. An organization team of this general design, working together, can do much to improve the maintenance effort in a manufacturing plant.

Work order system. One requirement of effective maintenance is a system of work order control. It should be set up to include the following steps:

1. Work order initiation.
2. Work order approval.
3. Work order investigation and priority.
4. Work order estimating, to include:
   a. Time, by craft.
   b. Material, by item.
   c. Total for each project.
5. Decision to—
   a. Perform work internally; or
   b. Purchase work from contractor.
6. Scheduling of orders:
   a. Daily, by shift.
   b. Weekly.
   c. Monthly.

7. Report on performance by—
    a. Orders completed.
    b. Orders pending.
    c. Backlog in hours, by craft.
8. Follow-up, including:
    a. Reporting of completions.
    b. Rescheduling as required.

Planned maintenance. One of the major means of reducing manufacturing costs is the proper management of equipment maintenance. Maintenance becomes even more important as machines become more complex and sophisticated in design and are used to produce high-quality parts at peak production levels.

To insure that proper maintenance is engineered into new equipment before its turnover to production is complete, the process engineer is responsible for devising a maintenance program for each new item. The maintenance engineer includes the program in the overall preventive maintenance effort. The requirement that a maintenance program be provided is written into the purchase specifications given to each vendor. The information we have received from vendors thus far, however, is evidence that we and they have not given enough thought to this question of built-in maintenance programs. Improvement in this respect would reduce the high costs incurred by machine and tool down time.

A machine's designers should plan and specify the required maintenance program for each component item; then, if the plan is followed, a significant manufacturing cost saving can be achieved.

Maintenance performance indicators. It is important to know the trends of performance in the maintenance business, and some of the cost indicators which can be utilized are outlined later, in the section of this paper on financial control. In addition, it is important to keep track of the down-time hours of direct labor caused by machine and tool failure to spot trends and developments in the plant which are wasting dollars. A budget by department can be established for the amount of direct labor down time, in hours, which is expected within a given time. Comparison against this budget can be used to measure the performance of each maintenance foreman and, in total, the performance of the maintenance manager. The budget can also be expressed as a ratio:

$$\text{Percent down time} = \frac{\text{Total production hours lost by equipment failure}}{\text{Total production hours worked}}$$

This indicator can be developed for total plant performance and itemized into failures caused by tools and equipment by department. Utilized properly, it will measure year-to-year trends and highlight troublesome areas. In Exhibit 6, for instance, trends in down-time hours of direct labor are plotted graphically.

PLANT ENGINEERING

Any company which is expanding in size and scope requires the service of a top-notch plant engineering organization. This group is responsible for the spending of large amounts of capital and expense for new and revised facilities; it also handles a large number of smaller projects. The organization at Whirlpool's St. Joseph Division is set up as shown in Exhibit 7.

Facility engineering. Of particular importance in the plant engineering function is the responsibility for administration and supervision of facilities projects assigned to outside contractors. It is part of Whirlpool's policy to hold a facility engineer responsible for the complete project which is to be executed. He makes the preliminary estimates, selects the contractors who are to quote on

EXHIBIT 6

TRENDS IN DOWN TIME

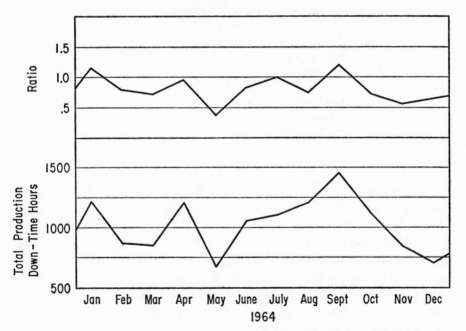

EXHIBIT 7

The Plant Engineering Organization

Manager Plant Engineering

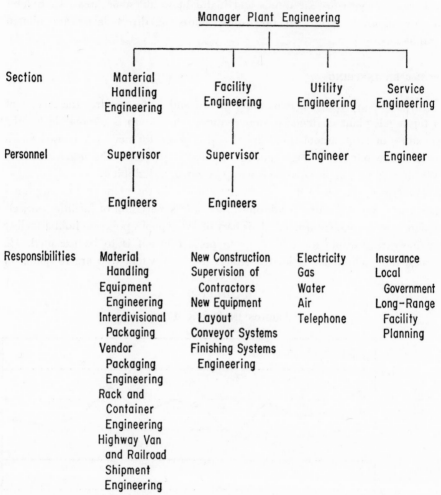

Section	Material Handling Engineering	Facility Engineering	Utility Engineering	Service Engineering
Personnel	Supervisor	Supervisor	Engineer	Engineer
	Engineers	Engineers		
Responsibilities	Material Handling Equipment Engineering Interdivisional Packaging Vendor Packaging Engineering Rack and Container Engineering Highway Van and Railroad Shipment Engineering	New Construction Supervision of Contractors New Equipment Layout Conveyor Systems Finishing Systems Engineering	Electricity Gas Water Air Telephone	Insurance Local Government Long-Range Facility Planning

the job, approves the engineering designs, handles the discussions with the contractors, and, with the concurrence of the buyer, makes the final award of the contract. He then supervises the job and is responsible for meeting the established targets of cost, quality, and schedule. He reports progress regularly against established cost checkpoints, and his performance is measured by the final outcome of the project against his goals.

By treating projects in this manner, we believe, each man is made to feel a personal responsibility for the total job and the most economical results are achieved in the shortest possible time.

Material handling and utilities engineering. A function which can add much to cost reduction results is material handling engineering. By looking at the utilization of the total space or "cube" of a plant, and the method by which its materials are handled, many improvements can be effected.

Some improvements which have resulted in major savings for us are as follows:

1. Durable containers for parts which permit high-density storage and low-cost handling.
2. Vendor parts shipped in durable containers, eliminating throwaway cartons.
3. High-density trailer loading.
4. Dunnage-free freight cars for finished-goods shipment.
5. Durable racks for finished-parts handling without damage.
6. Flow-through containers for supplying parts to stations on assembly lines.
7. Custom-design lift trucks for various plant operations.

The area of utilities is worth mentioning since it is normally responsible for a large amount of spending. A few innovations which have contributed to savings include:

1. Development of cost trends on various utilities used.
2. Organization of teams to investigate areas of potential savings.
3. Development of reports itemizing waste or overusage.
4. Installation of standby sources to obtain lower rates.
5. Engineering analysis of bills submitted over a period of time.

INDUSTRIAL ENGINEERING

In our system of management the industrial engineering department plays a key role. It is primarily the evaluation, measuring, and goal-setting operation within the manufacturing engineering section. Exhibit 8 shows how the unit is organized.

Labor standards. There are many labor standards systems in use. It would take considerable space to discuss the pros and cons of even a few of them; however, a few keys to good operation in this area can be mentioned.

There are many industrial engineers who believe an incentive wage system is more productive than a day-rate system, and vice-versa. For our operation we believe that the day-rate approach has many advantages over an incentive-rate structure, primarily because of its flexibility (it allows changes with minimum effect on labor relations), its contribution to quality improvement, and its low administration costs.

EXHIBIT 8

THE MANUFACTURING ENGINEERING ORGANIZATION

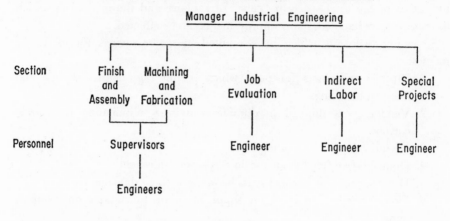

Manager Industrial Engineering

Section	Finish and Assembly	Machining and Fabrication	Job Evaluation	Indirect Labor	Special Projects
Personnel	Supervisors		Engineer	Engineer	Engineer
	Engineers				

Responsibilities	Work Measurements: Direct Labor Standards Manpower Control New-Model Evaluation Engineering Change Control Line Balances	Establishment of Rates Liaison with Union Committee Investigation of Methods Changes Labor Cost Analysis	Measurement Establishment of Controls	Evaluation of New Projects Financial Analysis Post Audits Special Studies

We call our hourly-wage program the Fair Day Work Plan. The system is based on the tenet that a properly managed employee will perform a Fair Day's Work for a Fair Day's Pay. We believe that in order to manage properly it is necessary to establish consistent standards for each operation. These standards are based on a consistent concept of the normal average work pace, which has been established and documented on films and in studies over the years. Furthermore, our standards, once established, will not be changed unless there has been a change in means, methods, or process on a particular job.

Another important aspect of our standards policy is to avoid building in allowances. Except for normal rest and lunch periods, measurable provision for tool changes, stock-up, or whatever, and a constant for personal needs, bad parts, and the like, we do not permit miscellaneous "slack" in our standards. As a result, we do not show 100 percent efficiency on every operation or throughout the plant on many complex processes; rather, our goal is to measure true efficiency and progress with the basic objective of stimulating improvements. A system which allows miscellaneous unmeasurable allowances to be arbitrarily added to standards may show 100 percent attainment of efficiency at a given time, but it doesn't measure progress or the lack of it over a long period. It measures performance with a "rubber yardstick" and can result in the industrial engineers' having to restudy operations to solve problems which should be handled by the foreman or process engineer.

For example, some companies provide allowances for the miscellaneous down time which may be experienced on a highly automated press line. In our opinion any unscheduled down time should be shown as a labor efficiency variance, thus stimulating those responsible to get at the cause of the down time and find a way to reduce or eliminate it.

Financial analysis. Still another important type of industrial engineering activity is the financial analysis service which is provided by each industrial engineer. Before a project is put in final form by a process engineer, the industrial engineering department is asked to prepare an analysis and make a recommendation. Since the industrial engineers cover each area of the plant, they are capable of providing the required information easily. They suggest new labor standards, compute the return on investment, estimate the time required to recapture the investment, and provide data on the effect on scrap, material costs, and other related factors.

For all new pieces of equipment, production standard estimates are outlined and start-up costs are established. New standard costs reflecting start-up and learning times are developed for the cost department. Generally, the production standards are given to the operating people as targets to be attained, and the cost department is informed of the estimated time it will take to achieve them.

PROCESS CAPABILITY

The primary responsibility of the process capability section is to provide an equipment evaluations service for the process people and to assist them in specifying and analyzing new and existing equipment capability in comparison with engineering tolerances.

Statistical analysis. The men in this group are skilled in the use of statistical analysis techniques of evaluating, identifying, and solving problems. (A recent study made at Whirlpool utilized a computer to analyze results. Another involved an equipment-replacement decision in which by testing various combinations of components in an assembly, it was determined that the existing equipment could satisfy quality reliability requirements with minor modification, thus preventing a major expenditure for new equipment.) Process capability people also train process personnel in the proper use of statistical analysis, which is one of the most important tools for determining adherence to engineering specifications. Finally, they assist in developing the proper specifications to be utilized under various production conditions. They work with the quality control department people and the process engineers in the areas of *reliability testing* and *equipment and process capability*.

Confirming engineering design reliability by testing production-tooled parts made to print is a very important step in most new-model programs. As soon as parts to print made on production equipment are available, pre-pilot assembly runs are completed and units are tested under various conditions of severe use. Weibull curves (shown in Exhibit 9) are statistical tools which are developed to compare results with current production tested under the same conditions. In addition, various combinations of parts are selected and tested under maximum tolerance conditions to prove that quality can be maintained during actual production. The test results in Exhibit 9 indicate that substantial improvements have been obtained.

EQUIPMENT AND PROCESS CAPABILITY

There also is a great need for, and an opportunity to develop further, the skills required to specify and analyze equipment capability. This need became apparent at Whirlpool in the past few years during discussions of specifications based on statistical analysis. Phrases such as "potential tolerance," "machine accuracy," and "process capability" were confusing and generally unfamiliar to many suppliers responsible for building the equipment. In order to maintain parts to print during the expected life of our equipment, we decided to specify that each machine must be capable of holding dimensions within 75 percent of print tolerances on the basis of a statistical analysis of 120 consecutive pieces.

EXHIBIT 9

WEIBULL CURVES

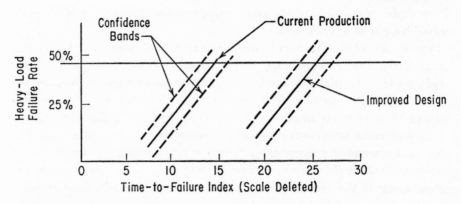

This specification was explained to each prospective vendor. Some refused to quote with such a requirement; others agreed to quote without fully realizing what it meant. In almost every case, extensive tryouts and debugging periods were required to satisfy the capability specs; however, in most instances we had anticipated this extra time in the original schedules.

Better understanding of machine and process capability analysis on the part of all concerned will be required in the future to keep pace with the demand for product reliability. The space industry is leading the way by writing specifications for space hardware with extensive quality and reliability requirements.

ADMINISTRATION AND CONTROL

The manufacturing engineering administration and control group is charged with overall coordination of the department's functions and programs. It is responsible for capital, tooling, and expense projects; coordination of engineering changes; cost reduction administration for the division; and maintenance material ordering and control. The department is organized as shown in Exhibit 10.

New-model and project program control. Effective timing control is as much a "must" in the appliance business as it is elsewhere. It is mandatory to know where we stand at all times in relation to new-model programs, material phase-outs, product assembly schedules, and so on. At the start of the new-model or other-type project, an overall schedule is established and detailed schedules are outlined for each major item of equipment. Establishing and meeting target dates are the responsibility of process engineers in the various areas. Coordination of the overall schedule is handled by the manufacturing engineering administrator, who meets regularly with the division's product scheduling people. Schedules are set up to outline dates for the following key activities:

1. Initial event—project estimate of capital, tooling, and expense.
2. Final engineering release.
3. Issuance of capital and tool appropriation.
   a. Issuance of the purchase order to selected builder.
   b. Approval of design.
4. Initial tryout machines in vendors' shops.
   a. Sample approval.
   b. Production run and machine capability analysis.
   c. Shipment and delivery date.
   d. Installation.
   e. Debugging.

EXHIBIT 10

THE MANUFACTURING ENGINEERING ADMINISTRATION
AND CONTROL GROUP

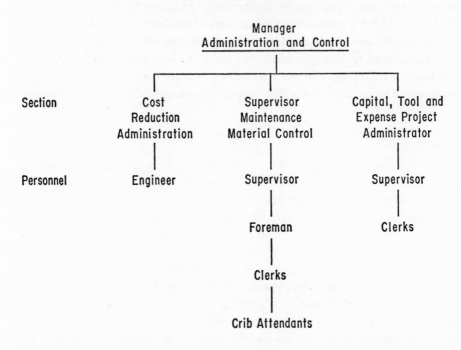

Responsibilities	Administration of	Maintenance of Crib	Post Audits
	Division Cost	System	Long-Range Planning
	Reduction	Development of Parts	Engineering Change
	Program	Catalogue	Control
	Initiation of	Inventory Control	Process Estimate
	Contests and	Follow-up	Control
	Special	Special Parts	Budgetary Control
	Programs	Order Parts	Tool and Equipment
	Monthly Progress		Records
	Reports		Appropriation Control
	Evaluation of		Project Administration
	Suggestions		
	Follow-up on		
	Projects		

    f. Pre-pilot run.

    g. Pilot run.

    h. Turnover to production.

Post audit. After each major project has been completed and turned over to production, it is given a post audit, which compares the actual outcome of the project with the established objectives in the areas outlined in Exhibit 11. The explanations of variations from forecast which are required serve as a factual record of performance for the people responsible.

Cost reduction. Each department has an established cost reduction program which is constantly stimulating its people to improve costs. Annual goals for accomplished savings are established, and progress each month is measured against these targets. Responsibility for coordinating the cost reduction pro-

EXHIBIT 11

POST AUDIT FORM

	Forecast	Actual
Capital		
Expense		
Tooling		
Total Investment		
Percent Return and Breakeven		
Savings:		
Labor		
Material		
Burden (effect)		
Quality and Capability and Reliability		
Delivery and Schedule		
Safety		
Vendor Performance		
Down Time		
Productivity		
Maintenance Costs		
Tools and Supplies		
Scrap and Rework		

gram is assigned to the manufacturing engineering administration section. Records of all suggestions are kept, and various programs to stimulate activity are conducted throughout the year. Team effort in installing cost reduction ideas is encouraged by giving "participation" credit to each individual who assists in the implementation of a suggestion. This credit, in the form of dollars equal to the value of the suggestion, is a key element of our program. Exhibit 12 shows the monthly status of the program versus the division goal.

FINANCIAL CONTROL

The subject of financial control is far too complex to handle within the scope of this chapter; however, let us at least mention briefly some of the key concepts which are followed in our company within the manufacturing engineering department.

EXHIBIT 12

STATUS OF COST REDUCTION PROGRAM

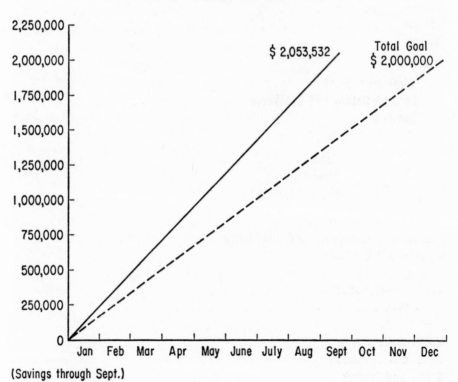

(Savings through Sept.)

FROM PROTOTYPE TO FULL PRODUCTION: PREPARING THE NEW PRODUCT FOR MARKETING

By JOHN V. SMONIG

There are four main areas to cover whenever we consider the preparation of a new product for marketing: (1) manufacturing's relationships with engineering and marketing and the resulting interplay; (2) the common denominator in all efforts—people, and their particular attributes, matched with functional requirements; (3) manufacturing input, to arrive at a market introduction date; and (4) manufacturing's internal objectives and its approaches to achieving them through planning, organizing, integrating, and controlling all the activities which will result in the successful introduction of a new product to the market.

MANUFACTURING'S RELATIONS WITH ENGINEERING AND MARKETING

Let us imagine a manager who will symbolize the essence of manufacturing. He stands for many people who are united and organized to achieve a common goal. He represents the proper blending of materials, machinery, money, and motivation guided and directed by a sense of accomplishment and individual recognition throughout the process of making a product which satisfies some sociological or psychological need in its buyers.

Time is never ample for this manager and should not be: Manufacturing feels as though a vise is closing in around it, one of its jaws being engineering and the other marketing. These two corporate divisions are indispensable to new product planning and introduction, and each contributes to the other's

JOHN V. SMONIG is Engineering Manager with Olivetti Underwood, New York.

survival. Engineering, of course, provides—through drawings and specifications—the "what" that must be produced; marketing represents the customer who requires ever higher levels of quality at ever lower prices.

When we examine the flow of a new product through engineering, manufacturing, and marketing, we find that as the efforts of each division expand and contract, there are areas of interaction, of overlapping responsibility, while the product progresses from idea to hardware to customer. And, as the program progresses toward reality, each succeeding function offers some resistance to the new product. This reluctance to accept innovation is one of our inhuman human characteristics. The product's newness, our own unsureness (due to the lack of knowledge about it), carry with them a threat to job security. Engineering conceives the product in the turmoil of many rejected efforts; it has pride of ownership and is reluctant to let *its* product go. On the other hand, manufacturing feels that it has not been exposed to the product early enough. Gradual, transitional exposure can minimize this interdepartmental conflict and hasten market introduction.

To eliminate conflict completely would destroy the essence of the human effort. We should not attempt to destroy this vital interaction of people in the advance of technology; rather, as managers we should recognize it and make use of it as an effective tool for group guidance and organizational control. The manager should make use of this created circumstance involving responsibility, authority, and power. If he keeps all these vital ingredients in proper balance and shows a complete awareness of them, the success of the program will be assured.

It then becomes the manager's task to provide symbols which may be used for identification within the program. One way this may be accomplished is to have each division participate in long-range planning, thereby committing the various suborganizations to the total program of readying a new product for the market. Top management should stress the importance of the program, set goals, and make them known throughout the organization. Association with a fruitful and profitable activity creates the strongest motivating factor for all personnel.

THE NEEDED MANUFACTURING SKILLS

Manufacturing's first exposure to a new product usually comes when it is asked to submit a cost estimate. This affords the opportunity to prepare some original manufacturing plans; to determine manufacturing engineering manpower requirements, new processes that may be encountered, and space and equipment needs; and to designate tentative major mileposts. After manufacturing has received engineering's model drawings or layouts, it documents the latest proposals for changes; prepares a rough process for each part or assembly, designating the sequence of operations, special tooling, machine-tool requirements, material usage, and the department where the work will be performed; determines the costs by breaking them down into their individual elements; and notifies engineering of how it is progressing. The transfer of knowledge has begun.

Some of the skills or characteristics that manufacturing personnel should have and that should be stressed in a start-up program are these:

- All employees should at all times be aware of time and control.
- They should be self-motivated; they should, that is, require no motivation outside themselves and their identification with a successful enterprise.
- They should be imaginative and be able to conceive new processes, techniques, and devices, no matter what level of organization they serve.
- They should be flexible and mature enough to adapt to the rapid change which is integral to the act of introducing a new product.
- They should be cost-conscious and able to control and reduce expenses.
- They should have a broad outlook and be able to coordinate and correlate internal and external forces.
- If supervisors, they should at all times maintain a sense of the program's importance and urgency.

We should not overhire either in quantity or in quality. We must, rather, make sure that the people we hire are able to grow. Many people work well under pressure; when they seem to be overworked, they are happier and their morale is higher. It is surprising what people can do when they are put to the task. Maintaining high productive standards and eliminating fill-in jobs often prevent bad group or individual habits from developing. Slowing people down always seems easier than getting them going. The challenge to the manager lies in coordinating and directing their energies. The process of selecting individuals to perform the various functions is of utmost importance. Each man must understand what responsibilities and tasks are to be assigned to him so that his personality, experience, and qualifications can be matched to them and be in agreement with the group image.

Supervisors or project managers must understand that the effectiveness of their actions should outweigh their efficiency. They should be able to stand back, analyze a problem, and decide what actions will be most effective in realizing their objective.

PRODUCT ORIGINALITY: SOURCES OF IDEAS

An idea for a new product may stem from any one of numerous sources, such as research, engineering, manufacturing, vendors, other outside influences, or competition. Many ideas are subjected to studies, testing, and evaluation from a variety of standpoints, including engineering feasibility, profit return, the satisfaction of market needs, and the enhancement of existing product lines. A product usually goes through four distinct phases: fundamental research, applied research, exploratory development, and development and design. At the end of each phase the product should be evaluated by a new product committee before the go-ahead is given to proceed with the next phase. The product should be reviewed periodically to see if it meets the original need. Many times changes are evident that destroy the original intent—or strengthen it.

The design and development group is the link between engineering and manufacturing. Here manufacturing has its first contact with and indoctrination about the proposed product. The group's engineering or product engineering responsibilities are these:

- Mechanical development and design.
- Product design and reliability.
- Electrical engineering.
- Standards engineering.
- Model-shop responsibilities.

Prototypes should be constructed by manufacturing. Design responsibilities rest with engineering, but we want to put this product to the production test early in the program. Supervisors should be selected from the assembly area in manufacturing. Of course, all the components or piece parts are purchased by manufacturing personnel, and the responsibility for their assembly as well as for the final assembly usually falls on one of manufacturing managers. At the same time, manufacturing engineers and quality control personnel see to the assembly of the prototype. Rough processing is developed which will be used to build the units. This helps firm up the final manufacturing process as well as define some of the trouble spots to be encountered as the program advances to completion. After the prototype has been built, engineering and quality control personnel test and evaluate it.

This blending of technical and practical backgrounds, rich with personal experience, creates an agonizing atmosphere; only mature individuals who recognize that exposing problems and finding solutions to them will result in a higher probability of success can tolerate the stresses inherent in the creation of a new product.

INTRODUCING THE PRODUCT TO THE MARKET

Now let us look at marketing. We in manufacturing require marketing people to forecast how many units of this new product they require and when they would like to introduce it. This forecast must also include some idea of the quarterly sales expected for at least the first year of production. In turn, marketing requires preproduction machines or hardware or whatever for advertising campaigns, service manuals and sales literature, and training programs for its sales and service personnel.

Briefly, marketing is responsible for advertising and sales promotion, sales and service training, determination of the product's price and sales cost, and distribution and installation techniques. At this point a top management group of executives from the engineering, manufacturing, and marketing divisions reviews initial plans, opinions, and other data to determine the earliest possible or most advantageous date at which the product can be brought out.

INTERNAL GOALS AND HURDLES

Now that manufacturing is committed to a market-introduction date, let us look at some of the internal objectives and detailed goals that must be set up, some of the hurdles that must be overcome by our symbolic manufacturing man. He must concern himself with four broad areas:

- Planning.
- Organizing.
- Integrating.
- Controlling.

Under planning, he must consider two major subordinate areas: first, arriving at a master plan or strategy that will be understood and accepted by all top manufacturing management and, second, determining resource allocations for facilities, manpower, finance, and operating plans and schedules.

The master plan fits into, and is actually one of the links in, the total corporate plan—which, at this point, usually takes on the appearance of a Gantt chart. A total corporate PERT (Program Evaluation and Review Technique) network has been used with considerable success to coordinate many product plans. One of its benefits has been to ease interdepartmental transfer of knowledge by allowing each department's manager to see the effect of his actions upon the other departments or divisions. Let us say, then, that we have organized a planning group whose responsibility it is to coordinate the total initial planning effort within manufacturing, thereby developing some mileposts for the detailed planning which will follow. The proper allocation of resources—men, money, material, time, and machines—is likewise determined by PERT.

A project manager is normally assigned early in the planning stage, if the project is large enough to warrant his presence. His talent for organization and administration serves us well at this time; he takes a leading part in determining project commitments and becomes familiar with total objectives. His prime responsibility is to assure that corporate strategy is fulfilled by developing the tactics necessary to product planning. He completes the communications link between other corporate efforts and the introduction of the new product. He should not exercise his authority in detail decisions, but should bring the parties together and allow them to resolve any problems through their own efforts. At all times he should be results-oriented rather than process-oriented.

At this point in the development of the program, engineering models (breadboards) have already been completed. Manufacturing should obtain from engineering further detailed drawings and specifications so as to update the information used in preparing the original cost estimate. An assembly bill of material is exploded (showing a breakdown of the work, principally to determine the interrelationships of parts and assemblies and affirm personnel, facilities, and skills requirements and the budget for total start-up costs).

"MAKE OR BUY" DECISIONS

A preliminary "make or buy" decision is made for all parts and assemblies by personnel in manufacturing engineering. It may be considered extreme to rely on just one group of people to make such an important judgment in relation to the entire program, but at this point we are primarily interested in expediting and this certainly will get us off dead center. If wrong decisions are made, they will become obvious, and other groups who have at their disposal firmer facts for decision making will make them known. In addition, these people apply some degree of intelligence to the various reports that should become available in such areas as machine loading, new skills and techniques, purchasing assurance, and internal manufacturing capabilities, skills, and physical facilities.

Let us consider for a moment how manufacturing engineering can by itself make such a major decision as whether to make or buy a new product—or at least its component parts. One of the reports which we have mentioned and which this group utilizes fully is a complete machine-load forecast which takes into account the existing products in production, service parts for replacement and retrofit, and parts requirements from overseas operations or other affiliates. This total forecast is supplied by a computer program and is extended for a five-year period. Another valuable bit of information available to the group is the new equipment installation and delivery schedule. A third has to do with production shrinkage factors; a fourth, with the financial commitments that management is willing to undertake for new or additional equipment and processes.

Parts and assemblies fall into the "subcontract" category when manufacturing engineering personnel believe that at some future date they will become "in house" or "make" items. These parts now are subject to overall control by manufacturing. Vendors must produce them in a prescribed manner utilizing machine tools and special tool design restrictions. Parts and assemblies drawings are designated "make," "buy," or "subcontract" and are distributed to the various responsible operating personnel, who estimate the time it will take to complete their tasks—primarily processing, tool design, fabrication, inspection, and tryout. On buy parts, these time estimates cover internal purchasing lead time, gauge design, gauge fabrication, and receiving inspection.

THE THREE MAJOR PLANS

The total program for new product introduction can now be broken down into its three major plans: (1) parts and assemblies; (2) facilities and equipment; and (3) preproduction schedule. The focal point for terminating the elapsed times and tying in the entire program should be the start of the first machine on the assembly line. All these plans have problems which are significant to the areas that they deal with and, therefore, make for a logical division into three separate entities. Let us look at some of the details involved in preparing each of the three.

Parts and assemblies. Here we should attempt to determine the elapsed time for each part and assembly in the entire program. When these times are applied to our bill-of-material explosion (work-breakdown structure), a total elapsed time from engineering issue to start of final assembly is obtained. Some of the factors that should be considered are:

- Program logic.
- Elapsed time necessary for completion of each activity or task.
  a. Make parts and assemblies:
     Processing.
     Tool design.
     Fabrication and inspection.
     Process tie-in.
  b. Buy parts and assemblies:
     Internal purchase lead time.
     External vendor lead time.
     Receiving inspection, gauge design, fabrication, and tie-in.
     Receiving inspection.
- Man-hours and skill code assignments.

Skill coding deserves elaboration. By assigning a code number to each skill required in the program (manufacturing engineer, 01; tool designer, 03; clerk typist, 04; and so on), we can develop a start-up manpower forecast by week and by skill required. The code number facilitates immediate input to a computer, and by programing we can sort this skill code by expected date of completion for the individual part or assembly. Additional refinements can be made by matching this date against the available time and showing the variance for any skill, by week, in hours. And, further, a valuable tool for planning future programs can be provided by developing a matrix which can be put into a computer memory and used for later estimating.

Developing a part-number coding for parts and assemblies of a particular class will permit tie-in with the matrix. If records of actual time expended are kept, a standard elapsed time can soon be developed which will improve the matrix's reliability. When a new program comes along, it becomes a simple matter to utilize the code numbers for needed classes of parts or assemblies as computer input and print out a total elapsed time.

The most important part of any start-up program for the introduction of a new product is defining where to start. Certainly, having a bill-of-material explosion and a matrix for time estimates puts us well down the road. In addition, as standard networks can be developed, including the major activities that are performed in the organization, they will represent the larger part of the time consumed from engineering issue to stock and will be of significant value. However, it must be remembered that the logic of these networks should be developed first, prior to applying time estimates or assigning responsibility.

The parts and assembly plan should take into account all the elements of work necessary for part and assembly preparation insofar as it concerns the stocking of these components for the final assembly line. Therefore, the end date or terminal objective should be, again, the start of final assembly.

Facilities and equipment. The next plan to be considered is what we can refer to as the facilities and equipment program. This may be a misnomer because what the plan primarily contains is all the elements of work necessary to complete the assembly of the final unit. But, for convenience, it may be advantageous to include some of the overall program tasks in this plan: building erection or alteration, personnel recruiting and training, capital budget preparation, and so on.

We can treat the completion of the first unit in the final assembly as our end date. Working back from that point, we must consider some of the following activities:

- Packaging requirements.
- Assembly procedure.
- Special tooling.
- Floor layout.
- Handling equipment.
- Test procedures and programs.
- Service procedures and tooling.

Many interfaces with marketing will be found in the development of this plan. The sales forecast will become a prime consideration and serve as the basis for manufacturing planning.

Preproduction schedule. We have only one remaining plan to develop: our preproduction schedule. We must determine the rate of build-up and the quantity of units that are to be considered adequate for preproduction. This plan will serve to provide manufacturing manpower schedules for the final assembly line, the final tests, and supporting functions. It will also give a machine schedule showing release dates. These are important in connection with manufacturing's responsibility for providing other divisions with machine availability for their testing and evaluation programs. Service training, advertising campaigns, and field-test programs are just a few of the efforts that machines will be used for during preproduction.

The number of machines turned out during preproduction will depend upon the total production schedule for the year.

RESPONSIBILITY AND AUTHORITY FOR THE PROGRAM

When all three detailed plans have been developed (parts and assembly, facilities and equipment, and preproduction), we have a completely new product plan which will encompass all the activities that manufacturing will undertake and establish the time necessary to carry out the entire program. Determining the relationships of production capability to changes in marketing requirements should be a prime consideration, as should providing operating personnel in manufacturing with information that will enable them to adjust to these new demands.

Responsibility and authority for this total program should rest with the new product task force. It will provide line operating personnel with methods, techniques, devices, and counseling—in short, facilitate the transition of the product from engineering drawing to production capability. Here again, as in the transition between divisions, there may be some conflict due to pride of ownership. A gradual changeover, and involvement of personnel throughout, should be helpful.

WHAT THE PROGRAM HAS ACHIEVED

What have we obtained from this total program in behalf of our representative manufacturing manager? That is, from plotting every activity and figuring the total elapsed time from the making or supplying of every part or assembly to product completion and the stage of preproduction? These activities all fall under the heading of logical planning and together provide a schedule for each function performed in manufacturing. In addition, we have provided a delivery schedule for purchasing and have a "feel" for manpower, equipment, and facilities requirements. And, with the help of engineering and marketing, we have participated in the establishment of a market introduction date.

Replanning is undertaken when and where needed. In fact, a number of refiguring or replanning maneuvers should be necessary. The project manager should probe constantly, asking himself and others such questions as, "What is going on here?" "Who does what?" "Is that essential?" Activities and tasks should be defined in such a way that there is no chance of misunderstanding. All hedges and slack should be removed. Where there are risks and alternative solutions to be considered, where there are doubts about accomplishments, we should set goals that stretch our capabilities fully.

The plan, in other words, is being updated constantly. New input is being supplied; recycling is taking place. Meanwhile, financing needs can be developed readily from the facilities, equipment, and manpower requirements, which enable us to determine what capital expenditures are necessary and for what period.

At this point, then, we have:

- A detailed plan which shows the completion date or the stock date for all necessary activities or for each part and assembly in the new product.
- An engineering issue schedule.

- Manpower requirements: the types of manpower that will be needed and when.
- Delivery schedules for all parts to be purchased.
- An equipment delivery schedule.
- A finance plan indicating what expenditures will be made over what period of time.

Information gathered from these detailed planning activities can of course tell us just what the program's status is at any given moment.

THE IMPORTANCE OF COMMUNICATION

One important area to be considered in developing the new product program is communication, or paper flow, which is concerned with—

- How to update the program.
- How to arrive at time estimates and their input to the program.
- How to show the completion of events and activities in the updating procedure.
- How often reports should be printed.
- How much tie-in is necessary with such existing systems and procedures as make or buy decisions, the ordering of tooling, and the issuing of engineering orders, hold orders, and change requests.

A simple, unrestricted method of updating must be established and made available to all parties involved in the program. Any and all communications media used should be fully understood by personnel at all levels. Many times the format, not the content, of a report causes confusion; therefore, it becomes necessary to indoctrinate people properly in the forms that are to serve as reporting and updating devices. These forms should, of course, be kept as simple as possible. Also, the frequency with which they are issued should not be determined solely by a fixed schedule; rather, they should appear when the need arises—at the discretion of the program manager or his counterpart.

ORGANIZATION AND STAFFING

Now the new product program is almost complete, but it is static, lifeless. We have to develop an organization and staff it with competent people.

There are two possible types of structure. In a *functional organization,* the product moves horizontally through all the functional operating departments, each of which assumes additional responsibility for the new product. This approach has its pros and cons. One disadvantage is that these departments are also concerned with the day-to-day problems of existing products and cannot devote enough of their time and effort to innovation. An advantage is that such a group will already have learned to work in unison and perform its specialized function efficiently.

A *product-oriented organization,* on the other hand, is essentially a miniature of the company as a whole; it contains the same functions and has the same structure but is set up solely to put the new product into production. In the military this is what is called a "task force." It is staffed with personnel selected from within the organization. Its advantage is that it has only one job and one objective; its disadvantage is that at the program's completion, when we are ready to put the new item into production with the regular organization in charge, transferring the task force members back into their "civilian" jobs sometimes becomes difficult. Yet the most expedient way to get an item into production is to use the product-oriented structure.

INTEGRATION AND CONTROL

Finally there is integration, a total mix of plan and organization. Its purpose is to inform the entire organization about the components of the new product program and to inform each individual concerned about his share of the work, the relationship of his share to the total, and his accountability for each of his activities or tasks. Here we encounter a very important motivating factor: the proper recognition of the individual by his superiors, for the job he has to do.

All program objectives, policies, and plans are carefully explained. Program and organization, properly merged, give us a dynamic invigorating force.

Control becomes necessary, and measuring is the essence of control. So, in our planning and scheduling, we have devised and established measuring systems and media. Performance is to be recorded and reported. Consideration is to be given to the type and frequency of reports; operating personnel require detailed, timely reports which give all the information necessary for making decisions; whereas top management may require only reports on exceptions or on major mileposts. Constant comparison of these status reports against the original plans will allow for replanning and updating to correspond with new areas of difficulty or of opportunity.

The sound judgment of competent manufacturing personnel can, in the last analysis, be relied upon to satisfy end objectives. People who have been properly selected and assigned and given full responsibility for results will, in fact, exceed any prescribed and limited goals we may have achieved in the past.

MANUFACTURING RESEARCH: DEVELOPING NEW PROCESSES AND EQUIPMENT

By GLEN R. SIMMONS

Manufacturing research is research in how to make things. This type of investigation has actually been going on ever since the Stone Age. The first man to punch holes in two pieces of deerskin and then tie them together with deer sinew was engaged in manufacturing process research. The man who first put a cylindrical stone on a stick and turned it while he held a weapon to it to be sharpened was engaged in process research. When Oliver Evans in 1787 designed, built, and operated a fully automatic flour mill, he was engaged in manufacturing process research.

Manufacturing research as a separate and special industrial activity is, however, relatively new. There are actually three types of activities which lead to new or improved manufacturing processes. They are:

1. The interrelated process research that is a necessary part of product design.
2. The work of factory cost reduction and process improvement, carried on by functional engineers of the manufacturing staff.
3. Organized and oriented manufacturing process research.

It is with this last activity that we are here concerned.

In the past, industrial research and development were focused on invention and the creation of new products. There was often a long lapse of time between a discovery in basic science and its practical application. For example, a gap of almost 75 years came between Faraday's discovery of electromagnetic induction and the development of power plants. Today, the gap between discovery

---

GLEN R. SIMMONS is Manager, Distribution and Systems Equipment Engineering Planning, Service Division, Western Electric Company, Inc., Newark, New Jersey. Dr. Simmons was formerly Director of Research and Development, Engineering Division, Western Electric Company, Princeton, New Jersey.

and application in some cases shrinks to a few months. With the flourishing of new arts—electronics, microminiaturization, solid-state devices, computers, magnetic alloys—and the concomitant tying together of manufacturing research and product design, manufacturing process research is coming into its own.

In manufacturing research, then, we look for new and better ways to make things. We seek new technologies of manufacture, and we endeavor thereby to reduce costs and to improve product quality. Capacitors for electrical circuits, for example, were once made by interleaving metal in alternate layers with paper or plastic. This process was costly because it used a great deal of metal. Today capacitors are made by evaporating thin films of metal on paper or plastic, which is then wound into a roll. This process uses less metal and produces a capacitor with improved properties.

LOCATION OF THE MANUFACTURING RESEARCH FACILITY

In present-day industry almost all manufacturing plants have engineers and scientists who develop better ways to make things. In large organizations each location of a company may have a corps of such people. Recently a new way of administering this activity has evolved—that is, the separately organized function. This may be effected by a separate laboratory within a plant or by a completely separate location. Western Electric, for example, has established a facility of the latter type. This is the Engineering Research Center at Princeton, New Jersey, where a staff, provided with modern buildings, excellent laboratories, and the proper equipment, devotes its efforts exclusively to manufacturing process research at some distance from the plants.

Some of us may argue that a separate facility, within the plant or at another location, is unnecessary. Improvement in manufacturing techniques is something that many people are engaged in at many locations. An operator working on an assembly line may suggest changes. The supervisors in charge of such work and the manufacturing or process engineers associated with it may think of, try out, and adopt modifications of processes. Individually or cumulatively they may produce the same final effect that can be accomplished by process research in a special laboratory.

True, the kind of work done in manufacturing research is not basically different from the process improvement that is being achieved at plant locations, but the pace, the intensity, and the total dedication to this one type of effort are different. Manufacturing process research requires freedom from the specific production commitments that are a primary concern in the factory.

In manufacturing plants production emergencies inevitably arise. In a separate facility scientists and engineers are not as easily diverted to solving such short-range problems.

The negative "Oh, that just won't work!" attitude, which is sometimes encountered in industrial plants, is less frequently heard in the research environment. Some scientists, who may be unwilling to accept employment in a factory, are attracted to a laboratory devoted to manufacturing research.

In a separate facility, in the large company, projects which have only limited application at many different locations can be justified in the overall view. Long-range projects, supported by companywide financing, become more possible and practical. They might not be readily authorized for an individual location where appraisals are made for short-range results.

In the manufacturing plant attention may be centered on better ways of performing old methods. At a manufacturing research facility it is easier to escape from the parochial, to step back and take a long look at all the operations throughout a company—perhaps to envision how to make things five and ten years hence, perhaps to apply new methods from the swiftly moving world of science and technology.

STAFFING THE ACTIVITY

Manufacturing research can, of course, be conducted without a separate location and without laboratories constructed for that purpose. It is well, however, to provide some sort of administrative separation for the manufacturing research facility within the plant. It is equally important not to allow research to divorce itself from the realities of the manufacturing plant.

The nature of the staff depends upon the type of industry. People may be needed who are trained in mechanical, metallurgical, electrical, chemical, or industrial engineering, in mathematics, in physics, in chemistry, in ceramics. Scientists and engineers can come from works locations and bring with them a background of understanding of company operations and the necessary awareness of current manufacturing problems. Fresh recruits can be brought in from colleges and universities.

The staff of a manufacturing research facility should be, on the whole, a youthful one, fully knowledgeable in scientific principles and in the latest technologies, with a leavening of older people to insure adequate experience and mature judgment. A substantial proportion should have graduate training at the master and doctoral levels. Attention in choice of staff must be primarily focused on technical excellence, but there should also be a strong emphasis on skill in communication, for these are two attributes which certainly do not always go hand in hand. Many, but not all, need to be able to work effectively in teams, since many large projects require group effort, but room should always be left for the lone worker who may be misanthropic but gifted.

ORIGIN OF MANUFACTURING RESEARCH PROJECTS

One of the first questions asked by visitors to a manufacturing research laboratory is, "Where do you get your projects?" This question has no single answer. Suggestions are obtained from many sources. Internally, projects may be proposed by top management, by manufacturing planning engineering, by the research staff members. They may arise from product research; they may be the outgrowth of previous or current projects. Externally, they may grow out of the general technological scene.

Fruitful areas for perusal are long-established operations and points in the manufacturing process where much of the cost lies. Standing back and looking over the entire manufacturing process often suggests projects. The systems approach may offer numerous leads as mathematical techniques, statistical techniques, and computer technology are utilized to control the operations of a manufacturing business. For the electronic computer enables us to do things that were previously impossible. Manufacturing plants may use literally billions of small parts for assembly into equipment, and sophisticated systems designed to forecast requirements and to order the manufacture or procurement of parts at the proper time are of tremendous value in making equipment available exactly at the time of need.

As an example of the evolution of projects, it may be fruitful to review the growth of just one part of one project at the Western Electric Engineering Research Center, a project first called Electronic Switching Systems. The general research area was first described as the need to reduce the cost of components expected to be used in very large volume in electronic switching central offices and private branch exchanges. One facet of this original program was a study of means of positioning certain transistors so that very thin stripes of aluminum on raised areas (mesas) could be oriented to permit automatic wiring.

A member of the manufacturing research staff accomplished this by illuminating the area of the stripes with bright light, reflecting the light through a microscope, and allowing it to fall upon photoelectric sensitive surfaces which sensed the differences in the amount of light reflected by the stripes and by the background. An electronic circuit, thus activated, then drove positioning motors to orient the transistors for attachment of wires.

During the period of this investigation, a team had been working on an interim solution for the transistor-wiring problem. It developed an ingenious tool that allowed an operator to turn out hundreds of transistors per hour. This method was so fast that it simply was not economically attractive to complete the automation on the basis of light-sensing.

This might seem discouraging, but several staff members became interested in light-sensing, acquired a great deal of knowledge in optics, and applied the same principles to other areas. The new knowledge was used in the development of a method for cutting tungsten filaments for switchboard lamps. These filaments consist of coiled sections alternating with straight sections. When exposed to light, the different sections cause corresponding changes in intercepted light which then permit the automatic placement of the center of the straight section between the blades of a cutter. Automatic equipment utilizing this method is now in use.

A second project which grew out of our discoveries in light-sensing involves the use of reflected light from the six differently colored wires in a Princess set telephone cord—green, yellow, white, blue, red, and black. The blue and yellow wires must be cut to lengths which are longer than the other four wires and different from each other. This work had been done by operators who positioned the wires and then activated an automatic terminating machine. The manufacturing research team developed a process which discriminated automatically between wire colors by light reflected from the wires through filters. An electro-optical device completely automated the operation by selecting the blue and yellow wires for automatic length control and by furnishing signals if cords do not conform to physical specifications.

The staff also applied its new insight to the development of an electro-optical sensing apparatus to inspect the Twistor memory cable. This cable is used in constructing a "memory" (similar to that in computers) in electronic switching systems to remember such things as special telephone numbers and switch-path selections. The spacing in this cable is extremely critical. A laborious test is run by an operator who checks visually, by means of an optical magnifying and special gauging apparatus, the precision spacing of wires in the Twistor cable. Manufacturing research designed an electro-optical sensing apparatus to replace the manual check. It inspects cable, records the exact wire position on paper tape, and shows systematic or cumulative error, all at rates which are impossible manually.

A fourth application is the detection of surface defects in great lengths of materials, such as copper tape employed as the conductor in submarine cable. This is accomplished by correlation of variations of light reflected from surface defects.

To sum up: Repetitive manufacturing operations that lead to boredom and fatigue, with the resultant poor response, can often be accomplished automatically through the use of electro-optical techniques. These applications, and the possibilities of many others, branching out from a small part of one project, provide an excellent example of the way in which manufacturing research works.

THE SELECTION OF WORTHWHILE PROJECTS

A problem in manufacturing research is often not so much the seeking of suggestions for projects but the selection of worthwhile projects from many possibilities. It is wise to set definite criteria for the selection process.

A project must offer an adequate rate of return. In cost reduction engineering projects, rate of return can be calculated by—

1. Estimating the cost of the engineering effort required to carry out the project.
2. Estimating the investment in plant facilities that will be required to implement the development.
3. Estimating the savings that will accrue over a period of years.
4. Calculating the average rate of return as a percentage.

The rate of return on research cannot be calculated as accurately as it can on cost reduction engineering projects, but the effort required and the potential benefits should be examined to make certain that the game is worth the candle.

A subfactor is long-term profitability. A plus factor in choosing a project exists if the successful completion of the work puts the company in a position to make profits over a long period of time.

There should, of course, be a reasonable probability of success. The certainty that worthwhile results will be obtained cannot be high on all projects. (In fact, success on all projects may indicate too cautious and conservative an approach.) The estimate of the probability of success should be compared with the estimated rate of return, and these factors should be balanced. If the probability of success is only moderate, there should be a higher estimated rate of return. Even if success is not likely but the rewards of success are enormous, the project may be worth taking a shot at.

A criterion which must be examined early is capability. Are space and facilities, including special instrumentation, available? Do rates of return and probability of success indicate the advisability of acquiring special instrumentation? The facilities of the manufacturing research laboratory often serve to direct the choice of projects—for example, possession of an electron microscope suggests projects using such an instrument.

There should be a reasonable time of completion. In the field of manufacturing technology, one does not ordinarily engage in manufacturing research if the project is so long-range that the benefits of success will be in the far distant future.

It is to be hoped that the project will have a wide scope of application. Sometimes, however, the possibility of extension will justify a project of more limited applicability. Even if the initial rate of return will be moderate, the project may be attractive if there is the possibility of extending the results to several similar fields of activity. For example, in early work on the development of powder metallurgy as a technique in making bearings, the porosity of the resulting product was a feature that made the process particularly desirable. It could be seen that, if the process was successful, the work expended on research and development could easily be applied to making other articles of intricate shapes, even though the porosity, which was a factor in the original case, might be relatively unimportant.

There should be a high likelihood that the results of a project will be utilized. Technically successful manufacturing research, if not utilized, is of no economic benefit to the company. It is often wise to review a project with those most likely to be concerned with the application of results, so that a decision to implement or adopt it may be made. Moreover, projects should be aimed at significant needs, so that pressure for adoption will make utilization more likely. Sometimes a little salesmanship may be necessary after the successful completion of a project.

Will it be necessary to carry the work far beyond the feasibility point, the borderline between research and development? The need for new or different factory skills to implement the successful project may be a negative value in selection. Will the company find it worthwhile to have a program of training for factory workers? If the project takes the manufacturer into an entirely new field in which he is not tooled, it will need especially careful examination before adoption.

The probability that patents will result is a definite plus value on our checklist. The protection of the company's investment in existing patents and know-how aids in justification of the proposed research. In some areas, however, the probability of acquiring patents is low. For example, research on statistical techniques as applied to quality assurance and quality control will probably produce no patents. Other aspects of such work must, therefore, justify the project.

If it is likely that the people who will perform the manufacturing research will not develop enthusiasm for the project, we can sometimes, especially in a large organization, substitute a different team, but it is often better simply to look for a new project. Uninterested research workers result in only a routine application of effort which is rarely productive. The personnel factor is important in work of this caliber; there, it is essential to consult with the professional staff who will be carrying out the research work itself. Again salesmanship is a factor, too. Enthusiasm can be built up by the proper approach.

The project should be compatible with existing staff skills. While the fresh outlook of a different discipline is sometimes productive, it would be unwise, for example, suddenly to switch research teams of organic and physical chemists to mechanical engineering. If the direction of projects is to be decidedly changed, it has to be done gradually. If no one in the organization possesses skills compatible with the project, but the other criteria give it very high plus values, addition of a small new group or groups is indicated.

Scientific significance is not a major criterion in manufacturing research project selection, but importance must be attached to it because of its effect on the motivation of engineers and scientists. One of the problems of manufacturing research is that some people who have the training, background, and intellectual capacity to do research in manufacturing technology have a strong bias toward pure or basic research. They are sometimes reluctant to engage in work primarily justified by practical needs. Changing such attitudes requires skilled administrative action—again with a large portion of salesmanship.

Projects with genuine scientific significance on a scale beyond immediate needs are beneficial to morale. Also, a successful piece of work of genuine scientific significance adds luster to a company's reputation and helps to attract desirable talent to its manufacturing research staff. And the public relations benefits are obviously considerable.

A value to be considered in selecting a project is the extent to which it increases a company's knowledge in current fields or in a new field. Manufacturing research not only provides answers to definite problems but also builds up a stock of knowledge on how to make things. The manufacturing arm may draw upon this stock of knowledge much as the prudent depositor may draw money from his bank account. The account of knowledge is a particularly satisfactory one; drawing upon it does not diminish its reserves.

Finally, the project should not be too big or too costly for the company undertaking it. Magnitude of project should be considered separately from rate of return. For example, it is usually unwise to tie up an entire organization in one or two gigantic projects, even if all other factors are favorable.

The order in which we have discussed these project-selection criteria is not especially significant. Their relative importance will no doubt differ from organization to organization. For most projects, it is valuable to consider criteria systematically; absolute rigidity is not desirable. Although 99 percent of possible projects may rise or fall when evaluated in detail with such a checklist, occasionally some project will not rate too well—but one or more persons may have what can almost be called a hunch about it. Now and then it is well at least to start such a project so that the research people can see whether there may possibly be something in it. On the whole, however, hit-or-miss estimates and cursory considerations are not desirable, and the choice of a research project should be a carefully considered action following an established procedure.

TERMINATION OF PROJECTS

As important as the establishment of criteria for the selection of manufacturing research projects is the decision on when and how to terminate them. Projects should be terminated when—

- Feasibility and preliminary know-how are established, and the manufacturing staff engineers take over.
- The probability of success becomes low, especially when other projects can be pursued more profitably by the same people.
- Another engineering organization in the company takes over the projects.

Termination of projects is often a painful, but necessary, action, and delay may make it all the more difficult. Termination will be accepted more willingly by the (possibly) reluctant scientist or engineer if the general climate of the manufacturing engineering organization is good.

Planned or unplanned, a climate of some sort always exists. It consists of the surroundings, both psychological and physical, which affect an engineer or scientist in discharging his assigned duties. It includes physical environment, recognition, status, approval authority for expenditures, attitudes of management, and many other tangible and intangible elements.

PLANNING A FAVORABLE CLIMATE

Recently management has made greater efforts to plan a more favorable climate for research, and this is true as well in manufacturing research no less than in any other area. An increasingly larger percentage of industrial development work is done in a manufacturing research environment; more and more of the costs of doing business are engineering costs. The principal end result of effective engineering and scientific work is cost reduction, which increases the relative cost of such effort in comparison with the costs of direct factory labor and materials. As new arts make industrial processes more complex, the influence of manufacturing research becomes more and more widespread, the services of engineers and scientists more and more necessary, and the establishment of a favorable climate more and more significant.

How is such a favorable climate established? Certain methods are obvious. Management must provide good working conditions, excellent equipment, adequate library facilities, and sufficient clerical, technical, and administrative personnel. The professional man should be assisted and encouraged in self-development by on-the-job training, released-time study, tuition refund plans, and graduate training programs. He should be provided with means of exchanging information and ideas by association with his peers, by in-company symposia, and, in the large organization, by interworks conferences. In-company technical journals and papers will help him with his problems and communication. He should be supported in his membership in scientific societies and engineering organizations and encouraged to attend their meetings. He should be given opportunities to write technical books and articles for publication. Most industrial organizations can improve their policies along some of these lines; many have already expended much sincere effort in these directions.

The idea of a parallel ladder of advancement within the scientific fields is applicable to manufacturing research personnel, but several points need emphasis. For one thing, management should state clearly its policy on salary for supervisory and nonsupervisory positions. In practice, equivalency in the two ladders usually brings the top of the engineer–scientist ladder up to the second or third level of supervisory positions. If management is actually operating on this basis, it should so inform the engineer–scientist.

Equivalency is not, however, completely a matter of salary. There should be equality in physical matters such as office space, type of desk, and so on. Issues of this sort may seem petty, but in the matter of status symbols wise management should maintain a high degree of tolerance if it wishes to keep a favorable climate. Levels of reporting are also important, since it is clear from the level to which a man reports where management believes he belongs in the structure of the organization.

Management may not always be aware of the frustrations of the professional man that result from subprofessional work—work which in some cases is actually done better by other types of skilled people, such as draftsmen and toolmakers. There should be a definite policy of assigning only challenging technical or scientific work to the highly professional employee.

Continuity of activity level in the manufacturing research organization also is an important aspect of climate. A vacillating policy, fluctuating with the economy, can have devastating effects. In view of the costs of recruiting and training professional personnel, a "yo-yo" policy can be very expensive too, but its principal drawback is its effect on morale. Equally injurious to morale is the initiation of large numbers of interesting projects in times of high business activity and subsequent cancellation in times of retrenchment. While such actions may be necessary at times, morale should be weighed in the administrative judgment.

On the other hand, boredom and ingrowth may result from too prolonged assignment within a restricted field. An expert is not necessarily produced by leaving a man in one narrow activity for long periods of time. One year of experience repeated 30 times with only very minor variations is very different from 30 years of diversified engineering and is likely to produce very different results.

Most important of all, the professional man in manufacturing research must be given freedom. We cannot expect him to be creative if he is told that a problem exists and is then required to solve it in a circumscribed way. If he is an expert in the field, *he* should decide what constitutes the most promising path to solution.

First-line supervisors are most likely to interfere in this respect. They usually are better informed on the details of a project than are middle or top managers, and they may have definite prejudices concerning avenues of approach. It may be necessary in some cases for upper management to state explicitly what is meant by "administrative help." The duty of the administrator is to do all in his power to produce results, to give the scientists and engineers all the assistance and support they need.

It is, unfortunately, quite difficult to measure to what extent proper climate improves results. To what extent does a climate of freedom increase profits? Companies would be reluctant to set up a controlled experiment in which one group of their professional people was subjected to coercive management of projects and another to permissive management. There is, on the whole, simply a strong general feeling that a climate which emphasizes freedom does, in the long run, pay off.

Communication is often problematic in manufacturing research. Technical report procedures, conferences with higher levels of management, visits by other groups, conferences with professional people working on day-to-day manufacturing problems, speakers, rotation of personnel, the establishment of a general communication medium such as a newsletter—all help in this area. Isolation from the real problems of the company, with resultant nonacceptance of results by the manufacturing arm, must be avoided. Nothing is more deadly to climate than ill-defined lines of communication.

THE FUTURE OF MANUFACTURING RESEARCH

What is the real importance of manufacturing process research, and what is its present and future impact on the economy? Manufacturing research is now being done by universities, research institutes, government, and competitive industry. There will be a great deal more of such research in the future, performed either in a separate location or in a special laboratory facility of the factory. Organizations can no longer afford to neglect it.

Increased work in this field will no doubt augment the tendencies noticeable in our manufacturing economy:

1. The amount of direct labor required to produce manufactured products will be reduced to an even greater extent.
2. The amount of material required to make these products will be lowered by the simple means of reducing waste in raw material and by the more complicated methods of miniaturization.

This should bring about a cycle of lower costs, lower prices to consumers, and greater demand.

Manufacturing process research leads to the reduction of the need for unskilled labor. The amount of clerical, professional, and administrative effort consumed in the production of manufactured goods increases in relationship to the reduction of direct labor. Integrated data processing of systems engineering will require still further growth in the professional ranks of engineers, scientists, systems analysts, and computer programers. In the future we may even computerize some parts of what is now considered professional activity.

Even with such revolutionary changes, we need not anticipate reductions in the demands for skills, and we may look forward to a continuing need for that interesting and satisfying activity—manufacturing process research.

COORDINATING PURCHASING WITH PRODUCTION REQUIREMENTS

By H. J. MOORE

To meet production requirements, the purchasing department must be involved with many types of activities. However, this chapter limits the discussion to those activities which relate to purchasing's responsibility to supply purchased goods at the "right time" and in the "right quantity." Purchasing's responsibility in cost control, of course, cannot ever be relaxed, but for the purpose of this discussion let us merely recognize the obvious impact upon cost of supplying goods and services at the right time and in the right quantity. Limiting the interest in this way should make at least the production control manager happy, if not the controller.

We must make one basic assumption—the factors which influence right time and right quantity decisions cannot be completely eliminated, nor can the problems they cause always be completely solved. If a company's business is such that time and quantity factors do not exist, or if the problems they cause can be easily solved, then the dynamics of its business are such that its ability to exist for any period of time within a competitive environment should be seriously questioned.

RIGHT TIME

The foremost factor limiting purchasing's ability to supply purchased goods according to the production schedule is lack of proper lead time. The first consideration in minimizing this problem should be one of proper organization

H. J. MOORE is Director of Purchasing for International Business Machines Corporation, in Armonk, New York.

or at least of setting up a communicational link between the purchasing staff and the person who originates the requisition. Obviously, the sooner the purchasing man can be brought into the development cycle, the better chance he has to lessen the vendor's lead time. The usual comment, however, from engineering or from the person originating the requisition is, "I don't really know what I want yet," or, "Purchasing will just confuse things if they get into the act at this point."

Two distinct advantages can be gained if the purchasing man is brought into the activity in its earliest stage. First, by the simple fact that he is aware of a potential requirement he can begin to do some preliminary planning about sources, production problems, capacity, and so on. This planning can shorten the time needed to select the vendor when the requisition is finally released. Second, industry knowledge concerning the item to be purchased can be made known by purchasing to the originator of the requisition. This knowledge may cause any number of changes in the requisition, such as specifying a different type of raw material, relaxing tolerances, or using a different design to make the manufacturing process easier and less costly. These changes can often reduce the time required for the vendor to produce the item and thus make it easier for purchasing to live with a short lead time.

To put purchasing into the early stages of the development cycle and the resulting creation of the requisition is a real challenge in most companies. Two elements are required if it is to be accomplished successfully. The first is top management understanding and support of the purchasing function. The second is purchasing's ability to exhibit its knowledge of supplying industries with needed goods and services and the use of this knowledge to meet the production requirement. Top management's understanding and support are often inherent. If this is the case, so much the better for purchasing. If this is not the case, however, purchasing must continually strive through its performance to increase its stature in the eyes of management.

Once company management is convinced of the value of purchasing's contribution, the question of how to put it into the development cycle can be considered. One direct approach is to make the buyer who will handle the production purchasing requirements responsible also for the buying connected with the development program.

In the past, unfortunately, buying for a development program has evolved along completely separate lines in most companies. The development buyer's primary responsibility has been to support the development engineer. Since the engineer's responsibility is aimed solely at developing one working model, such production factors as supplier capability to produce production quantities and cost reduction through vendor value engineering have not had sufficient emphasis.

Production considerations such as supplier capacity, manufacturing problems connected with production runs, and proprietary restrictions can and should be considered during the development period. The buyer who knows he must live with the problems during the entire life of the requirement and applies his experience in production buying to the job is in a much better position to reach balanced purchasing decisions than a buyer whose responsibilities and experience are limited to development buying. In some cases it may even be worthwhile to move the buyer physically into the engineering area. In this way he is continually involved with the engineering activities, and the very fact of his "just being there" makes it more convenient for the engineer to keep him continually advised of activities affecting purchasing.

When single purchasing responsibility (manufacturing and engineering) is not practical, a systems or product manager approach may be considered. Under this approach, a single buyer, quite often of management status, can be made responsible for establishing the necessary liaison between engineering and manufacturing. The systems or product manager must establish reporting controls which assure that information of importance to buying decisions is moved rapidly between the various functional areas. He should also be sensitive enough to know when he must personally bring together the individuals concerned in order to reach a balanced decision.

When the size of the buying program does not justify moving personnel or specially assigning a systems or product manager, consideration should be given to establishing two-way communication between the purchasing department and the man who originates the requisition. New and developing purchasing requirements must be made known to the department so that, in turn, pertinent vendor and industry information can be fed back to engineering. Both parties must cooperate fully so that purchasing can be brought directly into the activity at the earliest possible date and appropriate action can be taken to acquire what is needed. The objective, once again, is to give the vendor more lead time.

Regardless of the approach, however, the objective must be to focus within engineering as much purchasing information as possible and as early as practical in the development cycle of the requirement. Purchasing, consequently, must be made aware of requirements and changes affecting them as soon as possible. Early entry by purchasing into the development and release cycle can greatly reduce the problem of short lead time and thus improve purchasing's ability to supply at the right time.

Another factor which affects purchasing's ability to coordinate with production requirements, and one which quite often contributes to a too short lead time, is lack of complete specifications for the item to be purchased. These two factors (short lead time and lack of complete specifications) have to be balanced. For example, in order to arrange for a longer lead time, a requisition may be released to purchasing with fewer specifications than desired, while, conversely, in order to develop more complete specifications, an item may be held longer within engineering before release, and thus the lead time is shortened. Such situations cannot be eliminated, yet they do have an impact upon purchasing's ability to supply at the right time. Once again, the best way to minimize their effects is to make purchasing a party to the development and release cycle.

Purchasing's knowledge of outside companies may be the key needed by the engineer to determine how complete and detailed the specifications need to be. For example, in most cases a requirement is first generated on the basis of a functional need (such as a motor of certain physical dimensions to perform in a specific way). Purchasing's knowledge of the products and performance capabilities of suppliers may make it possible for the requirement to be released immediately without waiting for more detailed specifications to be developed. On the other hand, purchasing's knowledge of the product may indicate the costliness of acquiring the specific function and the engineer may find it advisable to redirect his efforts immediately toward a new functional approach.

Some purchasing departments have developed tables which relate purchased cost to often-used functions for use by the engineer during the development program. They tell him how much the cost of his product will be affected if he designs a particular function into it. Having this information on hand assists the engineer in reaching a specification decision at an early time, thus once again giving purchasing more lead time. A side effect of the use of these tables is directing the engineers to industry standards which not only lower cost but, because they are standards, can be purchased with shorter lead time, thus adding to purchasing's ability to supply at the right time.

A vendor's failure to perform is another factor which purchasing must learn to cope with if it is to meet production requirements at the right time. Failure to perform can occur for many good and valid reasons, but the two questions which purchasing must answer are: (1) What can purchasing do to reduce the chances of failure? and (2) How can the effects of failure be minimized? The answer to both of these questions is "knowledge and communication." One way the possibility of failure can be minimized is by making a "checkpoint" reporting program one of the responsibilities which purchasing places upon the vendor. Under this arrangement the vendor is required to submit periodic reports on the status of the various activities within his own organization which affect his ability to provide the product at the proper time.

Purchasing should be knowledgeable about the various steps which must be taken by the vendor in order to turn out the product and see that they are included in the checkpoint status reports. These should cover such factors as the following and relate them to a schedule to which both the vendor and purchasing have agreed: procurement of raw materials, including lead times; anticipated dates of purchase orders to be issued by the vendor for purchase requirements; inventory of purchased goods to be carried by the vendor; design, manufacture, and/or purchase of tooling required; manufacturing schedules; stocking of parts and assemblies; final assembling; test equipment required and inspection procedures; and shipping schedules.

The size and complexity of the purchase determine the detail and frequency of the checkpoint report. Its purpose is, of course, to establish an agreed-upon program of manufacture between purchasing and the vendor and to provide a means for both parties to evaluate continually the vendor's ability to meet the schedule established. Purchasing should not, of course, rely upon this report as the only means of evaluating a vendor's progress. If the size and complexity of the purchase warrant it, purchasing staff members should make periodic trips to the vendor for the purpose of personally evaluating his progress and measuring the effectiveness and accuracy of the checkpoint report. However, the report is an effective means of minimizing vendor failure if both parties look upon it as a "live" management tool and react promptly to the information it discloses.

The biggest problem caused by vendor failure is created when the purchasing department and the company of which it is part blindly assume that a purchased item will arrive at the right time, and then, a day or two before delivery is expected, a call comes through from the vendor to the effect that such and such has occurred and delivery will be late. The proper use of a checkpoint report can prevent this from happening, of course. If a problem does occur which will affect the delivery schedule, both parties are better off if it is brought out into the open at the earliest possible opportunity. Once the problem is known, it can be looked at and analyzed. It may be possible to vary the production plan so that purchasing can live with a new and later delivery date. On the other hand, if the lateness cannot be tolerated, learning about it at the earliest possible date gives purchasing and the vendor the chance to consider alternatives. Perhaps a substitute can be used temporarily, or extra effort can be applied by the vendor at least to minimize the delay in shipment.

A vendor's failure to perform is a problem which all buyers must face from time to time. The availability of prompt, accurate, and continuing information concerning the vendor's activities will help him, if not to prevent a missed delivery, at least to minimize the delay in delivery.

Quite often a vendor's failure to meet a schedule is caused by changes made by the purchaser in total quantity, delivery schedules, or specifications. Purchasing's success in coping with these changes depends primarily on three considerations: (1) selection of a vendor who can react quickly to changes; (2) establishment of efficient lines of communication among all parties concerned, both inside and outside the company; and (3) purchasing's ability, through its strength, knowledge, and stature within the company, to see that the external aspects of change—such as cost, the effect upon the schedule, and the impact upon the vendor—are properly weighed and considered before they are approved. Let us look briefly at each of these factors.

First, the selection of a vendor who can react quickly to change. Too often a product is selected without considering the production capabilities of the vendor. The ability to handle changes can be evaluated by comparing potential vendors in terms of such considerations as size, manufacturing capability, technical support, and financing. This need for ability to cope with change obviously varies according to what is purchased. Purchasing should, however, give major consideration to it when the buying program is of long duration, with major quantities involved, and where the product being purchased has a long or technically complicated manufacturing cycle.

The second consideration in lessening a vendor's likelihood of failing to meet a schedule is establishing proper lines of communication. When requirement changes are major, the line of communication must be extended to include any in-company areas that can cause these changes. Purchasing is too often at the end of the communication whip. By the time purchasing is informed about the change, all the problems have been enlarged. The lead time for the vendor to react is shortened; the vendor may be further through the manufacturing cycle and thus have created inventory that must be scrapped; and, when quantity changes are involved, the effects on inventory and production, either upward or downward, become more critical. This delay in receiving information concerning changes is undoubtedly the biggest obstacle which purchasing must face in handling them efficiently.

Purchasing's ability to mitigate the effects of poor communication is to a large extent determined by our third consideration—its strength, knowledge, and stature within its company. Too often the purchasing department is the "last to know," as we have seen. To operate efficiently it must be part of the decision-making cycle. At the time changes are being contemplated, purchasing people should be requested to place before management a rundown on all the external factors which will be affected by the changes. How often has a change in inventory practice not considered its effect upon the vendor and thus caused an increase in purchase cost which more than offset any saving? How often has a change in requirements which was intended to solve an in-plant workload problem not only increased the purchase cost substantially but even caused the supplier to cease production for a time, with such costly results as loss of experienced people and retraining when the job had to be started again?

Certainly many factors, both in the plant and out, must be considered if the proper decision is to be made about changes in requirements. The important point, however, is that purchase dollars have the same impact upon the profit of a company as dollars resulting from in-company expenditures. The effect of changes in requirements on purchasing dollars must be considered at the time a decision is made. The purchasing organization must have the stature, authority, and ability to see that such external aspects of change have been duly evaluated.

Although other factors such as transportation, industry capacity, and the state of the art affect purchasing's ability to supply purchased goods, the right time, lack of proper lead time, incomplete specifications, vendor failure to perform, and changes in requirements must, in most companies, be considered the most critical problems with which it has to cope. No purchasing organization will ever operate completely without such problems. Purchasing's objective must be to minimize their negative impact by continually improving lines of communication (internal and external), considering new and improved organizational and procedural relationships, and upgrading purchasing personnel through professional training and experience.

RIGHT QUANTITY

Some factors that affect the right time, such as lack of lead time and incomplete specifications, also affect the vendor's ability to manufacture and deliver the right quantity. Of course, other factors as well influence the purchasing objective of providing goods in the right quantity: one is inventory control practices when production schedule changes take place.

Inventory levels are usually calculated on the basis of current production schedules, and a change in production means that the inventory level must be adjusted accordingly. This adjustment in turn causes a change in the requirements from the vendor which is even greater than the increase or decrease in the production schedule alone. For example, the inventory level in most companies is set at "so many days of production." If production is to be increased or decreased by 25 percent, then the requirement change is 25 percent of the production change plus 25 percent of the previous inventory level. The production control department will normally include this desired change in inventory level when it issues the first purchase requisition to cover the production change. The inventory control department would naturally like to see all shipments stopped until such time as the inventory level is adjusted, and in some cases the vendor does completely stop production. The economics of this type of action, if brought to light, usually overshadow the inventory considerations. Purchasing must, therefore, accept the responsibility of smoothing out the impact of the change upon the vendor. What is right quantity to the individual whose interest is only inventory control may not be the right quantity that purchasing should request from the vendor. Purchasing must make information available to management so that a carefully weighed decision can be made concerning the quantities to be ordered from the vendor. The decision must compare the increase in purchase cost caused by placing a radical and abrupt production change upon the vendor with spreading the desired change over a period of time so that he can efficiently adjust his operation.

A change in inventory practice may also affect purchasing's ability to deliver the right quantity. For example, because of a lack of cash, the financial organization may request that ordering cycles be shortened so as to have fewer dollars tied up in inventory. A questionable market forecast or the possibility of changes in specifications may cause the same request to be made to purchasing so that there will be less chance of having to write off inventory because of technical obsolescence or lack of demand. These are good reasons for shortening the ordering cycles to reduce inventory, but they alone should not cause the reduction. Purchasing should be able to show management how the shortening of order cycles will increase the purchase cost and to what degree. This cost can then be compared to the possible saving and other advantages that would accrue through reducing the inventory. The increase in purchase cost can easily be determined by purchasing when one or two items are affected. The problem arises when a major program is affected and many purchased items must be considered. When this happens, the ability of purchasing to draw upon data maintained in a purchasing data processing system becomes important. The system should be able to analyze major programs in terms of the increase or decrease in purchase cost caused by varying ordering cycles. Purchasing management should continually explore the possible uses of data processing for this and other applications which assist in making balanced decisions.

"Right quantity" must be viewed as a combination of two factors—how much and how often delivered. Purchasing must provide information to assist management in reaching a decision by balancing such positive advantages as having inventory protection against stock-outs, lower purchase costs through larger quantities, and lower costs through fewer deliveries and larger inventories against the ultimate of inventory control, which is daily delivery to the production line with no inventory at all.

*   *   *

Throughout we have emphasized purchasing's responsibilities in coordinating production requirements. These responsibilities, however, require the support of, and at times direct assistance from, other functions such as finance, engineering, production control, inventory control, and quality control. In order to handle its responsibilities as related to these other functions, purchasing must maintain organizational and procedural relationships with them. It must also develop highly qualified and trained people in the other functions who work with them.

If the key to a good purchasing decision is the careful weighing of all information related to the subject, then why not make it possible to develop this information within a single organization? Where the purchasing activity is of sufficient magnitude, some companies have done just this by creating a separate group within purchasing that includes people with backgrounds in financial analysis, engineering, quality control, and purchasing specialties. Major purchasing programs can then be evaluated on a total basis within purchasing. This in no way eliminates the responsibility for final decisions within the particular functional area concerned, but it does assure continuing and professional analysis of all factors affecting the purchasing decision. The knowledge which a group of this type can bring to the purchasing function will go far in assuring the "balanced" decision for which the management of all companies must strive. In the long run, the reaching of "balanced decisions," based upon accurate and current information, supplied from both inside and outside a company, will be the major factor which assures that the purchasing activities are properly coordinated with production requirements.

THE "MAKE OR BUY" DECISION AS A FACTOR IN MANUFACTURING COSTS

By PETER DeK. DUSINBERRE, JR.

Although every segment of manufacturing operations contributes its share to the overall cost of a product, few decisions so directly affect cost as whether to manufacture some component internally or to depend upon a vendor. "Make or buy" decisions date from the earliest beginnings of American mass production; when Eli Whitney developed the technique for mass producing muskets by introducing into America the concept of interchangeable parts, he participated in one of the earliest of such decisions, since he did not make every component of every weapon. In the nearly two centuries which have elapsed, the factors which influence the make or buy decision have greatly multiplied. The complexity of today's operations demands careful evaluation of all these factors in order to increase the likelihood of profitable production.

ORGANIZING FOR THE MAKE OR BUY DECISION

Since the make or buy decision decreases or increases the current or potential scope of an operation, it is only proper that certain guidelines be established to help determine the best means of planning, organizing, and controlling the activities which result either from self-sufficiency or from reliance on the resources of others. In reviewing the elements of a workable make or buy program it is wise to begin with the organization, without which no decision making can be fully effective.

From the very top must come a description of the basic nature of a company's business. If it is a distribution warehouse, for instance, pressures for quick inventory turnover heavily influence the make or buy decision. If technical knowledge, market penetration, unavailability of competent suppliers, or

---

PETER DEK. DUSINBERRE, JR. is Works Manager for The Wilcolator Company, Elizabeth, New Jersey.

any other factor dictates total self-reliance, the policy decision about just what a company's business *is* must become the starting point for any make or buy program. As should be true of all management decisions, the policy defining the basic nature and extent of the company's business must be periodically reviewed.

In any series of independent judgments whose ultimate purpose is to aid in deciding whether to make or buy, the advantages and disadvantages must be subject to continuous scrutiny lest the correct decision under one set of circumstances should become unwise under changed conditions. Two cases in point will perhaps help clarify this statement. A company in the television receiver industry decided to reduce its dependence on its cabinet supplier; this operating decision was compatible with the nature of the business and was reached on the bases of cost, storage space, erratic delivery, and so on. The management decision to become self-supporting, it should be noted, evaluated cost as but *one* of many contributing factors. As industry techniques and consumer preferences changed, it became necessary to re-examine the decision, which in turn led to a decision to revert to buying. This second decision, too, was correct in the light of current conditions.

Another decision in the same industry dictated continued purchase of printed circuit boards, even though the investment in internal manufacturing equipment and staffing was small and the potential return was great, because the state of the art was undergoing such rapid change that equipment and technology could quickly become obsolete. The policy decision to defer internal manufacturing showed awareness of the valuable contribution that suppliers can make when a process is new and undergoing rapid change. The risks in entering a "new business" in its formative stage often outweigh the short-term cost and delivery advantages.

Thus no effective make or buy program exists unless the top management first defines the basic nature of the company's business, for such a policy decision prescribes the areas in which it shall make its own parts or components. It is always preferable if this policy can be made available in a formal statement with guidelines established for its administration. In the absence of a formal definition of business, however, guidelines become established merely from the accumulation of isolated decisions, and tradition can prove tyrannical and wrongheaded in the light of continuous change.

ANALYZING THE INTERNAL FACTORS

In establishing the guidelines for a make or buy program one of the first considerations of top management must be how to delegate authority to render the ultimate decision. Too often this authority is delegated to some committee. The continuous use of a formal committee with or without any decision-making authority is unwise, because ultimately the decision to make or procure can be made effectively only by a single person. In The Wilcolator Company, where all the factory operations are grouped to report to a single man, the logical focus for the make or buy decisions is the works manager. In an organization where the procurement and the quality functions report separately to top management it would seem wise to delegate the responsibility, to exercise at least the penultimate authority for the make or buy decision, to someone other than the top manager.

To be effective, the decision must be made as close to profit responsibility as is practical; to remain continuously effective, decision making is best vested in a single manager. However, the complexity of today's make or buy decision and the increasing number of factors which influence the decision makers dictate the need for a broad cross-section of opinion. For this reason a meeting to present the opposing points of view and to buttress recommendations with fact is an invaluable and a proper use of a committee. Regular meetings, nonetheless, can quickly become a mechanism to avoid all but follow-up action between the scheduled meeting dates and tend to make too many programs into projects.

Wilcolator's regular review of the decision to manufacture or procure is a direct byproduct of an ongoing cost reduction program. A two-man team receives cost reduction ideas from the manufacturing floor, from the design group, and from top management. As these men evaluate suggestions, they cause not only the process but also the source of related parts and assemblies to be reviewed as well. It is this forced review which triggers the meeting of the make or buy committee. When an alternate source of supply is indicated to the cost reduction team, one of its members requests review and analysis of the current practice.

To insure that all salient points of view are represented, the committee should include a design engineer familiar with the end product, the chief of quality control, the purchasing agent, a direct shop supervisor, the manufacturing engineer of the process under review, and the ultimate decision maker. The committee evaluates risks in order that the decision may be properly reached; thus it performs a staff function and provides the necessary cross-fertilization of ideas and objectives. Each member is expected to present and support arguments on issues relating to his own responsibilities; the coalescing of these ideas into a conclusion is a natural outcome of a well-ordered meeting.

Assuming, then, that the cost reduction team has made a recommendation which indicates a change in source, what are the factors which must be evaluated in order to insure that the decision will be effective? The current emphasis on product reliability and process control of quality increases the need to evaluate make or buy decisions from the point of view of product performance. In management's concern with the manufacturing process, guaranteeing product performance has assumed virtual equality with direct cost because of its long-term effect on product cost and acceptance. Although Wilcolator's industry does not yet demand certified reliability, product quality is a paramount requirement. In the defense industry and in certain segments of the auto industry reliability is the byword, and it will probably spread quickly into many other consumer areas. Thus the make or buy decision in the mid-1960's is much more heavily influenced by reliability and quality considerations than was true a decade ago.

Another factor which is often overlooked in arriving at an intelligent sourcing decision is the availability of talent to produce the part in question. The increasing complexity of manufacturing processes means that the availability of manpower can and should outweigh the availability of mechanical power. In a recent decision at Wilcolator the availability of manpower proved to be *the* significant factor, although cost and scheduling weighed heavily toward internal manufacture. Wilcolator requires an extremely precise and clean annealing operation on stainless steel tubes. It is essential that small orifices in the tubes remain absolutely clean and that no scale, flake, or foreign matter be present after the annealing operation. The configuration of the tubes must not be altered. Because cleanliness is to some extent insured by the heat-treating process, it is not practical to anneal the ware in advance; consequently, each lot must be processed daily. Since this operation was costly and made deliveries troublesome, it was closely examined to determine whether it could be made internally more economically. Equipment costs could be paid back quickly, it was discovered, but the critical nature of the process and the need for precise control and evaluation dictated regular attendance by a skilled technician if not, in fact, a qualified engineer.

We had to recognize, therefore, that quality could be sustained and delivery and cost improved only if we had technical talent available to insure that the process was continuously and accurately maintained. Although there are men in the company who have the talent to perform this function, they were already working full schedules, and the surveillance of the internal process would have warranted an addition of manpower. There was no assurance that the necessary skills were available in the marketplace or that, even if they were, they could be fully occupied in this particular project. Hence, Wilcolator decided to continue buying and simultaneously to continue examining other products which could be converted to the process in question in order to create a full-time occupation for an additional technician. A survey of the availability of talent in our market area quickly disclosed a distinct undersupply. Thus the compelling factor proved to be the availability of competent manpower.

The investigation itself, however, developed improvements in the vendor relationship which have relieved much of the pressure on scheduling. It also made possible a price reduction through the medium of a blanket order with a continuing commitment to use the services of the vendor. Here the effectiveness of re-examining an earlier decision to buy, although it did not generate a change from buy to make, did produce a precise definition of the marginal factor (manpower), an improvement in scheduling (daily vendor pickup and delivery), and a reduction in cost (through the use of a blanket order and the establishment of an annual commitment quantity). In view of these improvements in manufacturing effectiveness it would seem that the management of the make or buy program had made an effective decision.

ANALYZING THE EXTERNAL FACTORS

Examination of the procurement function quickly discloses certain key external factors which bear directly on the decision of whether to make or to buy. The responsiveness of many vendors to maturing and changing concepts of quality control indicates that it is wise to continue relations with outside suppliers. Among the more efficient vendors today are those whose customers include companies which manufacture missile components and other highly sophisticated devices for industry; they very often have developed a control organization which has available resources to provide equivalent control on *all* products. As the state of the quality control art progresses because of pressures from the defense industry and from certain segments of the auto industry, we can, if we are alert to these changes, take advantage of improved vendor quality at no increase in cost.

Among the external factors which regularly affect procurement decisions are competent international sources. American industry's constantly improving contacts and relationships with business firms in Europe and the Far East particularly are making it worthwhile to examine the availability of talent and material everywhere on this globe. During a recent review of one component Wilcolator uncovered a highly competent source just north of the border in Canada. This vendor, who had idle capacity, was able to quote on large volumes at sharply reduced cost and with relatively good insurance of delivery. Because his operation had previously catered primarily to lower-volume users, Wilcolator could quickly become his chief buyer and thus reap the benefits of his fully utilized capacity.

The search for vendors has taken us to one of the Common Market countries where tooling and material are attractively priced. Through indirect discussion with one of our licensees in the European Free Trade Area we have uncovered a fundamental change in process on one assembly which, with a minor design modification, may well dictate reversing a decision made six months ago to manufacture it rather than to continue buying it from a local source. It is such developments as this that point up the necessity for flexibility in the make or buy program.

A somewhat nebulous external factor which relates directly to the make or buy decision is information about the programs of competitors. It is normal for several major companies to use common supply sources. Even in a strictly proper relationship there are certain signs that indirectly lead to inferences about the activities of competitors, such as when a vendor declares that he is working heavily on overtime or, alternatively, has a great deal of idle capacity. While these bits of news are never conclusive and seldom extraordinary, they do nevertheless provide some touchstones by which a company can examine its present plans.

If a vendor that is supplying a critical part to a company and to one of its major competitors develops a delivery problem because of overdemand, it may mean that the competitor is increasing his activity. It may alert the company to the existence of a new-found market, or it may foreshadow a loss in its own markets. The opposite reaction from the vendor may signal a design change or slackening demand on the part of the competitor; when related to its own marketing forecasts, this knowledge, with the inference drawn from it, becomes one more piece of data on which one of the many key management decisions may be evaluated.

OPERATING PROBLEMS

Whether in the defense, the home receiver, or the controls industry, the lion's share of product cost comes from items procured outside. Since the major function of a manufacturing shop is to add value and to be rewarded proportionately, it is not surprising to find great pressures to reduce the imbalance between purchased parts and manufactured parts.

When a company is determining whether to introduce into its own manufacturing plans various items which it previously has purchased, it attempts to assess the added burden which must be recovered as a result of the added operation. To do this accurately requires answering certain key questions. The decision to introduce a product requiring 10,000 square feet of space to manufacture, for instance, may appear to demand an immediate acquisition of extra space. Unless this evaluation is made in the knowledge that the present space is being profitably utilized, the decision to expand may be in error. How often has a plant concluded that it is in need of additional space for storage when in fact it is using but one-third of the cubic feet which the storerooms now occupy because its racks and shelving terminate six feet above the floor while the ceiling is a dozen feet further away? And how frequently have the existing manufacturing operations been streamlined and consolidated to create the space needed for a new product or a new operation? When the efficiency of space utilization is analyzed, it often has the bilateral effects of improving the original internal operation and providing space for the introduction of new operations.

Much the same type of analysis must be made of overhead personnel. Is the foreman loaded to the point where he cannot reasonably expect to supervise additional people, or is he so overloaded that his function would be more efficient if it were divided and two foremen placed over a combined operation? Would the addition of the new operation mean hiring a large number of new employees for whom proper work scheduling would become a problem? These and other questions have a definite bearing on make or buy decisions. Analyses of these kinds must attempt to assess the burden only when introduction of the product or process into the manufacturing cycle clearly means an added cost. If the costs for outside expediting, telephone follow-up, handling purchase orders and invoices, and other related expenses of outside purchasing are subtracted, the newly introduced burden will be somewhat reduced. When the cost appraisal indicates a standoff between make or buy, the factors of quality, delivery, increased investment, and availability of talent weigh most heavily in the ultimate decision.

If a manufacturing operation is tautly run, there is seldom sufficient space, talent, or equipment available to take on efficiently a major segment of the product line which has previously been procured. Often the search leads to examination of an acquisition of a supplier company or of that portion of its operation which is profitable by reason of its sales to the acquiring company. By broadening investment through acquisition a company obtains tools, equipment, talent, often the assurance of an improved cost relationship, and an increased share of the added value from manufacturing. The great difficulty is to determine accurate costs of managing the new operation so that the imagined benefits are realized.

The gain in flexibility which comes with being one's own supplier can sometimes dictate investing in equipment. Recently one company decided to invest in coil-winding equipment in order to maintain competitive costs. The decision was amply justified by the ability of the manufacturing arm to respond quickly to engineering innovation and to examine promptly the effects of design change. Without this speed of reaction the project would not have been as successful as it was and the company's prominent position in the industry would have been jeopardized. At the same time a decision not to manufacture a basic component was dictated by rapid change in the state of the art; the available technical manpower was in such short supply that the company would have severely overextended itself by investing in internal manufacture. This decision, recently re-examined, was justified by substantial reductions in the supplier's prices. As costs came down rapidly and the number of suppliers increased sharply, the ability of the purchasing group to contribute to profit was greatly enhanced.

An industry where rapid response to changing customer requirements demands a foreshortened manufacturing cycle must continually evaluate the cost of carrying inventory to insure flexibility. Since many smaller vendors are anxious and willing to operate on broad-load planning, it is becoming easier to project long-term commitments (for six months to a year or more) within the range of possible requirements, including authorization for the vendor to obtain some materials and, at his discretion and risk, to perform some preliminary fabrication. Thus, each vendor becomes at his own expense a depository of inventory for which the purchaser is ultimately committed but which it is not required to store in its own facility and for which it is not required to post immediate funds.

APPRAISING THE MAKE OR BUY PROGRAM

When all the internal and external factors have been analyzed and the operating considerations evaluated, ultimately a decision is made to purchase or to manufacture a part, an assembly, or a component. By what yardstick is the wisdom of this decision to be evaluated?

The financial yardstick is most frequently the tool which top management uses to determine whether the make or buy program has been effectively managed. Has the product cost been reduced, has the margin between selling price and cost of goods sold improved, has the manufacturing operation been able to retain its profit margin in the face of declining demand or increasing price pressure? Customer satisfaction, as judged by reliability and quality, is rapidly approaching an equal status with financial measurements in appraising a make or buy program. As customer satisfaction has a direct influence on market penetration, it inevitably has long-term effects on profit. Since return on investment is increasingly cited as a measure of the use of the stockholders' funds, this point likewise assumes greater importance than previously. The foregoing discussion suggests a three-point examination on which to base a realistic evaluation and an objective appraisal of the management of a make or buy program.

1. Is there increased contribution to operating profits?
2. Has the customer relationship improved as a result of product reliability?
3. Is the return on investment reasonable when measured against that of competitors?

Since a great many other operating programs are evaluated by the same criteria, the make or buy program becomes more naturally one of the many tools used by manufacturing management to achieve its objectives. The well-rounded make or buy program keeps these criteria uppermost in mind and continually reviews prior decisions against current conditions. In noting the absence of growth as a viable criterion for measuring the make or buy program, we recognize that while corporate growth has often been held as a measurement of the efficiency of management, there are all too many examples of growth for its own sake without production of reasonable profits, adequate return on investment, or continuing customer satisfaction. Growth is a natural end product of objective and intelligent decision making in the make or buy program, and growth *per se* should not be a significant reason for reaching a make or buy decision.

Often a company committed to long-range planning finds it necessary to acquire skills, talents, and resources in an otherwise alien field in order to insure continued growth; when these needs are evaluated and articulated, a make decision to insure the continued orderly development of the company's products and its position within the industry is properly defined as the effect—not the cause—of growth.

SOME FURTHER COMMENTS

From the foregoing comments it may be inferred that no well-defined path to successful management of a make or buy program exists; or that so many paths exist that a company attempting to choose among them is certain to take a misstep. In truth there is no mystery in make or buy decisions, and the successful ingredients are not dissimilar from those used in all fundamental management decisions:

- Begin with a well-defined objective.
- Determine the significant critical factors bearing on the objective.

- Operate under accurately defined responsibility.
- Appraise against measurable results.

The foundation stone of these ingredients of success is the corporate statement of objectives. This rough framework covers the determination of the critical factors which bear on these objectives; the program is roofed with precisely defined responsibilities; and the finishing touches and final appraisal of results achieved are measured against the standard contained in the established objective.

An effective make or buy program must be so flexible that the manufacturing man can constantly reappraise decisions in the light of later developments, as we have seen. The dynamic change in worldwide manufacturing techniques, capabilities, processes, and manpower resources insures that any decision not subject to critical and periodic re-evaluation will become as valueless as yesterday's newspaper.

The make or buy decision must be based on considerations of profit performance, product reliability, and return on investment. Without excluding or diminishing the significance of peripheral evaluations, these three factors in most instances yield sufficient data on which to make a workable decision. If internal manufacture is preferable, the methods of achieving it are as varied as the problems presented. The competent manager will have little difficulty administering a make or buy program so long as he espouses flexibility and includes among his advisers the responsible proponents of quantity, quality, and cost. Lacking detailed information on any of these key ingredients, he must postpone his decision until the data can be obtained; once the best estimates are available, he must determine their values and render his judgment. While the element of risk varies inversely with the amount of study on the problem to be solved, the most agonizing phase of the modern manager's job is to decide when sufficient facts are in hand to warrant his decision. The execution of his decision can then be properly delegated to the appropriate line manager.

As is equally true of most of the other subjects covered in preceding and succeeding chapters in this book, the best knowledge available to any manager about the make or buy decision can be used only as a series of boundary lines and milestones; keeping within these boundaries while noting the milestones, he can fully expect to wander somewhat from decision to decision. If it is any consolation to him, he can rest assured that he is only one of a large group of managers who also wander from decision to decision with pangs of uncertainty. It is the fact that he is expected to make such high-level decisions that marks him as a manager.

PLANT AND WAREHOUSE RELOCATION, CONSTRUCTION, AND LAYOUT

By JAMES A. O'HARA

Plant and warehouse relocation presents management with a unique opportunity to install facilities which are capable of the best possible performance at the lowest operating cost. These benefits accrue, however, only if planning is sound and takes into account practical economic considerations. Planning, therefore, must be open-minded to the accomplishments of modern technology and to new ways of improving operating methods. It should be directed toward eliminating unfavorable traditions and bad habits and replacing them with whatever truly works.

New facilities planning requires the combined efforts of all managers, regardless of their level. Top management's responsibility includes overall planning and making financial decisions. It contributes information relating to the company's future that is significant to the work at hand. Middle management generally directs the planning work, assigning the detailed information collection to staff and first- and second-line employees.

After responsibilities have been assigned, the overall study logically divides itself into five phases:

1. Determination of facility requirements.
2. Choice of site.
3. Economic evaluation of facilities relocation.
4. Architectural detailing and construction.
5. Facilities start-up.

Each phase is comprised of a number of independent parts that can be carried on concurrently. The phases themselves, however, must be consecutive.

JAMES A. O'HARA is President, E. P. I. Associates, Inc., Ridgewood, New Jersey.

DETERMINATION OF FACILITY REQUIREMENTS

Facilities arrangement affects both direct and indirect labor cost. It is one of the few areas in which savings can be effected without changing pace or quality, a means for holding or reducing costs and increasing productivity while still maintaining an acceptable labor pace and a satisfactory level of quality.

Methods improvement must be effected at the facility start-up. When the facility is in operation, it is probably too late to introduce change because the machines have been installed and the employees are conditioned to the work techniques. New facilities planning starts with top management. The actions it takes first are covered in the following three paragraphs.

1. *Determining the true reason(s) for relocation.* The reason(s) for relocation may not basically influence facilities requirements but are nonetheless important to other planning phases, such as relocating to bring facilities closer to the source of material supply or to the finished-goods market. On the other hand, they could have a significant effect on planning and layout, as in relocating to allow for expansion or to make space available for consolidating the existing decentralized operations.

2. *Evaluating the company "course."* Long-range planning is important to make certain that facilities are not outdated before their construction is complete. Particular attention should be given to potential mergers and acquisitions by determining whether they are targeted to horizontal, vertical, or circular product integration and to management's policy about where and how operations are to be continued.

3. *Projecting the expansion of existing product volumes and lines.* Marketing and sales top management should furnish volume projections itemized by product and summarized by product line annually. The projection period should cover at least five years, but preferably ten. Projections for new products and additional product line volumes should be supplied for the same period by marketing and product development management. After these volumes are known, they are worked into physical distribution patterns for use during site selection.

Middle management generally draws up the detailed facility requirements. It takes the data contributed by top management and expresses them, through its process knowledge, in terms of building space, utility requirements, and yard area. A good start in establishing facilities requirements is to know the economic shortcomings of existing operations. In short, how much is inefficient facility arrangement costing now? Inefficiencies generally fall into one of two categories:

1. Antiquated processes or machines.
2. Substandard utilization of direct and indirect in-plant labor because of excessive handling and storage of goods in process.

The analyses which are intended to improve technology and methods should be made concurrently with the volume projections. Two separate groups should be set up, one to evaluate process technology and the economics of new equipment acquisition, the other to evaluate techniques for in-plant cost reduction through more effective facilities arrangement and methods improvement. The final requirements are determined through combining the efforts of the technology and methods groups, enabling management to express volume projections in terms of facilities space and utility requirements.

Advantages that can be realized through technological improvement cannot be forecast. They depend on technological advancement in the particular industry and the current stage of sophistication in technology of the company in question. It can be assumed, however, that developments in electronic controls and feeds have made possible productivity rates which were undreamed of ten years ago. Only through economic analyses of replacement costs, labor expense, and productivity can the advantages of improved technology be determined. The required information is obtained through vendor contact, by working with consultants, or by discussions with others in the industry who are knowledgeable in up-to-date process technology. As the process information accumulates, particular attention should be paid to such matters as equipment and machine utility requirements, dimensions, and foundations, for such information is vital later to the determination of facilities requirements.

Knowledge of what savings potential is inherent in improved in-plant handling and storage is best obtained by means of a realistic appraisal of existing operations. This evaluation should be made by the study group, and specific care is needed if the group is not to corrupt its work through its familiarity with methods. Too often, managers and supervisors merely assume that they know how much they are spending for in-plant storage and handling; time studies invariably prove them wrong. This is understandable; the average company can afford neither the time nor the expense to break down such costs in detail. Therefore, information about the costs of storing and handling stays buried in overall expense and is skimmed over lightly during a routine cost analysis.

It has been found in 10 years of observation and work with firms that only about one in ten records its handling costs. We can assume that the ones that keep such records have better control over costs than most that do not. Collectively, their data indicate that handling and storage represent almost 36 percent of total production costs. Personal experience validates this percentage, as we find about one-third of the operating employee's time is spent in picking up, shifting, and putting down materials. When the materials are put down, additional time is spent in bending, lifting, and carrying. Through improved facilities arrangement and investment in modern handling equipment it is possible to reduce handling to approximately 2 percent of the total production costs. Further savings can be effected at individual work stations where, through storage aids, proper tool positioning, and efficient layout, productivity increases up to 15 percent have been experienced. These improvements in combination can save as much as one and one-half hours per employee per day, or about 19 percent of the total day's work.

More and more attention has been paid to cost reduction during the past years because of increasing domestic and overseas competition. Thus the two suggested studies of existing operations should not be new. They are the basic analyses required by any cost reduction plan for improving operations within existing facilities. The approach generally accepted for attacking costs is summarized as follows:

1. Minimize raw materials expense.
2. Optimize raw materials usage.
3. Increase production per man hour.
4. Minimize in-process and finished-goods inventory.

The technological study is basically Phase 2. Methods improvement is the start of Phase 4. Phase 3 is a combination of both. Therefore, in carrying out the facilities requirement study we are basically making a cost reduction analysis.

The methods improvement study requires a more detailed approach than the technological study. First, let's review what can be expected through methods improvement. The specific advantages are:

1. Efficient product flow.
2. Effective utilization of direct labor.
3. Minimum of materials in-process.
4. Improved in-process materials handling and storage.
5. Better employee morale.
6. Most economical use of floor area.
7. An optimum base for evaluating new equipment acquisition and added facilities.
8. Some immediate economic return that will at least pay the cost of the study.

The methods improvement study begins with an examination of existing product flow patterns. This is best done by summarizing each process on standard industrial engineering flow sheets, indicating the sequence of operations, inspection, transport, storage, and delay. Next, we need to trace the physical in-plant routing; the overlay is probably the best device for this purpose. The method uses a base plan view layout of the manufacturing area as a master to which transparent overlay sheets are keyed. Each process flow is traced on a single transparency on which crossover, backtracking, and excess indirect labor operations also are noted. All transparencies are overlaid simultaneously to determine common points and areas of conflict.

With this unbiased view of the flow pattern as a base, the analysis of existing operations can start. The first requisite is a first-hand knowledge of operations. A recommended technique for gaining this familiarity is called the "hands in the pocket" approach. It consists in analyzing operations through personal observation, by talking with employees, noting problems, and constantly asking oneself: (1) Is this operation necessary? (2) Is there a better way of doing it? The advantages of using the technique are that observation time is spent in analyzing instead of writing, plant routines are not disrupted, and employee morale is not disturbed.

After the team has familiarized itself with operations, the depth study starts. As the study team works, it should check each area for utility requirements. Specific items include:

1. Availability and volume of utilities at various in-plant locations.
2. Equipment restrictions because of limited facilities.
3. Steam shortages and overall balance.
4. Air shortages and distribution.
5. Power factor.
6. Utilities waste.
7. Availability of process chemicals and their costs.

Items to consider in analyzing individual departments include the following:

Receiving:

1. Congested hold areas.
2. Limited maneuvering space for over-the-road trucks and in-plant equipment.
3. Truck-line complaints about vehicle delay, either in spotting or because of unloading.
4. High demurrage costs.
5. Employees not working.
6. Difficult manual handling.
7. Extensive rehandling.
8. Materials damage due either to weather or handling.
9. Paperwork procedures and flow.
10. Flow bottlenecks.

Storerooms:

1. Congestion in receiving, storing, or dispensing materials.
2. Materials damage.
3. "Can't find" situations.
4. Frequent out-of-stock conditions.
5. Materials rehandling.
6. High ratio of storeroom and handling personnel to production workers.
7. Employee inactivity.
8. Paperwork procedures on receipts, charge-outs, and returns.
9. Average time materials are held in inventory.

Processing:

1. Congestion in either flow or storage.
2. Poor product quality.
3. Excessive storage of goods in process.
4. Inability to supply raw materials easily to production workers.
5. Conflict between feeding machines and scrap removal.
6. Excessive handling of materials by operators.
7. High maintenance costs from causes other than wear.
8. Constant repetitive requests for equipment additions and more working space.
9. Excessive worker rest and delay time.
10. High accident rates.
11. High labor turnover.
12. Supervisory and employee complaints involving hazards, heat, light, ventilation, rest rooms.

Inspection areas:

1. Congestion in receiving, holding, inspecting, and forwarding areas.
2. Excessive accumulation of finished goods entering or leaving the inspection area.
3. Excessive inspector rest and delay time.
4. Poor quality control.
5. Inefficient flow of work between and among test stations.
6. Complaints (same as processing).

Warehousing:

1. Congestion in receiving from production.
2. Layout problems that restrict product accessibility or prohibit inventory turn.

3. Poor use of floor area or building cube.
4. Excessive manual handling.
5. Extensive rehandling.
6. Types of transport equipment and storage aids used.
7. Flow bottlenecks.
8. Paperwork procedures.

Shipping:

1. Congested areas.
2. Finished goods delays.
3. Truck-line complaints about delays due to vehicle spotting or loading.
4. Carrier scheduling for outloading.
5. Excessive rehandling.
6. Methods of order accumulation.
7. Paperwork procedures.
8. Use of common carrier drivers on premises.

Assuming the initial evaluation indicates that problems do exist, we must next define these problems to determine their magnitude and significance. Questions that must be answered include:

1. What is the problem?
2. Can it be corrected?
3. How much must be spent for correction?
4. Is the money spent for correction the best use of funds for both now and the future?
5. What savings will result?
6. Will production be affected?
7. Can improved quality be expected?
8. What labor problems are involved?

Very often a problem arises in one place because of difficulties in others. Consequently, all operating departments and most support functions eventually will be included in the methods improvement study. In this depth analysis the work sampling technique of ratio-delay is most helpful, since it forces a listing of work elements by the employee and indicates the percentage of working time spent on each element.

As these studies progress (they usually can be made concurrently), the data collected should be periodically summarized and analyzed. Additional deficiencies, bottlenecks, and inefficient labor areas should be noted, as well as their cause and their effect on other operations. Consideration should also be given to the service and office departments and their interrelation to operations. The service departments include stockrooms, tool rooms, repair shops, utilities, hospital, and cafeteria. Office departments include production control, engineering, accounting, purchasing, sales, inventory control, and administrative services. If necessary, the same study techniques can be used to evaluate these operations as are used for production.

During the methods improvement study those changes should be made which are of immediate benefit to operations. The savings that can be achieved through them often pay the complete study's cost.

The information gathered by the technical evaluation and the methods improvement groups should be combined as work is completed in one area or department so that decisions can be made about process alterations and equipment replacement. On the basis of what is decided plus the projected product volumes, a complete machine load analysis can be set up for both current production volume requirements and for the other specific time intervals accepted for planning. These loading statistics are then expressed in equipment requirements.

Area requirements are determined by equipment needs and operations data for each of the time intervals used in the machine-loading analysis. Each area should be expressed in terms of perimeter dimensions. To specify dimensions, the flow pattern must be considered. Naturally, straight-line flow is the easiest, but it is practical in very few operations because of dual machine utilization within and among departments, which means that flow patterns must be compromised for the sake of overall efficiency.

Numerous complex mathematical techniques assist in determining the most efficient flow pattern, including matrix algebra, linear programing, and gaming theory. Other techniques are much easier to use and give substantially as good results, however. The simplest uses templates (magnetic or adhesive backing) from which emerges a pattern that is easily understood.

The physical limitations of proposed facilities must be considered at this point. If they have been preselected and the building's perimeter is known, the overall layout, including space for expansion, must be contained within the bounds of existing walls, and the need for additional construction must be minimized. If no facility is preselected, the layout should be made independently of any perimeter restrictions. Later, the walls and roofs are designed as a shell to enclose the chosen areas and activities.

A master template flow chart can be prepared which combines the equipment and department layouts. This chart, too, is often best made by laying out individual flow sheets for each department and then superimposing transparencies on a master to discover points of conflict and common endeavor.

The end result of combining all transparencies is the master proposed flow diagram arranged for optimum overall efficiency.

Next, the layout of each individual work station is reviewed. Here again templates can be used to advantage. Indications of where improvement is possible originate in the ratio-delay studies which have been made for the operations, in the knowledge contributed by the technical evaluation group, and in the principles of motion economy. Specific actions to consider while contemplating a work station layout improvement are:

1. Keep the operator at the machine.
2. Combine two or more machines when practical.
3. Deliver materials to the point of use.
4. Relieve the hands of all work that can be done better mechanically.
5. Rotate the work-station functions to permit the best sequence of motion and the simultaneous and symmetrical use of the hands.
6. Provide a definite place for every item used, such as tools, gauges, and reference parts. Make certain these are all positioned close to or in front of the operator.
7. Make sure work-station heights do not necessitate stretching or stooping.
8. Make provision for removing finished products, either in tote boxes or on conveyors, using gravity where possible.
9. Arrange for scrap removal with all scrap containerized or palletized as it is made.
10. Provide maximum employee safety and good access to exits and safety stops.
11. Provide adequate work space so that the operator is not crowded. However, be careful not to provide too much space, or excess walking will result.
12. Allow for maneuvering industrial transport equipment if stock is delivered in this way.
13. Provide for machine parts travel devices such as sliding beds.
14. Give adequate room for projection of work, as with bar stock feeding through a turret lathe.
15. Provide adequate storage so that enough work is on hand to keep the operator busy at all times. Allow for holding finished goods until they can be removed without delaying operations. Make certain there is a minimum of natural congestion in the work area.
16. Use materials handling equipment that can be integrated with the rest of the operation, preferably equipment that can be used in common.

17. Make certain that material arrival and departure conform to the overall flow pattern desired.
18. Provide machine access to ease maintenance and facilitate setup.
19. Make certain the rules of good shop housekeeping can be followed.
20. Evaluate the need to brighten the equipment with paint and to designate aisle and operating areas with paint or tape.

The work-station layouts should now be arranged on a master layout plan in conformity with the best flow pattern. Space conflicts should be resolved either by altering the overall pattern or by changing the work station layout. Aisles must be kept open for the delivery and take-away of stock and the removal of scrap. Rest rooms must be accessible. Foremen must be situated so that they can supervise efficiently. Heat, light, ventilation, noise levels, and vibration must all be considered.

The open areas that remain after the work stations are positioned on the master template represent the space available for support functions such as tool cribs, store rooms, and machine repair shops. If insufficient space is left for these functions, it is best to review them to make certain that prime operating area is not being recommended to store infrequently used dies and jigs. There are many advantages to having an efficient on-hand store room for frequently used equipment and a remote storage location for others. If the service functions cannot be positioned properly, the layout must be altered to accommodate them.

Expansion areas included in the overall layout should be planned so as to permit maximum flexibility. Very often one operation will not expand at the expected rate, whereas another will increase substantially more than expected.

The final test for the layout requires simulating production for a predetermined period of time, including as many exceptions to the rule as are practical. Problems should be resolved through altering the layout and operating methods until production needs are satisfied.

Utilities requirements can be determined as soon as the layout is complete. The information required is the specific location for the utility connection (point and height) and the capacity, pressure, power, and flow needed. Allowances for expansion and preferred manifolding or bus ducting should also be specified.

CHOICE OF SITE

Which plant or warehouse site is preferable depends greatly on what the relocation is expected to accomplish and on the requirements of the particular company and industry. The ideal site is one that provides sufficient land to accommodate the required buildings, meets yard and utilities needs, and is the most economical for labor, utilities, and the transportation of raw materials and finished products. Very few companies are ever able to find Utopia. Compromise and evaluation assure that management will obtain the best possible location.

If no property has been preselected, the site search starts with eliminating totally undesirable areas. A recommended method of elimination again involves the use of overlays. Let us assume that the plant's location may be anywhere within the boundaries of the continental United States. The first step is to have a number of transparencies made showing the outline of the U.S.A., state lines, and county boundaries. We designate one transparency for each of the major items that we consider important in the choice of site, such as raw material source, supply of labor skills, labor cost, finished goods distribution, transportation availability, unity rates, water supply, adequate land areas available, and construction costs.

Next, each county, by state, should be stratified according to its importance in each category. Stratification is by volume, dollars, or both; no more than five categories should be used. To each category we assign a cross-hatch designation which we place on its transparency. The transparencies are overlaid, and those areas that have no concentration of cross-hatching are eliminated. The remaining areas are then evaluated separately, and potential sites are thus selected. We start with at least seven or eight possible choices and through economic analysis reduce them to no more than three.

We now must consider each in terms of—
1. Size and dimensions of area needed.
2. Electric power required.
3. Water capacity and hardness.
4. Availability of gas or other heating media.
5. Subsoil conditions.
6. Storm and sanitary sewage availability.
7. Transportation needed.
8. Zoning requirements.
9. Property configuration.

A number of proposed lots within the specified county groupings should be selected for final evaluation, which, in addition to the items already specified, includes the following:
1. Influence of local industry on labor.
2. Labor history of the community.

3. Community tax allowances.
4. Accommodations for relocated employees.
5. Educational facilities.
6. Health and welfare provisions.
7. Cultural and recreational facilities.
8. Commercial services to complement operations.
9. Community police and fire services.
10. Planning and zoning trends.
11. Any other requirements peculiar to the specific manufacturing process involved.

The best site is selected after the overall evaluation has been made. Next, the purchase conditions of the chosen site are negotiated. During negotiations it should be determined whether the property has any specific restrictions or right-of-way limitations. If none materially affects the proposed facility, a non-cash option should be arranged to cover a time sufficient for a complete engineering study.

ECONOMIC EVALUATION OF FACILITIES RELOCATION

While this study is going forward, the economic evaluation of the relocation should be carried out. For it a tentative plant layout can now be prepared that includes facilities. In all likelihood this layout will be the same as the one which was developed to accommodate the facilities requirements, but it could vary because of site configuration or other influences.

The overall operations economics are calculated on the basis of the preliminary layout. Cost factors may require negotiations with local utilities, contractors, and specific vendors, and any negotiated rates should be formally stated in contracts that can be executed when and if management decides to go ahead. Cost factors from local and other sources to be included in the operations cost analysis are:

1. Land cost.
2. Site-preparation cost.
3. Construction cost, including floors, walls, utility connections, and yard facilities.
4. New equipment cost, including on-site utilities which must be paid for by the company such as power substations, stand-by fuel systems to compensate for interruptible utilities, fuel storage, and process chemical storage.

5. Taxes, including property, personal, and inventory.
6. Cost of transporting existing equipment.
7. Cost of relocating employees.
8. Employee-termination costs.
9. Transport expense for raw materials and finished product.
10. Production delay costs resulting from taking equipment off stream.
11. Administration cost.
12. Restoration cost of present facilities (if applicable).

Some savings can and should be expected through relocation:

1. Tax grace.
2. Increased productivity (direct labor).
3. Decrease in indirect labor doing materials handling.
4. Reduced number of employees through more efficient work methods.
5. Reduction in setup time.
6. Improved access for machine maintenance.
7. Lower building maintenance.
8. Increased use of floor space.
9. Reduction of goods in process.
10. Reduction of finished-goods inventory.
11. Savings in administrative personnel.

The final economic evaluation is a comparison of cost to savings, complemented by the engineering analysis of the site. Management decides on the basis of this summary whether to proceed or not. If the answer is negative, the land option is dropped and the only expense incurred is for the study and the engineering analysis, which in all probability is more than paid for by those operational improvements that have already been made. Or management may decide to test another site, in which case the procedure is repeated.

ARCHITECTURAL DETAILING AND CONSTRUCTION

A firm decision to relocate leads to the next phases of the overall program, which are detailing the plant's structure and then arranging for actual construction.

The building's design should conform to managerial policy and to industrial dictates. Construction materials vary from stainless steel and glass to glazed brick and concrete block. Naturally, the more detailed the construction, the higher its cost. Preliminary meetings with competent architects should quickly establish the design criteria.

Next, management must decide who is going to supervise the actual construction. The choices are as follows:

1. Having the company serve as its own general contractor and place bids for each phase of the work.
2. Designating the architectural and engineering firm as the general contractor and coordinating with this group in awarding bids.
3. Designating all work in one contract and making the successful bidder the general contractor.
4. Arranging to have design and construction done as a package.

No matter who supervises construction, the architectural and design group has sole responsibility for obtaining all state and local approvals and for assuring the conformance of the building to applicable codes and variances.

Companies with internal architectural capability can proceed with their own design. Organizations without this capability should select an outside architectural and engineering firm. In either case the objective is to develop drawings that are sufficiently detailed for competitive contractor bidding.

To coordinate design, one individual—usually called a project manager—should be appointed to represent the company. He must be intimate with the facility needs and have sufficient construction knowledge to act as liaison between management and the design firm. His job is primarily coordination; the final approval of plans and specifications remains management's responsibility.

Plant design details depend on requirements. Such items as bay size, clear height under the beam, floor loadings, and hazard area design will vary by industry. The current trend is toward large bay dimensions, and bay sizes of 50 by 50 feet now are common. Clear height under the beam is also maximized, and 30 to 40 feet is common. Naturally, the cost per square foot increases as spans and heights are enlarged. Consequently, building costs vary from approximately $4.50 per square foot for tilt-slab-type construction upward to $10 and even $12. Office construction is substantially more expensive because of air conditioning and elaborate décor. Generally this space costs upward of $12 a square foot.

As soon as a final construction price is determined, one last economic analysis should be made. A Gantt chart can be devised which illustrates what money must be expended and when. On the basis of this information financial arrangements can be made and money scheduled as needed.

Simultaneously, a network analysis should be prepared detailing the step-by-step time elements in the relocation. Individual lead and installation times must be determined for each construction phase as well as for new equipment acquisition. Moving the existing plant must also be timetabled. Complete, the network analysis gives management the critical path for relocation, indicates milestones for measuring progress, and points out areas where money might be best spent to expedite any or all phases of the work.

FACILITIES START-UP

Some inefficiencies can be expected in start-up. The length of time it takes to settle down depends on how well the planning has been done, the moving schedule, and the extent to which all employees have been trained in the new methods.

Facilities design alone does not guarantee either best performance or least cost. Any facility is only as effective as supervisors and operating employees make it. To guide them and evaluate their performance, targets and milestones should be established for each operation. These can be piecework standards, group rates, or measured day work. If the employees are to understand their goals, they should be completely knowledgeable about the work methods on which they are based. Training in these work methods should be complete before they are put into use, which means before the facility starts operation.

A training team consisting of the key employees responsible for operating the new facility should be selected well in advance of cutover. Each member prepares a formal written training program for his work area, assisted by industrial relations and other group members.

Timetabling the facility move is also important to start-up. Everyone knows that there is a difference between theory and practice. Any new operation or relocation generally requires a debugging period. Therefore, considerable advantage can be gained through relocating small segments of the operation at a time. These segments should be scheduled so that there is sufficient time between moves for consolidation and settling down. If the relocation has been well planned and executed, after the settling-down period operations should proceed smoothly and probably more efficiently than before the move.

MAJOR ACTION POINTS IN PLANT RELOCATION

By FRANK BUESE

Among the activities which ordinarily precede the decision to move the plant are carrying out a feasibility study; making a forecast of capacity; drawing up a list of equipment required; preparing outline specifications for land, building, and services; and making financial projections of investments and operating profits. Next comes the executive order to proceed with relocation. The necessary appropriations have been approved, and management is informed that the necessary cash will be available. The site has been selected. Now the manufacturing manager must answer several major questions. How does he implement this executive order? What are the tasks that he must supervise? What sequence of action should he follow?

He will be responsible for the expenditure of vast sums of money. A substantial proportion of the $44 billion which is spent annually for improvement of facilities goes for building new modern plants. Because of the sizable investment required, relocation has a long-term effect on the financial well-being of the company—for better or for worse. A move is generally irreversible without substantial loss. Yet new plants have been abandoned because their relocation was improperly conceived or poorly executed. One which made the annual "Ten Best" list was abandoned within a few years and sold for a small proportion of its original cost.

THE PROJECT MANAGER'S JOB AND ORGANIZATION

The financial impact and the finality of the decision make the relocation of a plant a full-time job to manage. Therefore, the first step the manufactur-

FRANK BUESE is a management consultant with A. T. Kearney & Company, Inc., in Chicago, Illinois.

ing manager should take is to appoint a project manager. What qualifications should the latter possess?

1. He must have executive ability.
2. He must have unflagging energy.
3. He must be cost-conscious.
4. He may well be a future plant executive—even the plant manager—which means that he must be knowledgeable not only in manufacturing techniques but also in the specific skills of management.

How does the project manager go about managing? He has many duties, some of which he delegates to a specially selected staff. He is expected to engineer the plant, then to build it. He selects and buys the equipment and sees that it is properly installed. Moving equipment from the old plant is also his responsibility, as is starting up the plant—which means securing a labor supply, establishing an organization, and devising the necessary controls for operation to minimize start-up loss. All these jobs must be completed on schedule.

Throughout the project the manager is to maintain communication with members of his own firm and with outsiders. He is to insure a smooth flow of customer relations. In addition, good labor relations at both the new plant and the old will be important for the success of the new one and for a reasonably happy termination of operations at the old one (if it is being closed). Public relations is important at all times since it affects both employees and customers. Finally, the project manager is expected to control the numerous and substantial expenditures.

WHICH KEY PEOPLE TO MOVE?

Planning the operating organization for the new plant and getting it manned require the manufacturing manager to select his key people early. Some of them may well be in the project management group; for example, the future plant engineer and future chief industrial engineer should be valuable both in carrying out the project and in starting and operating the plant later. The project group can be coordinated and integrated with the permanent management group more easily if the selection and organization plans are complete before the building is finished and equipment moving begins. A survey of the key people at the old plant is essential at this time if it is to be closed or if the existing organization is going to be drawn on for key men.

In selecting these key people the manufacturing man has a chance to screen them carefully and invite those he believes will contribute most in the new organization. But some of the men he wants to have in his new organization may question seriously whether they should move. The site was undoubtedly selected with pleasant living conditions for key employees in mind; so visits at company expense (preferably with their wives) should help them decide favorably.

What is the company policy on financing the sale (sometimes at a loss) of a present home owned by a key employee, and what will it do about helping him find and finance a new home? Since key people are at a premium, many companies find it necessary to absorb part of the loss on the old homes and to arrange for financing the new ones.

Moving expenses are, of course, generally paid by the company. Since this expenditure is the project manager's responsibility, he will want to take steps to see that the moving is done at a cost which is as low as is consistent with employee satisfaction.

In handling key people as in other aspects of relocation, it is well to write out the policies to be followed. Then everyone will know what the policies are, and all will be treated consistently as the move progresses.

WORK CONTROL: "GET IT DONE"

The task of relocation is complex. Its many divisions are diverse in nature, and all require careful attention and control to get them done in the proper sequence. Fortunately, there are techniques and control devices to help. One of the simplest is the Gantt chart in Exhibit 1 which shows when each task is to begin and when it is to be completed. It also shows which tasks may be carried on simultaneously. For example, building construction cannot begin until the architectural plans are complete, but the selection of a workforce may begin before the building is finished.

In addition to the Gantt chart there are such techniques as PERT (Program Evaluation Review Technique), CPM (Critical Path Method), and MAP (Multiple-Resource Allocation Procedure). A large project may be expedited by electronic data processing.

Even with all these aids, it is still the project manager's responsibility to see that each portion of his project begins on time. It's his job to follow up and take the necessary measures to prevent anyone from falling behind schedule. It may seem discouraging to suggest that revisions of schedules may be necessary. However, if strikes, natural catastrophes, or other events cause the

EXHIBIT 1
GANTT CHART OF AN IMPLEMENTATION SCHEDULE

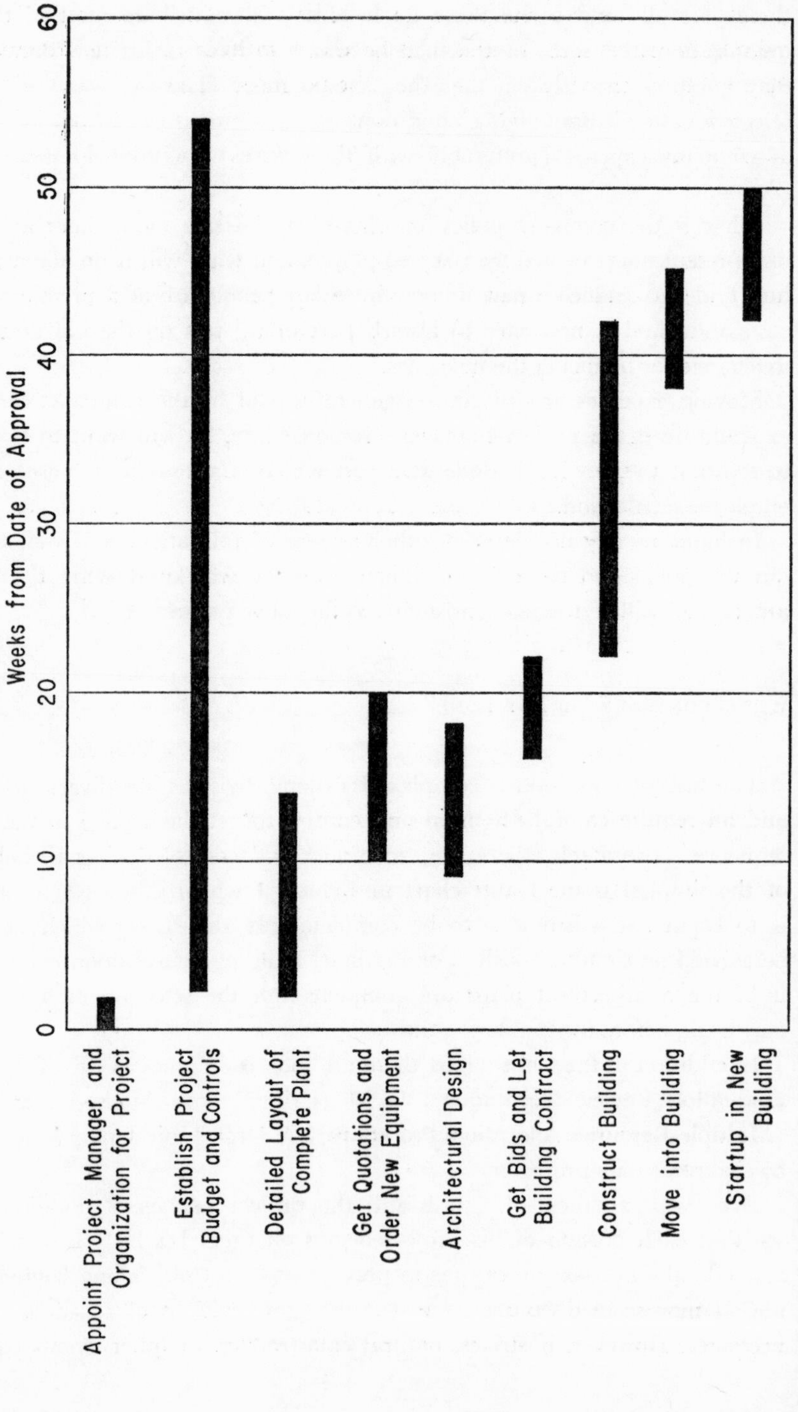

Weeks from Date of Approval

project to fall behind, the target dates will be respected more if the remaining portion is rescheduled. If delays have been excessive, the project manager can hardly expect his people to make up large blocks of time.

EXPENDITURE CONTROL

There's no disagreement on the importance of controlling expenditure. The only question is: How? A relocation project allows but a single chance to meet the established goals. It is not like production, where a failure today may be made up by better than average performance tomorrow. If the plant relocation cost is too high, there is no way to "average it out." Second chances are rare.

Feasibility studies of the project before deciding to relocate have approximated the budgets for capital expenditures, relocation expenses, and start-up. Now the project manager must subdivide these budgets into more detailed statements and refine them as he gets additional information. The major budgets are for equipment, land, and building and the noncapital expenses of moving people, equipment, and inventories and starting the plant.

The cash approved for the project is not lying idle in the bank. A well-run firm has little nonworking cash, but it will make money available when the project requires. Therefore, the financial executive will expect a schedule of cash needs—to pay the architect, the contractor, and the suppliers and to meet new payrolls.

Obviously, expenditures must be followed up frequently; weekly is none too often. The manager and the various individuals in responsible assignments under his direction receive reports that show them—

1. The budget for their portion of the project.
2. Expenditures to date.
3. The proportion of the tasks completed.
4. Any variances: Are they over- or underbudget to date?
5. Amount remaining in the budget.

It is the manager's responsibility to keep everyone alert about expenditures and well informed on progress, to assist anyone having difficulty in meeting his budget.

CUSTOMER RELATIONS

A customer (particularly if the company is moving farther away from him) may well wonder whether relocation spells progress or regression. He wonders

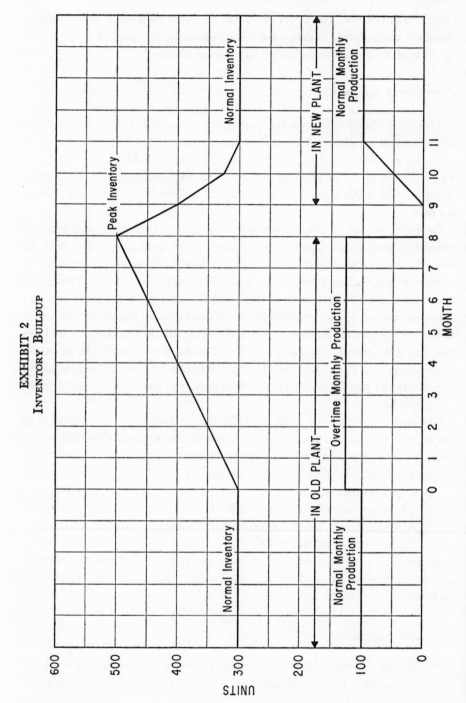

EXHIBIT 2
INVENTORY BUILDUP

what deliveries and prices will be like afterward and what the company is going to do to protect his supply while it is moving.

To quiet these apprehensions, the company through its project manager should keep its sales force well informed of objectives and progress. Perhaps salesmen should increase the frequency of their contact with customers to keep them informed. They can emphasize the advantages of the new plant in terms of delivery, costs, warehousing service, development of better products, and other customer benefits.

INVENTORY BUILD-UP

Moving generally disrupts plant operations for a time. To prevent customer dissatisfaction and loss of sales due to poor delivery, the project manager plans to build an inventory. Quite soon after the project is authorized, he decides to what peak the inventory is to be built to carry the company over the moving and start-up period. The graphs of Exhibit 2 show the reasoning behind inventory buildup. Production must be above sales for as long as it takes to build an inventory which will permit shipments to continue without interruption. Therefore, the first step is to determine the length of time that the company will be out of production entirely and the length of time when production in the new plant will be at less than the level of sales. From these answers and the predicted sales volume is calculated the amount of inventory increase.

If the company can produce, say, up to 25 percent above the normal sales demand, the number of months it must operate at the higher level in order to reach this peak inventory can be calculated. It is also necessary to decide where the inventory is to be stored and shipped.

LABOR RELATIONS IN THE PRESENT PLANT

A first step in maintaining sound labor relations in the present plant is to read the contract carefully. It may cover the company's responsibilities in relocation. If it doesn't, the next step is to find out what the law is.

In addition to consulting the wording of the contract and the provisions of the law, a relocating company should firmly establish and put in writing its policies on labor relations at the old plant. Such policies should obviously include provisions for separation pay (preferably with a proviso for keeping people on the job in the old plant until the company is ready to release them). Any unemployment funds with state authorities may or may not be transferable, depending upon the conditions of the move.

Announcements are necessary to the union, the employees, and the public. The company decides whether it will offer jobs in the new plant to current hourly paid employees and under what conditions. If some employees are to be released, all possible local aid should be sought in finding jobs for them. Aside from the humanitarian aspects of such a policy, it preserves a good public image.

PUBLIC RELATIONS

Public relations more than likely will be strained at the present location if the plant is being closed down but will be less strained if the company is expanding at a new location and keeping the present plant open. Even then, there will be a question: Why didn't the company expand in the old home town? Consequently, it is desirable to enlist the aid of the public relations department to put the best foot forward in the local newspapers and other news media.

Generally, a company is welcome in the new location because it is bringing in a payroll. It normally makes the most of this friendly reception. The public relations department can be of assistance in getting favorable publicity.

NEW EQUIPMENT

The feasibility study which led to the decision to relocate, if it was properly carried out, dealt with the selection of new equipment only to the degree which permitted an approximation of the investment required. The selections are usually refined in the implementation stages. The project manager obtains quotations through the purchasing department or someone specifically assigned to choose and buy the equipment. With due consideration to quality and price, orders are placed. "Turn key" installations, which assure that the machines are ready to operate at the push of a button, minimize start-up delays.

Work schedules include delivery and installation dates for each item of equipment. Frequent progress checks insure that absence of equipment does not delay the starting date. The investment in equipment, with current revisions, is correlated with the capital budget, which was established at the time of the feasibility study.

LAYOUT

The block layout of the feasibility study shows departmental boundaries but not the exact location of equipment. The time has now arrived for a detailed layout with templates to get the best work flow and to make the best use of space in the new plant. This is a time to forget the limitations of the old plant and to place the equipment where the operating people can realize the lowest-cost operation.

A layout is generally most successful if it is planned with the collaboration of the foremen and other key people who will have to live with it after the project has been completed and the plant is started. The architect can point out any limiting building restrictions. The layout and the design of the building should be compatible and practical for both operation and construction.

BUILDING

Complete specifications for the plant can now be sent out for quotations from contractors. Enough bids should be obtained from reputable sources that the company can be sure it has selected the lowest one which is consistent with reliability. In contracts with builders (as well as with suppliers of equipment and services) the company's attorney can protect it against uncertainty in case of strikes or other unfortunate delaying events. A schedule of completion should be part of the agreement, possibly with penalty clauses for late finish.

Because of the importance of a building and its long life, it is customary to follow up on quality while it is being erected. This may be done by the architect or by someone in the project group. And work control, remember, includes the erection schedule. A building late in completion will delay the entire project.

To repeat: When the building is finished, it should be in "turn key" shape—offices, cafeteria, washroom facilities, receiving and shipping docks, power, lighting, water, and everything else it takes to run a successful factory all ready for use.

WHAT LOCAL GOVERNMENTS AND AGENCIES DO

When building a plant in a new location, a company is dependent upon local agencies for much assistance—water supply, sewer connections, electricity, gas, and other services. It may be necessary to improve, widen, or build a street to the site. Failure by any one of the local agencies to produce the required service on time delays the construction and opening of a new plant. Therefore, it is safer before purchasing the site to procure a written agreement from all the private or government agencies concerned to assure complete agreement on what they are to do and when.

It may be desirable to obtain an ordinance. For example, one manufacturer bought a plant site served only by a narrow dirt road, with only verbal assurance that the road would be completed. The manufacturer wisely insisted upon an ordinance from the city council which appropriated money for a street capable of carrying large trucks.

The project manager follows up frequently to be sure that the requisite services are available on schedule and that they meet the specification agreed upon. This is part of the work control discussed earlier.

LABOR RELATIONS IN THE NEW LOCATION

The announcement of the company's coming to the new location has probably been made. Even if it hasn't, the local citizens know of the impending arrival. Quite early in the project it is desirable to set up wage scales and fringe benefits in conformity with the prevailing practice in the area. Consultation with local employers will help.

When the wage scales, the fringe benefits, and the labor policies have been decided upon, it is advisable to state them formally in a pamphlet. This has the dual purpose of telling prospective employees what the work agreement will be and insuring consistency in labor relations in the new location.

It should be decided early in the project what to do if a union approaches the new plant. A company may be taking the union with it because of a present contract, because it is not moving very far, or because relations with the union have been agreeable and it wishes to continue them. If this is not the case, will the company accept the union and proceed to bargain with it? Will it suggest to the organizers that they wait until after a bargaining group is elected under the auspices of the National Labor Relations Board?

Local agencies are sometimes of assistance in training employees. If the skills needed are not available, even for the more routine occupations, the company may take advantage of the local vocational school system with some assistance in the form of machines, materials, and instructors. This sort of training will enable it to reduce its start-up time because it can hire employees with at least a rudimentary knowledge of the more common operations.

MOVING EQUIPMENT

As with all other facets of a relocation project, careful planning of equipment moving will save much difficulty and loss of time in start-up. If possible, it should be scheduled at a time of the year when seasonal production is low.

One of the early decisions is to select the operations which should be moved first. Should the job start by moving the initial operations and shipping the material back to the old plant as needed? Or the opposite? That is, by first moving the shipping department with necessary storage and transporting the work in process and finished goods to the new plant to ship from there, gradually increasing the new manufacturing activity?

It may be more economical to shut down the plant completely and move all the equipment in a relatively short time. For example, complete stoppage is easier in the garment industry, with its sewing machines, than in an industry which requires moving large machine tools with special foundations.

Congestion and confusion in the arrival of equipment at the new site will be lessened by making aisles and numbering bays in the new building. Placing the machine or equipment numbers on the new plant's floor is a good investment of time. A tag on each item to be moved showing the bay destination will enable the riggers to set up equipment without delay. If the new structure is a "turn key" building, complete with all electricity, gas, water, compressed air, and other services, as soon as a machine is placed it can be quickly connected to any of the utilities which are necessary for operation.

To control cost it is advantageous to get firm bids from the riggers or other companies which are to do the moving. A budget in sufficient detail guarantees good cost control. Insurance should be carefully worked out so that the relocating company will incur no liability. Many companies insist on "hold harmless" clauses in all moving and rigging contracts. This protects the company against liability in case of an accident during the moving process. On all contracts it is essential to consult with the attorney to be sure that the company's rights are protected and liabilities limited.

Dispatching the loads of equipment should be coordinated with receiving at the other end. Where the plan calls for putting each piece of equipment in its proper place in the new building, a glut of items at the receiving dock defeats this purpose and delays installation. If the company falls behind in its moving schedule (because of unfavorable weather, strikes, or other problems), it is better to revise the schedule than to attempt to adhere to one which may have become impractical and is no longer respected.

WHAT ABOUT THE VACANT OLD PLANT?

The company may still own the old plant after it has moved. If so, what plans are there for disposal? It may be necessary to prepare the plant for sale and eventual delivery by cleaning it, removing loose ends of piping and wiring, and otherwise making it acceptable to the purchaser.

If some time is to elapse before the plant can be sold and turned over to a new owner, maintenance will be necessary. In many climates heat will be needed to prevent the wet sprinkler system from freezing. Watchman service may be required as well as a certain minimum level of housekeeping including the replacement of broken window panes, repair of roof leaks, and prevention of damage from trespassers or rodents.

The company, in other words, must include in the cost of the relocation the full expense of protecting the old plant until it is sold. And these expenditures, like all segments of the project's cost, must be covered by the overall cost control techniques.

MINIMIZATION OF LOSSES DURING START-UP

Getting a new plant into operation is an obvious source of potential loss. We have all read news items about companies that are earning less than in the previous year, with the explanation that "this is due to starting up our new plant." Start-up costs money, but the project manager's efforts should be devoted to assuring that it costs as little as possible.

If the company has insisted on "turn key" facilities and machine installations, it should now realize both financial benefits and the satisfaction of a job well done. By this time the staff departments in the new plant manned by the selected people will be functioning. They include production control, manufacturing engineering, industrial relations, maintenance, tool repair, and others. The foremen of the various departments will have been selected, and a nucleus of a workforce will be at hand. Production control and purchasing will have brought in the material needed to begin work.

Machinery and tools, new or old, will have been checked out and the bugs removed. Perhaps the company has been fortunate in getting some trained employees from local sources and has had some help in training prospective workers in the rudiments of plant operations. Nonetheless, much training has to be done on the job as the plant approaches its start-up. To make it effective someone must direct the training, and the company may well consider the Job Instructor Training (JIT) technique, which was employed with considerable success during World War II. (This simple but effective technique is designed to teach foremen or other instructors how to train employees.)

Immediately upon start-up the company should institute progress measurements. The "learning curve" or "improvement curve" (Exhibit 3) can be begun almost immediately with little preparation. Supervisors and staff track down bottlenecks in the operations so that production starts to flow smoothly through the plant. The learning curve, it should be pointed out, represents learning by the employee as well.

Work sampling is an inexpensive technique which helps in finding the causes of delay and in quickly checking the activities of employees and equipment. As most readers probably know, it is a procedure for making periodic observations, not with a stopwatch, but by observing the state of activity or inactivity. It identifies the reasons for the inactivity of each piece of equipment. It also can be used for studying the activity of employees and the reasons for their inactivity. The results can thus be used to improve the operation. Work sampling, like the improvement curve, has the advantage of lending itself to immediate application when the start-up begins.

A third method of controlling costs is, of course, using previous costs (or time records) as bench marks which supervisors and the employees under their direction are expected to beat by increasing margins. This method is illustrated in Exhibit 4.

These start-up cost controls apply not only to manufacturing operations but to the office, the warehouse, and all service operations.

PRODUCTION STANDARDS

Production standards are effective in controlling and reducing manufacturing costs. Therefore, a logical question is: When should production standards be applied in the new plant?

The answer depends upon the nature of the product and the degree of

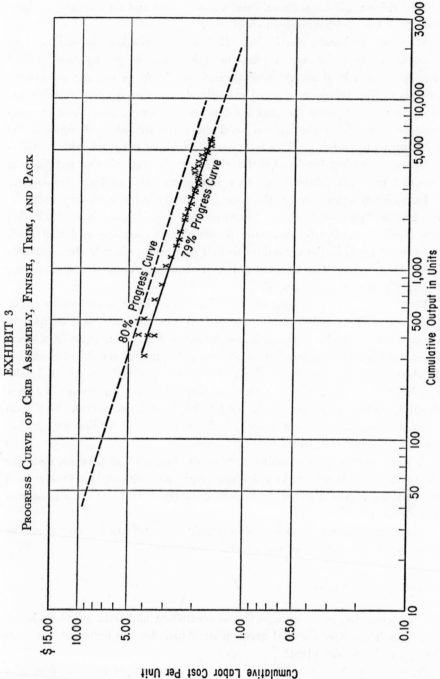

EXHIBIT 3

PROGRESS CURVE OF CRIB ASSEMBLY, FINISH, TRIM, AND PACK

EXHIBIT 4

COST PROGRESS REPORT

TO: MESSRS. _____

PLANT 1
DEPARTMENT Packaging
Direct LABOR

P.O. NO.	DATE	ITEM-NAME	OUTPUT	QUANTITY	ACTUAL COST PER	ACTUAL COST TOTAL	BENCH MARK COST PER	BENCH MARK COST TOTAL	GAIN	LOSS	REMARKS
648	5/ 5	# 951	each	622	$.0835	$ 52	$.0853	$ 53	1		
669	5/26	Loose W/O Callo	dozen	10,336	.0095	98	.0117	121	23		
626	5/18	Chipbd. Cont.	15c.dozen	1,573	.0404	64	.0406	64			
652	5/ 6	5 gr. 50's Loose	"	807	.0565	46	.0462	37		(9)	
653	5/11	5 gr. 50's Ldz. Disp.	"	7,696	.0447	344	.0471	362	18		
654	5/25	100's Ldz. Disp.	"	14,660	.0479	702	.0384	563		(139)	
641	4/28	2/Shelf Extenders	each	2,676	.0665	178	.0665	178			1st. Run
660	5/28	1/SW	dozen	121,190	.0142	1,721	.0159	1,927	206		
650	5/25	1/Cont	"	70,680	.0236	1,668	.0307	2,170	502		
659	5/28	S/M	"	4,518	.0718	324	.1061	479	155		
4861	5/15	Cement Tube 24cc.	"	2,000	.0901	180	.0863	173		(7)	
634	5/13	4 oz.	"	4,234	.0533	226	.0567	240	14		
635	5/ 8	4 oz. Loose	"	875	.0586	51	.0618	54	3		
		TOTALS FOR PERIOD				$ 18,649		$ 19,318	$1,586	($ 917)	
		ACCUMULATED TOTALS-YEAR TO DATE				$ 85,685		$ 91,882			

NET GAIN/THIS PERIOD $ 669 OR 3.6 % OF TOTAL ACTUAL

NET GAIN/YEAR-TO-DATE $ 6,197 OR 7.2 % OF TOTAL ACTUAL ACCUMULATED standardization. The company may be fortunate in being able to bring its production standards from the old plant to the new. More commonly, employers find a move an opportunity to improve methods and therefore set new and more accurate standards. If the operations are well standardized, it is possible to set standards quickly. Predetermined time systems like Methods Time Measurement (MTM) are helpful in presetting standards because the observer doesn't have to wait until the operator reaches a reasonable degree of skill, as is generally necessary with time study.

A problem of production standards even in old plants and certainly in new ones is "coverage." In plants which have been in operation for years it is not infrequent to find that only 60 percent of the direct labor hours are covered by production standards and that even fewer of the indirect hours are so controlled. In a new plant even that much coverage may be months or even years away.

There are distinct hazards to setting temporary or makeshift standards. One company, which moved successfully otherwise, failed in this respect because its standards (together with incentives) were set hastily. Within a year the company had a "runaway earnings" problem. Its employees were profiting, but management had failed to realize a substantial portion of the savings which it had anticipated. It also had troubled industrial relations.

Because of low coverage with resultant poor control and the hazards of temporary standards, a company may defer setting standards until after the shakedown period. It can then set accurate production standards when the curve of cost progress stops moving downward. This decidedly does not mean that the operation should not be under some form of control from the beginning. Other devices described previously (such as learning curves, work sampling, and bench marks) can be applied immediately to help reduce and control the high costs which typically are the mark of start-up.

QUALITY CONTROL, SCRAP, WASTE

Anyone who has ever started up an operation in a new plant knows that losses from scrap tend to run high. Whether it's called "scrap," "waste," or "broke," it's a costly element. The "turn key" policy, however, helps to minimize loss due to tooling and equipment failure.

Quality standards and specifications which existed at the old plant may be applicable in the new. They should be available before the start-up begins, not after. New employees can then be trained to the quality level to which they are to become accustomed. If statistical quality control is applicable (as it is to most manufacturing operations), this is an excellent time to begin it under the direction of someone skilled in the SQC technique.

The improvement curve principle is as applicable to reduction of scrap as it is to reduction in costs. A curve can be plotted for the manufacturing organization to adhere to in progressive reduction of scrap.

During this critical start-up time, processes may need more frequent inspection or more inspection stations. They can be reduced in frequency or number later when the operators have learned what is wanted in the way of quality and can do their own checking.

LET'S LOOK AT THE RECORD

The manager of the relocation project has completed his job. The new plant is in operation. Here are the results: He has met his budgets—capital, moving, and start-up. He has hit his start-up production and quality goals. The new organization is functioning well. Employee relations in the new plant are satisfactory, judging by low labor turnover and comparatively few complaints to the industrial relations department. Key people have been accepted and are taking an appropriate part in community life. Customers are pleased because buildup of inventory and careful scheduling have insured them against any hiatus in deliveries. The cost of moving and start-up has had its impact on profits, but the current profit trend is up.

Planning and "turnkeyism" have paid off.

PLANNING AND PREPARING FOR EXPANSION

By EDWARD M. BRABANT

In the small, medium-size, or large company it is absolutely essential as a first step to crystallize corporate concepts, philosophies, and policies as well as possible before planning any expansion program. Once these are defined, communicated, and, above all, understood by all concerned, then the company can set its targets and objectives for growth. Then it can lay out its short- and long-range plans. No one should ever think that doing these things takes too much time and that they are worthless tasks!

The short-range plan can be set up for the first year on a monthly, three-month, four-month, or half-year basis, depending upon how sensitive and responsive to change management wants the company to be run. A semi-long-range plan should be set up on a year-by-year basis for the first five years.

The long range is figured in increments of 5, 10, 15, and 20 years. The longer the range the more flexible the plan, but at least the plan should try to set up an intelligent growth pattern in sales units (assuming a larger share of the market) and, more importantly, a proper return on investment (profitability). It takes more than increased volume for a company to be successful.

HOW NOT TO GROW

Because planning and preparing for manufacturing expansion are only two of many elements to be considered in fulfilling a company's growth needs, any discussion of expansion and growth must take into account the interrelated areas of the business that contribute to, even dictate, the need for the manufacturing or supply function to expand.

EDWARD M. BRABANT is Assistant to the President, Applied Power Industries, Inc., Milwaukee, Wisconsin.

Too much of the expansion of manufacturing in the past has been piecemeal. Too few businesses have really carried on any intelligent long-range planning. If sales volume increased, sales departments would naturally clamor for more goods. Too often the request was fulfilled by "crashing" on the production line. We are all aware of occasions when the sales bubble had burst and the bloom had faded from the marketplace by the time the extra capacity was fully operational. Sales had leveled off for one reason or another, and the company was stuck with the by now useless extra capacity. This situation sometimes arose because of poor sales forecasting and improperly executed marketing research.

The tragedy is that the company in such straits ends up by having to support and absorb these additional expenses in its cost of goods produced. When this happens, everyone concerned feels the buildup of internal pressure. This is when heads begin to roll and everyone gets jittery. Being human, the managers become greatly concerned about what is going to happen to them personally; no matter how hard they try, they just can't keep their minds and efforts on the job the company needs to have done to pull it through the stormy period. Here we see one of the major reasons why it sometimes takes so long to "recover."

Some companies that have expanded without proper planning have wound up looking like crazy quilts. Additions were sewn on here and there without regard for pattern or shape. The expense of creating the monstrosity was probably three times that of doing it right through proper planning and programing. And not only was the initial cost excessive, but the built-in costs of material processing and handling cannot now be eliminated unless or until a complete new manufacturing facility were to be laid out, built, and put into operation.

APPLIED POWER INDUSTRIES, INC., AND HOW IT GREW

An outline of many of the questions we ask ourselves in Applied Power Industries, Inc., and the steps we take in our divisions in planning for expansion is printed at the end of this chapter. Before referring to the outline, however, it will perhaps be worthwhile to explain how Applied Power Industries grew by acquisition and expansion. Perhaps another company with a similar growth pattern can benefit from a brief recital of our tragedies and triumphs.

For 50 years we were known and respected primarily in the automotive aftermarket as the Blackhawk Manufacturing Company, of Milwaukee, Wisconsin. The aftermarket includes upkeep and maintenance of a new vehicle and the purchase and care of a "used" vehicle. Everything we did, made, and sold was controlled by one management group in one location under one roof. Blackhawk made, and Applied Power, through its divisions, still manufactures, high-pressure hydraulic lifting devices for trucks and cars. It also made a complete line of hand tools—open end, box, and ratchet wrenches.

In the 1930's Blackhawk conceived, engineered, and successfully built a line of hydraulic portable tools, known as "Porto-Power," which it has sold ever since. These tools were specifically designed to aid in the repair of damaged automobiles. As the design of the automobiles changed, Blackhawk would introduce new attachments to satisfy the new repair requirements. Further, as these tools were exposed to the end users, and in turn to customers who came in while their automobiles were being repaired, new applications were found. Industry began to use the high-pressure portable tools for maintenance repair work within plants for moving machinery, pulling gears, moving dies, and other activities. Blackhawk also developed pipe and conduit benders, knockout punches, and other attachments to serve specific industrial needs. And new uses were found increasingly for the two basic components: the high-pressure pump and the ram. One example is the hydraulic pump and ram system used for lifting and lowering the snowplow blades on the front of trucks and jeeps.

This pattern of growth continued until the 1950's—slow, steady, without much long-range planning and programing for expansion. It was accepted and handled piecemeal, and an impressive crazy quilt was emerging.

Early in 1952 Blackhawk spun off its first satellite facility. We knew pretty well what we wanted to achieve in manufacturing over the long range. In the latter part of 1952 we spun off another, and since then we have set up still more, until in 1965 we had 23 different kinds and sizes of organizations. We are currently looking for an acquisition compatible with our technological know-how and markets. In short, we have planned and programed more than in the past.

In 1954 we stated as one of our corporate objectives that we were in business "to serve the true needs of the markets." Obviously this phrase implies both the markets we were in as well as any new and attractive markets where we could meet our objectives. We also made it clearly understood internally that we were not in the business of manufacturing merely for the sake of manufacturing. In serving the needs of the market it does not necessarily follow that we or any other company has to do all things and make all or most of our parts. We decided to buy instead of make when the economics justified it. Scheduling problems, machine loading, parts interference, and inventory buildup at all levels should be considered when looking at the economic justification of "buy versus make." There are many people in business who can do certain things better than we can do them ourselves. (Some of us in the business world are reluctant to admit this fact, which is understandable—human nature being what it is.)

We decided to keep our new satellite operations relatively small in both size and number of people because of the many advantages we felt we would enjoy through being able to communicate with our employees and really get to "know" them. Our expectations have been fulfilled and have proved very rewarding.

Our sales organization did a fine job. The salesmen were all on our Blackhawk payroll and sold only our products through automotive jobbers. As we began to concentrate on multimarkets and definite submarkets within a major market, we had to take the next step and split up our sales organization so that special concentrated attention could be given to specific market and submarket needs. We developed corps of personnel to handle sales, advertising, engineering, manufacturing, personnel, supply, and anything else we needed to aid us in obtaining our objectives.

In manufacturing we broke out distinct families of products from what was once a conglomeration of all parts for all products moving through a job shop. We set up homogeneous parts for line production and assembly and reserved areas in the shop for these specific groups of products. As requirements for these products increased and volume rose accordingly, we would plan to move them to a satellite operation.

We would communicate to all employees at an early date so that we could expect maximum support and productivity, and, at the same time, we would assure them that volume was increasing in other lines and that therefore the contemplated move would not affect their job security. On the contrary, the moves often led to job and skill upgrading. By setting a limit on the total number of people we would like to have in any one of our operations, it became a relatively simple procedure to forecast one, two, three, or four years in advance of an actual spin-off.

Another point of possible interest is the change we went through in our concepts of how engineering should be "run." In the past, sales usually told engineering what products it should design, how the products should look, and just what they should do. (Communication is one of the biggest hurdles in the race of industrial growth. As somebody has said, it's "an incurable disease that will be with us as long as we live, so let's learn and find out how best to live with it.") Sales thus practically dictated the needs of the market—as it saw them—to engineering. But too often, when the products were ready and had actually hit the marketplace, we found they didn't quite suit or fit the true market needs. Why? Because salesmen and engineers, in those days, were speaking different languages, and neither could quite comprehend what the other really meant.

Administration of engineering today allows for our project and design engineers to spend a great deal of time in the field at the site of the tool user. Our sales personnel like it, our customers like it, and we design products which are better suited to the actual and anticipated needs of the market.

Because of this ability to be more sensitive to the *true* needs of the market, we know we do a better job of planning and programing for expansion. And there are other aspects of expansion a company should get control of before launching an intelligent expansion program. Let us hope that the majority of them are at least hinted at in the checklists that follow.

PLANNING AND PREPARING FOR EXPANSION
Suggested outline of some questions to ask and steps to take

I. CHARACTER OF THE COMPANY
   Ask:
     Who are we?
     What are we?
     Where are we?
     What are we doing?
     What is our image with—
       customers?
       stockholders?
       competitors?
       bankers?
       public?
       employees?

II. PRODUCT INFORMATION
   Ask:
     What have our products been?
     What are our products today?
     What is our history and reputation?
     What market or markets are they being sold in?
     What market needs do they serve?
     Is the product line too short, just right, or too long?
     What is our products' quality, and what is our customers' attitude
       toward them?
     How competitive are these products from the standpoint of—
       quality?
       price?

features?
availability?
patent protection?

III. MARKETING

A. *Research*

Ask:

What is the market?
Where is the market?
Who makes up the market?
Who serves the market?
What kinds of competitors do we have?
What is their size?
How many are there?
How good are they (competitors)?
Who else might enter the market?
What is the market potential?
What percentage are we getting?
What percentage do we want?
What submarkets are there?
Should we change our selling techniques?
Should we change our advertising techniques?
Should we concentrate on the whole market or on subsections of it?
What kind of image do we want to create in the long pull?

B. *Selling*

Ask:

How do we sell?
Whom do we sell to?
How good is our advertising?
How close are we to the end user?
What types of selling do we do?
Should we change the sales organization?
Are our products best sold through—
  our sales force?
  factory representatives?
  OEM accounts?
  chain stores?
  mill houses?
  warehouse distribution?
  others?
Do we have long- and short-range plans of selling?
Are we sensitive to market needs?
Are we sensitive to product obsolescence?
Are we sensitive to product revision?

Are we sensitive to product appeal?
Do we know and understand our products?
Do our customers know and understand our products?
What kind of image does the customer have of our products?
What kind of customer service do we have?
What kind of product service do we have?
Does the sales force know which products or product line to sell (profitability of product line versus loss lead items)?

IV. ENGINEERING
   A. *Product Design plus Research & Development*
      Ask:
         What will our products be?
         Will we have new ones? How many?
         What will they do?
         What will they look like?
         What will be their purpose?
         What need will they serve?
         Will they have patent protection?
         Will they be competitive?
         Will they be profitable?
         Are our products sensitive to market changes?
         Are we keeping all products in the line?
         Should we keep all products?
         Should we obsolete some?
         Should we redesign for profit?
         Should we add features?
         Should we add functions?
         Should we add consumer appeal?
         Should we revise and innovate?
         Will these products serve future market needs?

   B. *Industrial or Manufacturing Engineering*
      Ask:
         Should we update our processes?
         Should we take advantage of creeping changes?
         Should we retool?
         Should we take advantage of new materials?
         Should we change our methodology?
         Should we invest in new equipment?
         Should we invest in new machines?
         Should we invest (more or less) in brick and mortar?
         Should we develop new techniques of manufacturing?
         Should we stop manufacturing (buy versus make on some parts)?
         Should we change our AQL?

Should we automate?
Should we improve our material flow?
Can we shorten in-plant lead time?
Can we redesign to reduce the number of parts?
Can we standardize more parts across product lines?
Can we get an adequate ROI (return on investment) on any of these investments?

V. Purchasing and Material Control
Ask:

Can we improve vendor relations?
Can we improve vendor quality?
Can we improve vendor lead times?
Can we reduce vendor prices?
Can we help vendors in improving methods?
Can we minimize in-plant interference?
Can we minimize in-process inventory?
Can we minimize raw material stores?
Can we minimize finished goods inventory—and still have the products available when customers need them?
Do we buy parts in proper purchase lot sizes?
Do we run parts in proper economic lot sizes?
Does the sales department give us adequate lead time to process?
Does the sales department forecast its needs in realistic quantities?
Do we need new systems and controls?
Do we need to abolish antiquated systems?

VI. Manufacturing
Ask:

Are our facilities adequate?
Are our facilities too large?
Are our facilities too small?
Are our facilities up to date?
Are our facilities obsolete?
How long before they are obsolete?
Are our facilities too elaborate?
What about manpower?
Are we in a good labor market?
Are we getting cooperation (high productivity)?
Are we sensitive to the employees' needs?
Are we too autocratic?
Are we too paternal?
Are we too democratic?
Do we have good first-line management?
Do we have, or want, good communication?
Do we have, or want, good employee relations?

Are our production costs in line?
Are direct and indirect labor in control?
How bad or good are employee turnover and absenteeism?

VII. FINANCIAL
Ask:
Do we have good cost control?
Do we have long-range financial planning?
What are our needs for money?
Are our fixed costs under control?
Are our variable costs under control?
Do we have sound financial ratios on total investment to sales?
Do we have good ratios on receivables to sales?
Do we have good ratios on inventory to sales?
Do we have good ratios on fixed assets to sales?
Do we have a realistic ROI after taxes on present as well as planned business?
Do we have good sales forecasts and sales quotas, short- and long-range?
Do we have good budget control?
Do we know our cost on each product line?
Do we know our cost on selling each product line?
Do we know what random changes in product mix will do to our profitability?
Do we want to sell a product line?
Do we want to get out of a certain type of business?

VIII. MANAGEMENT
Ask:
Are we training key men for long-range growth needs?
Are we grooming our organization to serve needs of specific market subsections?
Are we programing and planning for product line spin-offs into new markets?
Are we going to have separate sales, engineering, finance, manufacturing, and personnel departments for the expansion?
Are we going to set up satellite facilities?
Are we going to locate near the user?
Are we going to locate near the raw material source?
Are we checking into diversified markets?
Are we checking into diversified products?
Are we checking into diversified services?
Are we using specialists in and out of the company?

AUTOMATION: PROSPECTS AND PROBLEMS

By ROGER W. BOLZ

Automation technology offers an economic solution to some knotty manufacturing problems, yet simultaneously presents a need to break radically with past practices. The increased tempo of business with its host of related individual changes has focused intense interest, and sometimes resentment, on the automation of manufacturing processes. The forces that resist change are not a whit less in evidence today than they were in the past.

Because of people's inherent resistance to change, far more find—yes, we may truly say, actually labor to develop—reasons why a new method is not suitable or will not work than are willing to try something different. As a result, the larger the organization the greater the difficulty it has in adapting to rapid change.

Automation today is synonymous with change. But the change goes beyond the productive machinery, and so resistance shows up more importantly in management circles than in labor circles. Even engineering people tend to wish it away through the mediums of confusion and gloomy social forecasts.

To remain competitive in the age of automation any management must be sensitive to the need for change. It must also be ready to accept all the risks that accompany the new and at times be ready to cope with the unpopular if the business is to survive.

In all probability the biggest hindrance to accomplishing significant advance through automation techniques is the well-established and well-routinized management organization. Although some routine is necessary, any company with too highly developed routine will not make much progress. Automation holds great promise and, in fact, few problems for the wide-awake company. If management has a broad and commanding technical capability, it has the major

---

ROGER W. BOLZ is Editor-in-Chief, *Automation*, Penton Publishing Co., Cleveland, Ohio.

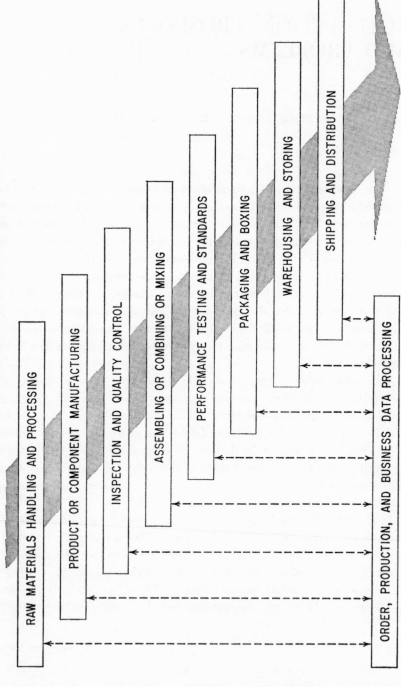

EXHIBIT 1
EIGHT INTEGRATED STEPS OF MODERN MANUFACTURING

asset required for progress. Along with this capability must go an understanding of personnel and their changing motivations.

A Matter of Semantics

Many companies have fallen on hard times insofar as profits are concerned, not because the efficiency necessary to maintain or improve productivity was unattainable but because resistance to change manifested itself in a long fruitless battle of words. Today we still find those who forgo the benefits of automating because of sterile arguments over whether the system has electronic feedback or not. Actually, the use of automation techniques has only one fundamental reason for being—more economic manufacture. Practical automation must be recognized as the technology of manufacturing, processing, or performing services as automatically and continuously as business economics demand. The system may or may not utilize feedback, depending on cost and quality requirements. A complicated gas control valve, used in large quantities, must meet rigid quality requirements but sells competitively for 67 cents. To charge more would be to price oneself out of the market. Although an automated quality-monitoring system for the valve would be desirable, the competitive selling price makes it impractical. On the other hand, some sophisticated chemicals are impossible to produce economically without equally sophisticated instrumentation for control.

Management must recognize that it is involved not in formulating sophisticated definitions but rather in finding more sophisticated solutions to the problems of manufacturing products competitively. The major hurdle for management is to recognize that the key to its efficient use lies not so much in the equipment itself as in adapting to continuing change throughout the entire company. Significant accomplishment in automating requires successful adjustment to change in every segment of the enterprise. In this adjustment all the earlier, neatly erected departmental barriers in a company may be shattered, for data processing tears down arbitrary walls between manufacturing functions and integrates them all into one functioning whole, as can be seen in Exhibit 1.

When the gradual introduction of automation has not been planned over the long range, sooner or later changing economic pressures will force the issue. The real troubles arise when sufficient time has not been made available to anticipate and assimilate the severe changes that must take place. However, these changes are identical to those that beset any company that has remained in a static condition overlong and is forced into rapid corrective moves to avoid disaster. They are depicted graphically in Exhibit 2, and we shall have more to say about them later.

No matter what the circumstances, the wide-awake manager must be conversant with the industrial facts of life in order to deal adequately with everyday problems. Today, automation applications can be found throughout all of industry. In spite of the many negative comments we hear, is automation really a problem? Does it in fact create unemployment? What has actually been happening in the American economy as the use of these techniques by business and industry has grown? What does the future hold?

Faced with such queries not only from his own organization but also from the general public, the manager should know the facts. For the most part they are not only of good report; they are promising. Today, everyone has a legitimate interest in automation. The word—in its broad significance to industry and business—has social and economic importance. Few industries

EXHIBIT 2

REAL CAUSES FOR RAPID CHANGE IN MANUFACTURING

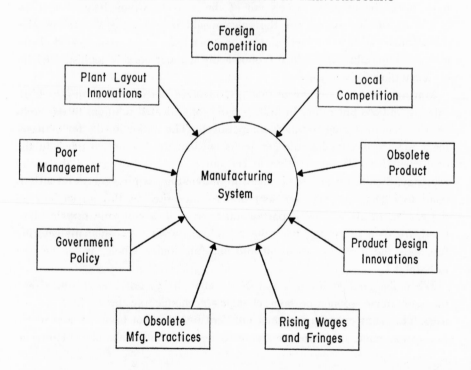

are totally unaffected by automation or can afford to ignore its possibilities and promise.

A few years back, it was commonplace to find the word "automation" being given science-fiction attributes. Having survived the onslaught of the fiction writers, the true character of automation, which has been emerging gradually in recent years, is almost prosaic in comparison—actually, to some, it is disappointing. Nevertheless, its scope, accomplishments, applications, and opportunities can be truly breathtaking.

What Is Automation?

Automation implies continuous or cyclic arrangements for manufacturing products, goods, or services. Its accomplishment rests upon several important developments: (1) principles of mass production, (2) mechanization, and (3) power and control equipment.

Mass production in the past was attained largely by manual methods—often by making the workman virtually a machine. Mechanization—doing things by or with machines—for the most part merely made the workman another part in a mechanical cycle which was seldom automatic. Exhibit 3 shows the evolutionary phases of production with their concomitant freeing of man from menial labor and the enhanced possibilities of increasing production and improving productivity.

Mass production made possible the manufacture of products at diverse locations with controlled specifications, all sufficiently identical to permit random use or random assembly in other products. Mass production and mechanization techniques constituted a major step in providing large quantities of complex products with superior quality and uniformity at lower cost in time and money. But, today, manual methods often fail to fulfill the requirements of mass production because of economics, market demand, quality, time, and other factors. Industry is turning to the succeeding step in the manufacturing picture—automation—to regain the benefits of mass production with assured quality control.

UNDERSTANDING AUTOMATION ECONOMICS AND TECHNOLOGY

Manufacturing managers must recognize the practical character and scope of automation, for its use in manufacturing has been expanding rapidly in

EXHIBIT 3

EVOLUTIONARY PHASES OF PRODUCTION

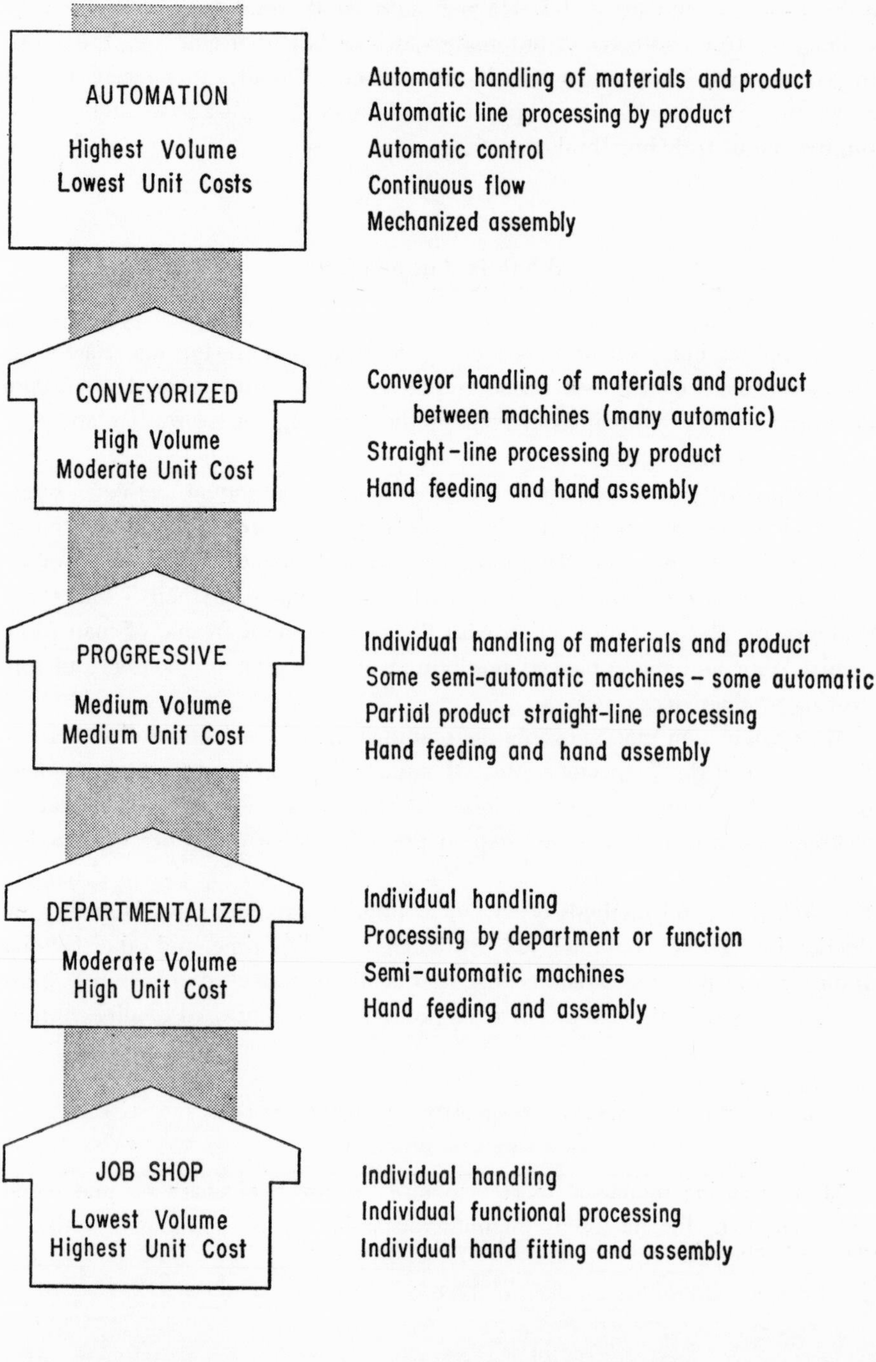

AUTOMATION

Highest Volume
Lowest Unit Costs

Automatic handling of materials and product
Automatic line processing by product
Automatic control
Continuous flow
Mechanized assembly

CONVEYORIZED

High Volume
Moderate Unit Cost

Conveyor handling of materials and product
    between machines (many automatic)
Straight-line processing by product
Hand feeding and hand assembly

PROGRESSIVE

Medium Volume
Medium Unit Cost

Individual handling of materials and product
Some semi-automatic machines — some automatic
Partial product straight-line processing
Hand feeding and hand assembly

DEPARTMENTALIZED

Moderate Volume
High Unit Cost

Individual handling
Processing by department or function
Semi-automatic machines
Hand feeding and assembly

JOB SHOP

Lowest Volume
Highest Unit Cost

Individual handling
Individual functional processing
Individual hand fitting and assembly

recent years. We are obliged to recognize its major contribution to and other effects on our standard of living.

Properly applied, automation makes possible desired goods and services with two advantages: more for a dollar plus more wage dollars. Growth in total wages paid (and taxes as well) and total employment attests to this. The contrast between wages, labor cost, and productivity over the 50-year period

EXHIBIT 4

UNIT LABOR COSTS
(*Private Nonfarm 1939 = 100*)

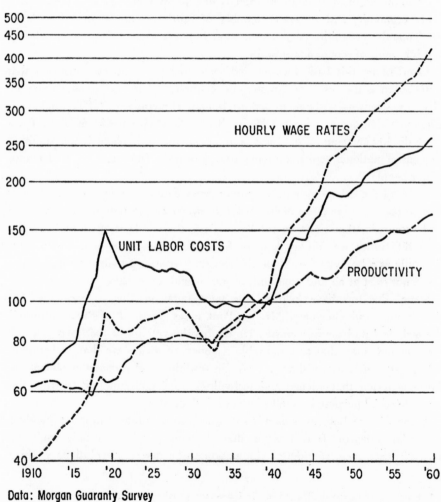

Data: Morgan Guaranty Survey

1910–1960 is clearly shown in Exhibit 4. In spite of the record many still cling to the discredited theory that computerization leads to limited jobs and a general lack of remunerative work. The most extensive user of computers—the banking industry—has an employment rate that is increasing three times as fast as the average for all other industries combined. And yet the fears remain.

To build solidly for the future, therefore, something more than imagination and conjecture is needed. Sincere concern about improved job opportunities and employment demands equally sincere effort by management to provide a more thorough understanding of how a free economy functions. It demands an acknowledgment that automation is merely another tool by which better, more economic, and a greater number of products can be made available. It demands recognition that automation is not a *cause* of economic change but is a *result* of economic pressures.

Overlooking this basic fact has led some to the erroneous conclusion that automation is the result of "mysterious technological forces imposed upon society by scientists without regard to human consequences." "Technology is everybody's business," observes Henry B. du Pont, vice president of E. I. du Pont de Nemours and Co., Inc.; "our advancing technology is the result of the entire national effort, deriving its importance from the rising demands of our people."[1]

Much of the debate over these contemporary issues, says du Pont, emphasizes the problems without examining the full sweep of the national needs, social and economic, that must be fulfilled. When the whole story is told, despite some difficulties, we find ample cause for gratification. Those who see automation only as a bogeyman overlook the fact that without it many useful products could not exist at all and thousands of jobs would never have come into being.

Some educators have followed the same fallacious line of reasoning. On the campus and elsewhere. Mr. du Pont notes, we hear of "two cultures," the technical and the humanistic. He doubts the validity of the "two culture" premise and states that as responsible members of society we share a common culture as clearly as we share a common tradition and a common obligation. Any suggestion that science and technology serve ends that differ from the common social purpose is as fallacious as it is dangerous.

Automation technology is merely a continuing development in our expanding industrial endeavor. It is amazing that so many people, especially engineers and scientists, have considered automation to be new or revolutionary, since

---

[1] Speech given at the dedication of the University of Rhode Island College of Engineering, Kingston, R.I., April 20, 1963.

the fundamental concept of continuous systems is so old. History reveals a long, arduous endeavor by inventors to create the machinery, devices, and processes which led to today's achievements.

The principles of manufacturing automation are based on almost 180 years of endless engineering research and development that began with the fundamental concept for a continuous automatic flour mill invented by Oliver Evans in 1783. In his book *Mechanization Takes Command,* S. Giedion makes the significant comment that, "Evans' invention opened a new chapter in the history of mankind." Giedion credits Evans with being the first man to see the opportunities of integrated manufacture. Ours is the job to write the next successful chapters of an outstanding American heritage. In so doing managers in manufacturing must become organizers and creators of change.

The problems of consumer demand, job availability, production efficiency, and related areas of economic life have changed little over the years. The cry, "Machines have taken your place," which was heard following the Civil War, has now been replaced by a new theme, "automation." In reality, there are no "easy" answers to the problems of changing job requirements, but individual interest and enterprise among managers will help tremendously. Careful study of the economic structure, renewed interest in our free enterprise heritage, and consideration of the common good are needed. Education and training for management—as well as the workforce—are key factors in making the most of our rich opportunities.

CHANGE AND GROWTH

Economic growth entails change, and change is always disturbing and unsettling. Societies which have not been willing to pay the costs of growth in economic, social, and cultural changes have also been stagnant economically. The United States has a notable record of adapting to the changes involved in growth. As a result, its long-term record of economic success is unmatched.

If automation truly is beneficial, what then are the main causes of unemployment and displacement? They are the same as those that cause change, as indicated in Exhibit 2—competition, taxes, products obsoleted by others of newer design, improved plant layouts, better plant locations, and obsolete manufacturing practices. As a rule, automation is introduced to save a failing business, to hold the cost line, or to provide products and services which are otherwise unavailable.

Without a careful analysis of what is happening in business and industry, many statements have been made regarding methods to limit or control the introduction of automation. Analysis calls for rather extensive knowledge of all the economic cause-and-effect phenomena which are not yet well understood. To forecast influences and control them effectively has little chance for success. Professor Van Rensselaer Potter states in the November 20, 1964, issue of *Science* that "it is now realized by many that science is in fact a source of considerable disorder and knowledge that science is by no means prepared to manage." Professor Potter notes that life itself is ordered by a certain amount of unpredictable disorder, without which no improvement would be possible. It is almost axiomatic that without some small percentage of disorder through changes, shifts, and displacement a business too would degenerate until it ceased to function at all.

What does a close look at current total employment data show? The total employment base has grown to more than 71 million, and over the past decade 96 percent of those interested in working have been employed. Compared with 1947, the number of farm and manufacturing production workers in 1963 had dropped 2.6 million, but white-collar jobs had grown by 10 million. Technical jobs had risen 112 percent, managers and proprietors 28 percent, office workers 40 percent, sales workers 28 percent, and service 5 percent, as we see in Exhibit 5. This picture is certainly much different from what a look at only one segment reveals. Employment is the highest in history. With critical

EXHIBIT 5

EMPLOYMENT, BY TYPE OF OCCUPATION, 1947–62

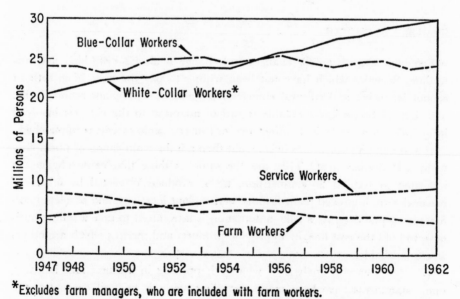

*Excludes farm managers, who are included with farm workers.

(bread-winner) unemployment running at less than a million persons (the total turning over at least four times during the year), for all practical purposes this figure is probably close to a minimum condition in a free-enterprise economy. Job openings also stand at an all-time high, and technicians are scarce. Demand as measured by unofficial estimates of openings is some five to ten times what it was five years ago.

But what of the story we hear that many jobs are going begging? Here is where automation has its most significant effect. It increases the need for engineers, technicians, and craftsmen. The growing complexity and number of products have helped, but expanding manufacturing enterprise along with increasing automation has made the greatest impact in this regard.

An interesting facet that emphasizes the growing demand for special skills is moonlighting. Present estimates indicate that more than 4 million persons hold two or more jobs in special fields, almost double that of a decade ago. This, along with the unfilled jobs available, creates a total that far overshadows any unemployment figure. But the vast majority of moonlighting work falls into the skilled or highly skilled category. The moonlighters, that is, are not depriving anyone of a job who is qualified to hold it.

MANUFACTURING EDUCATION AND TRAINING

Managers must be concerned with the need for broadening education and training. Studies show that results among those whose jobs are obsolescing are insignificant where the offer of job training or transfer is ineffectively communicated. Without a deeper understanding of their plight by the very workers whose jobs are affected by automation and the march of technology, the offer of free choice more often than not merely maintains the status quo. Surveys show that even engineers are reluctant to return to school for advanced studies. On the other hand, a prevalent view is that the future holds promise only for scientists and researchers. Those who make this claim have overlooked the greatest need of all—for skilled craftsmen, technicians, and engineers.

In a recent study made by the National Fluid Power Association it was found that severe shortages have arisen in these areas: 65 percent of the respondents indicated that there was a shortage of technicians in design, 60 percent in installation, 49 percent in operations, 57 percent in maintenance, and 62 percent in manufacturing. Studies made by *Automation* magazine show that roughly half the automated plants require significantly larger maintenance staffs, but nearly all such plants call for much higher skills than formerly, even if the number of employees remains the same.

The shortage of technicians is not restricted to manufacturing. An area of growing need today is service—servicing consumer products and servicing industrial machinery that is becoming more and more automatic because of growing economic pressures and advancing technology.

A Look at the Future

Certainly the history of industrial growth has *not* been one of machine-created problems. Consumer interests and influence on the business outlook have in large part been the troublemakers. Technological development to a great degree results from the stimulus of consumer actions. As the consumer's attitude, desires, and outlook swing in wide variations, industrial effort to serve them follows suit, with a tremendous backwash effect on the fortunes of all workmen involved throughout a great interwoven maze of connected services. The consumer—whether industry, commerce, or jobholder—for the most part is the victim of his own choices and whims.

Not even the computer technologist or the computer builder gleefully contemplates a future of uncontrolled growth in data processing. In the face of the many improper uses of EDP equipment and the web of complete information being spun about the individual, concerning both his private and his public lives, there may be little to be cheerful about. Uneconomical or unnecessary uses of computers in this manner offer little value to the individual and forecast a growing degree of rigidity in his choice of work careers, pointing toward immobility and widespread frustration. It is to be sincerely hoped that the values inherent in EDP for providing more and better goods and services by industry will predominate and will work to insure maximum freedom for all individuals. Yet wishing well will not make it so, and one of management's new concerns is learning not to violate a worker's rights by perverting the intended uses of EDP into ends for which it was never intended. Man's mind was nimble and imaginative enough to conceive the computer, and the machine must not be allowed to regimentalize and dull that mind in return.

WHAT THE MANUFACTURING MANAGER CAN EXPECT

What is the promising outlook for the future in a much more highly competitive world, with spreading automation and rapidly changing product demands? First and foremost are increased opportunities in education, the arts, and leisure. The education of our workforce and our supervisory and managerial classes must be broader and better than at any time in the past if we expect to survive the impact of world competition.

What of manufacturing men's jobs? The future calls for increasing individual enterprise and continual advancement in their educational base. The educated and skilled managers in our modern economy will adapt and fit easily into the changing environment, provided, that is, that they never stagnate, that they keep abreast of innovation. Manufacturing managers of the future will be highly skilled creators of change—innovators and motivators. Change will hold no terrors; it will be their milieu.

The development of better business conditions to stimulate new enterprise will require that we avoid any moves by business or government (no matter how socially desirable) that in the end militate against employment or that create unnecessary barriers to expansion, research, and productivity advances. Oversimplified temporary remedies must be carefully evaluated so that in helping to alleviate some localized hardship, an irreparable long-range problem is not created. Managers can assist in this area by careful study and application of the highest principles in labor negotiations. John F. Adams and Benjamin S. Kirsh suggest that unless managers develop a broader outlook in these dealings, they will become prisoners of their short-range decisions.[2]

Every man who aspires to success in managing manufacturing operations will have to set aside enough time to make a reasonable effort toward continuing self-improvement, to recognize his responsibility to contribute to the total enterprise. And, indeed, his rewards will be commensurate with the interest, quality, and effort he expends. In short—the manufacturing manager will be the uncommon man. We cannot expect improvement unless we stimulate it. We must create the climate that motivates workmen to look for and thrive on change. Manufacturing men, as the progenitors of change, must be the leaders in this area.

Alfred North Whitehead once said, using a phrase in a way which anticipates the meaning recently assigned to it by President Johnson: "A great society is a society in which its men of business think greatly of their functions. Low thoughts mean low behavior, and after a brief orgy of exploitation low behavior means a descending standard of life. The general greatness of a community is the first condition for steady prosperity."

---

[2] John F. Adams, "7 Challenges to Management," *Automation*, June 1964, page 54; and Benjamin S. Kirsh, "Labor Bargaining Must Protect Management's Rights," *Automation*, August 1964, page 50.

These are wise words for manufacturing people to ponder today. For one thing, industry itself has need to study and fully understand changing trends. Silence or platitude on the part of business will more and more be taken as evidence of unconcern over most problems that arise from the complex shifts and changes taking place. Failure of industrial leaders to take the forefront in explaining the issues at stake, in proposing suitable solutions, and in actively educating the general public as well as employees will result in increasing disregard and criticism of business. The expected growth in the ranks of job seekers in the coming years makes the issue crystal clear. Better communication must be forthcoming from manufacturing men.

THE EFFECTS ON THE WORKFORCE

New incentive measures are needed to promote in-plant apprenticeships, on-the-job training courses, and special technician educational plans. Certainly it is utterly unrealistic for state or Federal Government to express concern over job changes while maintaining a tax system that is distinctly punitive to individuals who are spending money to advance their educational status. All money spent on education of any kind will of necessity eventually be made taxfree.

The education and training of employees by their employers will increase considerably. Chase Manhattan Bank estimated the cost of on-the-job training by industry in 1963 to run to about $17 billion for the year. This has been growing at a rate of 5.5 percent a year, but the biggest area for expected growth to come is still rather dormant—individually inspired advancement. Therefore, it is desirable to stimulate personal incentives to help inspire initiative and to make it easy to adapt to and grow with technological change. Today's workman or technician *must* become a vital part of the industrial scene, not a bystander, as he too often has been made to be in the past.

To maintain an efficient automated operation, planned management development programs should be created for supervisory personnel. Even though specialists can be brought in to help, there can be no sidestepping of this major issue. Only through a continuing program of training for existing supervisors can practical working results be expected. Training and education must be focused on the system concept, handling and control of new types of equipment, changing job responsibilities, and practical solutions for growing technical problems.

THE DUTY TO ADJUST TO CHANGE

Automation and technological change will continue to have profound effects on the industrial scene.[3] Our job today is to determine what automation can accomplish, to use it wisely, and to continue to explain at every opportunity what we are doing.

Hickman Price, Jr., Assistant Secretary of Commerce for Domestic Affairs, forcefully emphasized our position with his comment that "we must cease being children playing at games in this great international marketplace. To meet the challenge of foreign productive enterprise, a re-evaluation of the seriousness of our work and labor outlook is imperative." To make the promise of automation come true, not only labor but management as well must accept and encourage change. We must stop deploring change and keep up with the expanding needs of a dynamic age. Every civilization must either adapt to its times or perish.

One of manufacturing management's major problems was summarized recently by Dr. Lloyd P. Smith, director of Philco Research Laboratories, with the comment that "we are living in the first period in human history wherein the time span of a host of significant changes is considerably shorter than the production lifetime of a single individual. . . . Nevertheless, the forces which resist change are still predominant and I believe constitute the greatest single cause of poor performance and self-generated management problems in a fast-moving environment. In fact, the assumption persists in people's minds to a substantial degree that conditions governing the lives of their fathers will to a great extent mold their lives."

The areas of major activity for both creating and handling technological change are to be found in science, engineering, and related professions. If management is to obtain high performance from its organization in the future, it must have a broad and commanding technical knowledge. In the future better understanding of personnel and their motivations to achieve success will also be required. Most of all, management will have to improve its sensitivity to the need for the disposition and readiness to make changes with all their attendant risks and, at times, their unpopularity.

It is now within our grasp to create whatever equipment systems are needed

---

[3] John A. Bekker, "Modern Manufacturing Environment Is Creating New Work Concepts," *Automation,* October 1964, page 58.

to manufacture efficiently in the competitive climate of the years ahead. The critical part of the problem will be related to the meager supply of staff and management personnel who have the broad technical background and experience to recognize the need for and ability to use the systems approach in manufacturing research. There will be a growing pressure to develop the new skills needed for applying the systems concept, which Frederick R. Kappel, Chairman of the Board of the American Telephone and Telegraph Company, describes as getting, "first, a clear view of what is both needed and potentially feasible; second, a closely reasoned determination of the best course for achieving the desired result; and third, a dependable measure of the means already available, and those we must still discover in order to make doable what we are setting out to do."

A forward-looking program for management in the era of automation will include the introduction of new blood into the organization. Not only can successful transfer of know-how be accomplished in this manner, but also the base of total corporate knowledge will be broadened.

Along with such efforts an economic cross-breeding of successful subsystem elements will be possible. As the pace of technology increases, a narrow, parochial approach to manufacturing will become untenable. Management will have to become more flexible and adjustable to suit the changing economic picture. The challenge to manufacturing management today is to understand the technological changes taking place and to prepare itself to meet them responsibly and eagerly.

POSTSCRIPT: THE FUTURE OF THE MANUFACTURING FUNCTION

By EDWARD WISNEWSKY

Three factors differentiate the manufacturing strategy of the past from that of the future and, in fact, promise to shape its destiny. The first is a surplus of capacity which forces us to seek a manufacturing ideology better suited to our day than the one we have inherited from the past. The second is the tremendous proliferation in recent years of technical knowledge with its own concomitant effect on our actions. The third is the fact that society as a whole has proclaimed its interest in economic growth and also its obvious intent to affect by political means the commodities produced, their quantity, and their price. Though each of these factors has a different origin, they are interrelated and must be dealt with accordingly. They give old problems new urgencies, and they also bring new problems.

What we must face is a condition in which these factors are interwoven. Sometimes one may seem dominant over the rest, and at other times all three may operate with equal strength; however, for the sake of this discussion, it should be clearly understood that the order imposed is more a matter of convenience than a reflection of underlying reality. We need a total picture, and this is difficult to give ready-made. To a considerable degree, any attempt to anticipate the effect of each of these factors resolves itself into a matter of opinion, but the conclusion that all of them will shape our strategy is something more than mere opinion.

THE NEW NEED FOR ANTICIPATION

The surplus of manufacturing capacity has produced several effects which are closely related to the growth of technical knowledge. Today most products,

EDWARD WISNEWSKY is a consultant with offices in Milwaukee, Wisconsin.

processes, and methods are satisfactory only for a short period of time; obsolescence of equipment, practices, and knowledge is a fact of manufacturing life. From this statement we can draw three specific observations.

1. An accurate determination of the life expectancy of products, processes, and methods is absolutely necessary for planning strategy.

2. Managers are being forced to pay closer attention to the technological capabilities of their own organizations instead of the capabilities existing elsewhere, whether domestic or international.

3. The nature of profits has changed; no longer are they derived from exploiting shortages of supply in the face of demand, nor are they made by setting profit-returning prices alone. Instead, they depend on the skillful use of working capital, the ability to produce within a fixed period of time, and the firm's success in increasing its share of the market.

While technological capabilities are important, in order to be profit-oriented we must also consider the nature of the total environment in which we operate. All the factors cited have made it essential to concentrate on what we are going to make and how we are going to make it in a way which takes into account tomorrow and the day after tomorrow. The future has taken on a new character in that we need to anticipate it in today's operating plans. This is a practical consequence of history.

The manufacturer who fails to keep pace with improvements among his competitors has always courted trouble, but today it is nearly disastrous to fail to anticipate new developments and their possibilities. To keep up to date in practice, we have to stay ahead in our thinking. One result of this is that often the advantage of innovation is short-lived; by orienting their thinking toward the future, competitors anticipate innovation and plot a counter-strategy.

To assure that no one can use protective agreements to thwart aggressive competition, society first acts through government channels to police stabilization efforts by agreement among industries. This policing technique will assuredly be refined in the future to become more effective. The second social objective, linked to the first, is a definite interest in stimulating the diffusion and wider utilization of knowledge and innovation. The large-scale attempt to improve managerial capabilities through educational programs is nearly worldwide. A movement has arisen in our country to discover ways of removing financial barriers to innovation; tax reform is only one element in this movement. All these trends undoubtedly have their wider political motivation, but at the same time they must be viewed as steps in the process of making sure that competition is as dynamic as possible.

What promises to make such public activity meaningful is that manufacturers themselves are aware of the need to change. An estimated 80 percent of all technical knowledge has been developed in the last generation; obviously there is still a great deal of knowledge yet to be assimilated and used. In manufacturing we are faced with this explosion of technical information, and we really don't know how to use it effectively. When we draw from this storehouse, we are running the risk that some part of the available knowledge we have ignored may be the very source of action which makes what we have done useless in the immediate future. But in general there is some hope that emphasis on the assimilation of such knowledge may lead to the kind of success which will reduce the effect of manufacturing capacity surplus by making some competitors hopelessly obsolete and thus ineffective.

But, for this to happen, two conditions must be met. First, the opportunity to put new knowledge to work must be recognized; and, second, the opportunity must be acted on quickly and used to capture the major share of the market so that competitors will be forced to buy back their place in the market. It is not enough to build a shield of patent rights and trade secrets. If a company is to gain the maximum competitive advantage on the basis of its technological achievement, it must have better knowledge and linkage to the marketplace. This idea leads to an observation we would all do well to remember: The advantage of technical innovation can be dissipated by slow marketing action.

This rise in the functional significance of the marketplace in determining immediate strategy is the most significant development for the future of manufacturing, since it promises to revolutionize our approach to the organization structure and the role of the individual. The emphasis on the market means that we have to visualize the manufacturing enterprise in essentially ecological terms; that is, we must realize that the plant is not a separate and isolated entity but a larger complex which includes the customer and supplier. The organization has an environment, and the relations of its internal structure to the surroundings must influence our decisions.

There is nothing new in this thought, for as long ago as 1938 Chester I. Barnard was pointing out the need for concepts of this nature in his book, *The Functions of the Executive*. But what *is* new is that common practice is taking us beyond the reaches of our theory. Thus the salesman is included as a creative partner along with the financial, production, administrative, and engineering experts. The proper way to regard the firm today is as an entity seeking to perpetuate its existence through adjustments to a changing environment, but for reasons which make good sense to individuals in the organization.

We have to accept this conclusion for a variety of reasons stemming in the final analysis from the three factors originally mentioned as shaping manufacturing strategy: surplus of capacity, proliferation of technologically significant knowledge, and the impact of culture or society on applied technology.

SELF- VERSUS THE COMMON INTEREST

Manufacturing in the United States is often a cultural phenomenon rather than an economic necessity. It is one of the most important ways in which men in a private-enterprise economy make themselves a livelihood. The pertinence of a cultural perspective can be established on a variety of grounds. One of these is that the shutdown of hundreds of factories would have no appreciable effect on the economic foundations of the general standard of living. The capacity to produce would still be there. In some cases we know that shutting down our factories and importing the goods they make would result in a net profit improvement.

But perhaps the better way of approaching an understanding of this cultural-economic dichotomy is not from the perspective of society but rather from that of the individual. Justice Brandeis wrote in 1912:

> Half a century ago nearly every American boy could look forward to becoming independent as a farmer or mechanic, in business or professional life; and nearly every American girl might expect to be the wife of such a man. Today most American boys have reason to believe that throughout life they will work in some capacity as employees of others, either in private or public business; and a large percentage of women occupy like positions.

Events of the past 50 years have substantiated the pertinence of this observation. More and more educated men live on pay checks, not on dividends, rents, or interest and certainly not on earnings as self-employed persons. Even the farmer now depends on nonfarm activities, in his role as an employee, for a large part of his income. Management thinking has responded to the increase in life-long employees and their changed nature. Sociologists, notably David Reisman and the late C. Wright Mills, have commented on the implications for American culture.

As it seems less and less possible for each of us to attain financial independence through individual efforts, we seek to attain it collectively for each other. We are not yet completely comfortable in admitting this. We have not yet discovered a way of being socially conscious that is psychologically healthy and in conformity with our traditional values. The old traditions of morality favor individualistic economic action—the battles over trade unionism and the philosophy of the "welfare state" make us uneasy. But, even though we are not sure of where the road may take us, the time has come to acknowledge this aspect of the social climate and to see that the need to develop a self-perpetuating organizational form which does indeed take into account our self-interest as employees, managers, and owners will definitely shape our future actions.

If we managers do nothing to meet this need, we will become merely an association of overspecialized professionals who think that our actions must be justified in terms of values independent of one another. Our specialties will make us tools of some master-minding fellow manager as we assert that "it's not our field" or "we were not hired to do that."

A "common interest" in the success of the firm as a result of getting pay checks from a common source is not enough to support the attitudes required for success today. When attention is directed at workplace activity, it is easy to see that the interests of the manager, the employee, and the owner are not the same. What we need to see is that the organization should be viewed as a common vehicle for the attainment of different interests.

Yet at the same time the organization itself does impose restraints on how these various interests can be accommodated and realized. The manager's task requires him to be aware of both the possibilities and the limitations which arise when the organization is regarded as the common vehicle for a variety of human aspirations. Because it must serve as such a common vehicle, the profit-making organization's logical nature dictates the selection of strategies.

PRODUCT OR INCOME ORIENTATION?

There are three basic requirements for a self-perpetuating enterprise. First, we need an organization which is not bound in time; second, one which is not product-bound; and, finally, one which can take fullest advantage of these two freedoms. Structural demands must be faced by every manager. Let's be clear about what we want: (1) We seek a form of organization which can survive the removal of any person. (2) We seek the ability to anticipate the events of the future and their impact on us. (3) We seek a way of breaking with the past so as to make new patterns of action effective. (4) Finally, we seek access to resources which are necessary for survival in the future. These are concepts of life rather than of mechanics—which indicates that it is a mistake to evaluate a company strictly in terms of its product output. What we make is secondary to the kind of success we have when we consciously regard the product only as a focus around which the manufacturing activity is organized.

This attitude is not easy to acquire. For centuries work was associated with its result in the form of a product. A man could see what he did; his activities made sense in a tangible way, which strengthened his awareness of personality and individuality. As a result, the yeoman and the guild member had broad time horizons, a life program with a cultural and historic significance. But, if we try to maintain such a craftsmanlike, product-oriented view today, we are going to be unhappy. We naturally outlive the evidence of our work, unless we are in the nonperforming arts.

For manufacturing survival and the sake of our own sanity we must shed our tradition-bound bias and realize that our work has meaning primarily in terms of its effect on our personal income level and on the stability, or improvement, of that level. This significant factor is what binds the fate of the individual to the future of the organization as a whole; it must be a keystone in our philosophy. The welfare of our society demands that we accept this tenet. Economic growth and acceleration in the production of social surplus both demand the kind of aggressive action which men put forth only when they are convinced that what they are doing is valuable to themselves. We can't talk of motivation and its importance and ignore this fact.

We can call this an "income orientation" if we are aware that all social benefits, including career opportunities, social status, and retirement financing, are included in the concept. The term has value in that it recognizes the role of the human being in the collective symbolized as "the firm" in traditional economic theory. It serves to draw attention to the fact that individual activity and interpersonal transactions in the firm are as much economic units for analytical purposes as the transactions between firms. We can apply concepts of utility, exchange, and opportunity costs to this area as validly as we apply these concepts to the larger economic scene. These define a way of participating rather than an attitude of cooperation.

Does "income orientation" then mean that any judgment about the worth of the concrete output of our factories has no role in our world of values? Are we not to care what we make, what we do, so long as the final product sells? These questions are rhetorical only, for by and large we cannot separate values from the judgments made by those who buy. This is certainly true for shops where the customer specifies the product, and it also applies to those which sell to industrial and large-scale buyers. The images men tend to imitate in our culture are not created by manufacturers. They are the gifts of our culture to which we as manufacturers must respond; certainly Detroit did not originate the small car.

MANUFACTURING AND SOCIETY

Our personal salvation in an age in which surplus manufacturing capacity is the rule and self-employment is exceptional depends on the fact that those who buy have a great influence in determining what we make. By exercising their power, they rationally save us from socially meaningless lives. The importance of the moral role of the customer in our society is largely unexplored. Improving mass morals is not a legitimate goal of manufacturing practice; however, adapting to cultural change is indeed a condition of economic survival.

This is not to say that the product itself is insignificant; however, its significance must be sought outside the structure of the organization, for its utility to the organization is one thing and the utility it has to those who buy is still another. Without the one the other cannot be present. It is thus possible to nullify the argument over whether the function of a manufacturing organization is to provide service or to make profits. This argument arises only when we look for purpose and justification in the wrong place. The social service we render in manufacturing is the result of competition in the development and production of those goods which the customer wants, and only in that. (This, however, does not entirely hold true for institutional organizations.)

To develop an effective rationale for the future in terms of manufacturing practices, we must view manufacturing as a struggle for existence, for this is the meaning of competition that society wants to impose on us. Such a struggle between producers would be insane were there not special benefits for those willing to risk themselves in the process. And we have missed our calling if we do not concentrate on winning these benefits.

One of the consequences of the continuing antitrust investigations may be a more explicit recognition of why society should encourage profit making, including a better definition of the success that accrues as a result. For a long time the real social meaning of competition was ignored by the public, by industry, and by government. Manufacturing was not so much interested in the increase in social surplus as it was in receiving its share of the profits. But the emergence of rivals in foreign lands has emphasized the need to make progress in creating social surplus by actively using all the knowledge mankind has made available. Profits are bound to become respectable and legitimate in the fullest sense if technology itself comes to be regarded as something to be developed to the fullest. It is quite apparent that to maintain progress it is necessary to attract the right kind of talent and to encourage risk taking.

The net result is that in the foreseeable future a manufacturing enterprise, from the standpoint of its participants, will exist primarily to provide them with an income—or the kind of wealth which gives value to purchasing power—but only if they can be made to earn their income through a special kind of success. From society's standpoint this success is to be evaluated in terms of the prices, kinds, and quantities of goods and services it wants.

THE PROPER USE OF WORKING CAPITAL

We can arrive at the guiding principles manufacturing needs by realizing that the real source of income for owners, workers, and managers lies in the efficient use of working capital. The functional value rather than the cash value of assets is the vital issue. Functional value is not static but is in fact subject to violent change. Book value by itself is a meaningless figure for operations. Would the money invested in plant and equipment have produced a greater return if it were used as working capital to finance sales? What would the effect have been on future prospects? Could the money have been more profitably spent on manpower? Questions about the utilization of working capital are always pertinent. What counts for the investor is the use of working capital to achieve a satisfactory return. What counts for the employee is the use of working capital to provide both a socially meaningful career and a satisfactory level of personal income. It is this last expectation which relates the interest of the investor to that of the employee, and vice versa.

We have only to observe day-to-day manufacturing problems to see how frequently they are traceable to faulty management decisions regarding working capital. Evidence of concern with the proper use of working capital is the proliferation of abstract models, conferences, institutes, and seminars devoted primarily to educating all levels of management about the effect of their decisions on profit. We have not yet learned to act consistently in this question of profit. The chief obstacle in the way of improved, rational behavior is that we still think that the product orientation of the craftsman or the process orientation of the professional belongs in the profit picture somewhere. Future progress in management training and development will eliminate these vestiges of a dead tradition.

One of the necessary early steps in making such progress is to get a clearer idea about the nature of profit. Profit is essentially a bonus—a bonus earned if production volume goes beyond the breakeven point. It depends on the achievement of a certain relationship between internal activities and the world external to the organization. Not profit, but potential for profit, is included in the prices charged. Such potential profit depends far less on the ownership of assets than it does on their use in a way that is meaningful to the customers. Our incomes derive from the effective use of assets whose value is determined by what we can do with them in a world which offers only a limited opportunity to us.

A word of caution is in order here. There is not so much a right to a monetary reward as there is a discovery of a possible opportunity to affect our income level by our daily activities and decisions in a specific manufacturing organization. This opportunity must be presented in meaningful terms to all the members of the organization. Unfortunately, a good deal of traditional organizational practice makes this very difficult, as Mr. Wade points out in the introduction to this book. The situation will have to be changed for two reasons: As employees, we need to see that the real importance of our jobs is solely determined by the contribution we make toward overall organizational objectives, and we need to see that this importance can change. As managers, we have to learn that value analysis cannot stop with the purchasing department but must embrace the measurement of everyone's work, including our own, in terms which take into account the interests of the customers.

One of the things which will differentiate the future manufacturing organization from its present counterpart is that in the future each man will know how his activities affect the earnings of the company and how they can contribute to its future survival. We are currently moving in the direction of such a widespread understanding. Even the most casual observation of manufacturing practices reveals that we are striving to develop methods and processes which lead to predetermined results—predetermined not only in output but also in time. We are trying to organize men to diagnose problematic situations quickly so as to anticipate and correct, with minimum delay, any conditions which could interfere with the continuation of the program for utilization of working capital—in short, to respond more to situations than to each other. What remains to be done is to develop a continuous means of evaluating the results of our corrections in terms of their relation to the market and to expected future changes in it.

SELF-IDENTIFICATION WITH CORPORATE ENDEAVORS

What are some of the characteristics of present-day manufacturing practices? Seven appear most significant.

1. The manufacturing executive of today is far more interested than were

his predecessors in general principles which can be applied to a wide range of products. The greater use of highly sophisticated and generalized mathematical techniques is an important evidence of this interest.

2. Since the manager is working against time and realizes that a given product may produce profits only for a limited period, he must appraise an employee not just on the basis of his ability to do the current job but also on the basis of his ability to learn skills which will be needed later on.

3. Waste is defined primarily as lost time, not lost materials. Efficiency tends to be equated with that which takes the least time for satisfactory completion. The manufacturing objective thus becomes the integration of effort, materials, and processes in a pattern which gives management the least wasted time, the minimum total time, and the maximum output per unit of time with the given technological system.

4. The kinds of schedules a firm can meet regularly determine to a large degree the kind of manufacturing success it will enjoy. Decisions as well as machine operations have to meet a timetable in modern manufacturing.

5. Reliability in scheduled or programed work means not only that its quality has a certain character but also that its completion (delivery) is on schedule.

6. Unless there is a substantial volume of orders to fill, operating personnel have little opportunity to realize the profit potential in the pricing system. The increasing importance of the breakeven point in determining profits means that, more than ever before, success in selling is a condition of earning ability.

7. Internal policies assume that able department heads, if assigned objectives, provided with solution boundaries by means of definite guides, and given means which are practical and useful, will do two things: accomplish what management asks of them and be able to recommend the means required to improve the efficiency with which the objectives are attained.

A working-capital orientation is inherent in all these practices. And it is obvious that they will be enlarged upon and developed in the future and that part of our task in manufacturing will be to participate in developing operational definitions. But more than this is required of us. Specifically, we will have to relate our activities and those we direct to the organization's need to survive and perpetuate itself, because we are unconsciously moving in a direction which emphasizes "job descriptions" and in so doing introduces sources of conflict. We want to simplify life, and one way to do it is to develop a "logic" or "universal algebra" of action. In this case we are trying to define job assignments in such a way that the required output is predetermined. Efficiency becomes almost completely the effort to eliminate ambiguity in action. This can be done, but only if we work with end goals which are fixed. One of our great problems for the future is that we need to be able to change end goals to reflect actions by our competitors, the assimilation of new knowledge, and the cultural changes which themselves affect the market. Changes, for example, like the current preference for smaller cars or the social rise of repressed classes and races.

In order to disorient ourselves from fixed goals we have to discover just what kind of unity is currently present in the organization and change it to achieve a unity of purpose, act, and result. Job descriptions have their place, and the logic behind them has its value, in a well-functioning organization, but we must make certain that they don't take on independent life and meaning. We need ways of measuring what we do so that it has a meaning, a value, and a direct connection to overall organizational performance. This identification with companywide endeavor is not something given to us by the organization chart; rather, it is one of the premises on which the chart itself must rest. As a consequence, we all have to accept the fact that our real job is to learn how to alter our own behavior, how to change the operational definitions of our own jobs, in order to contribute more effectively to the total company output.

GUIDEPOSTS AND OBSERVATIONS

We can best fulfill this responsibility by minutely examining the logical premises on which the organization has evolved. In the process we will have to accept a variety of management objectives as valid and ruling. Among these, five are predominant:

1. Get the most in the way of salable results from the working capital available.
2. Secure the largest gross profit possible under the established price and production levels.
3. Make sure that at some definite future time the working capital is all recaptured in the form of cash.
4. Foresee the life and extent of usefulness of the products being made.
5. Replace old products and old methods, not just to be competitive, but to gain competitive advantages.

If we try to operate according to these guideposts, then we will have to add four more observations to our ideological know-how. These guideposts will in the future most likely be the core around which we as employees organize our own perspectives toward the organization.

1. We have to realize that the prime function of any system is to reduce our need to think and thereby improve our speed and predictability of performance. *Work is the application of an acquired skill.* Both the acquired skill and its application have their own significance.

2. We have to realize that as the environment changes, the ideas on which a system is erected lose their universality and become less effective in dealing with realities; thus its ideological framework limits the usefulness of any system. *Work content itself can give us no meaning.* This is apparent in the fact that many jobs, when thought of as separate from the organization, become meaningless, whether that of the manager or that of the press operator.

3. We have to realize that in the history of the firm come periods in which it needs (*a*) the application of more effective systems and (*b*) new ways of seeing old problems. The real meaning of work for most of us then comes from its relation to the problems of the organization, and these can change.

4. Finally, we have to accept the fact that the leadership needed may be fundamentally different at each stage of a business's history. We can generalize this idea into the following statement: *The value of a set of skills fluctuates over periods of time, and the ability to acquire new skills becomes important to the individual as well as to the organization.*

The meaning of work involves a notion of partnership but does not include the concept of "equal partners." Our partnership status is defined by the extent to which our activities contribute to earnings and the extent to which we can alter that influence by using our unique individual capacities to respond to the total situation. At the same time, however, even a small degree of partnership does give us some right to demand, from those with greater positional influence on earnings, that they live up to their responsibilities.

EXTENSION OF THE ENTREPRENEURIAL FUNCTION

The variety of factors so far considered points up the need for a rational extension of the entrepreneurial function to everyone in an organization. There are many knotty problems here, which, if they are ever to be solved, require participation and wisdom from all of us. But the general notion that we must act in such a way as to be aware of the marketplace and to make our performance self-correcting with respect to wasted effort and time is not to be debated. There is no alternative; we have to be efficient in our use of working capital. The three factors of surplus capacity, technological explosion, and the interest of society in economic growth define the areas of opportunity in manufacturing. It is our job to learn to live with the opportunities thus presented and take advantage of them.

Obviously, all this has pertinence for the structure of union-management relationships. In the past these have been built on the premise that rights and obligations can be fixed and linked to occupational roles. As such they logically tend to supplement the usual industrial job descriptions. But once the job role is seen as a derived concept, rather than as an independent entity, the premise becomes a source of trouble and an obstacle to the attainment of the legitimate goals of a manufacturing enterprise in our culture and in a competitive order. In general, it produces this effect by reducing the range of alternatives available for coping with changes in expectations of participants and with changes in the external environment.

Profit-sharing plans and programs such as the Scanlon and Rucker cost-reduction-sharing plans represent an effort to enlarge the alternatives for the organization by recognizing, first, the interdependence of specialized effort (as well as its derived nature) and, second, the contingencies upon which personal expectations depend. The record shows that such approaches often do accomplish these ends. Success appears to depend on two factors: The past history of the firm limits the possibilities since it affects the way people perceive any proposal for change. In addition, effective managerial leadership requires an ability to demonstrate in acceptable concrete terms the economic consequences of change in behavior as well as a willingness to distribute gains resulting from such change so that the individual can act rationally to promote his self-interest without injuring the interests of others.

What is promising in these approaches, providing operational definitions of possibilities open to individuals as participants in a collective effort, is that the cooperation sought is pragmatically limited to the degree and scope appropriate to solving specific problems and is thus linked to the given circumstances and not to some ideal in which all behavior is subordinated to some one principle. We learn as a result that cooperation, if it is to have value, must be aimed at preserving freedom of action—or alternatives—further down the line along which work flows. Men faced with as yet unforeseen problems will have then the maximum freedom with which to deal with such problems because others took steps to make this possible. Otherwise we are forced to scrap pieces or go into overtime, for example. Only a keen sense of interdependence among participants makes possible the required communication and problem identification on an anticipatory basis.

To say this is to acknowledge that the individual has a way of influencing final results, that the choices open to him have consequences, and that delay in action at one point closes the door to opportunities at other points. What we seek, then, is a method of participation appropriate for solving *classes* of problems rather than the condition expressed by the ambiguous term "cooperation," which so often expresses a classification of attitudes toward direction.

The highly achievement-oriented manager knows this almost intuitively. The difficulty is to get a wider understanding among other organizational participants of this problem-solving approach. That understanding may be promoted by our willingness to admit others to a partnership role defined by the nature of the problem. A willingness associated with a managerial initiative aimed at improving the ability of participants at all levels to act responsibly as they become aware of their gain in freedom—a gain whose foundation rests on the appreciation of the various cause-and-effect connections that exist in the ways the organization transforms its various inputs into the final salable output. Obviously, these cause-and-effect relationships must be seen in their concrete forms in the workplace; it is here where technology is applied that the adequacy of our generalized concepts meets its test.

*   *   *

There is an intellectual revolution going on among managers—and for good reasons. It is essentially aimed at closing the gap between our more effective actions and our traditional rationale. We are more or less blindly struggling toward knowledge and a theory of action appropriate to the problems given us by our culture and the state of the arts. Philosophically speaking, the unknown frontier is the concrete form in which the generalized factors discussed will affect our organization's capacity to act effectively. The development of a broader perspective for coping with problems which can't be programed until the parameters are revealed is necessary so that we may learn not only to assure the survival of our enterprise as a whole but also to develop that character and personality which alone can save us from becoming a white-collar proletariat and a social menace because we are *only* experts.

In the process of defining our functions for the future we may also find a way to redefine freedom so that it becomes more meaningful for the individual in a profit-making enterprise. This last transcends by far a given organization's hope for survival; it is one of the desperate needs of our day.

INDEX

* Italicized Index entries are titles of exhibits reproduced in the text and of publications cited in the text.